COOKING LIGHT '88

Oxmoor House

Copyright 1987 by Oxmoor House, Inc.
Book Division of Southern Progress Corporation
P.O. Box 2463, Birmingham, Alabama 35201

Library of Congress Catalog Number: 87-061020
ISBN: 0-8487-0714-1
ISSN: 0884-2922

Manufactured in the United States of America
First Printing 1987

Executive Editor: Ann H. Harvey
Production Manager: Jerry Higdon
Associate Production Manager: Rick Litton
Art Director: Bob Nance

Cooking Light® '88

Editor: Ellen de Lathouder
Assistant Foods Editor: Janice L. Krahn
Copy Editors: Melinda E. West, Mary Ann Laurens
Editorial Assistant: Joan R. Winstead
Director, Test Kitchen: Laura N. Massey
Test Kitchen Home Economists: Rebecca D. Bryant, Julie Fisher, Lisa Glass
Photographer: Jim Bathie
Photo Stylist: Kay E. Clarke
Designer: Faith Nance
Recipe Developers: Carroll Sessions Flowers, R.D., Marilyn Wyrick Ingram
Menu Developers: Lee Cannon, Marilyn Wyrick Ingram, Donna Land, Lisa Weiss

Consultants, University of Alabama School of Medicine in Birmingham:
Julius Linn, M.D.
Susan Brown, Assistant Editor
Charlotte Bragg, M.S., R.D.
Karen Counts, R.D.
Heidi Hataway, M.S., R.D.
Laura Dunnam, Exercise Physiologist
Angela Shorter, Exercise Specialist
Julie Sulentic, Exercise Physiologist

Paper Sculpture Illustration (page 8): Barbara Ball

Cover: *California Veal Cutlets (page 148).*
Back cover: *Herbed Asparagus Sauté (page 207).*
Page ii: *A bountiful harvest of fresh, wholesome fruit.*

Contents

Living Well Is The Best Reward

The "Spockian" salutation "Live long and prosper" is the modern-day American dream. And *Cooking Light '88* is just the resource you and your family need to help make that dream a reality. Use this book to stay informed about food and fitness, to prepare healthful meals, gourmet dinners, and festive flourishes. But most importantly, use it to stay healthy for a long, long time.

A team of nutrition and fitness professionals worked with *Cooking Light '88* editors to translate scientific studies into bottom-line strategies for living defensively in today's world. In this all-new volume, you'll find tips that infect you with enthusiasm and make you want to take charge. You'll discover how to fill up—without filling out. When you visit this year's "Kitchen," you'll glean culinary know-how for becoming a *Cooking Light* cook and if you follow the simple prescription for exercise on page 18, you'll be on your way to cardiovascular fitness. Introduced for the first time in a *Cooking Light* annual is a weekly menu plan. You can follow these balanced meals with the sensible goal of losing about two pounds a week.

But mention of weight loss doesn't mean *Cooking Light '88* is a dieter's manual. On the contrary, the dishes in this volume are created by "hungry" people who like to eat real food. But our home economists also understand the culinary trends in "light" American cuisine and are skilled at merging our desire for simple elegance with our growing interest in nutrition. Each menu and each recipe is relatively light in calories, light in fat, light in sodium and processed sugar. But the pleasure and flavor factors remain intact.

The good life—good weather, good exercise, and good, wholesome foods: Herbed Pita Toast (page 102), Chinese Chicken Barbecue (page 161), and Broccoli-Garbanzo Bean Salad (page 178).

Update '88

America, How Are You?

Healthier and Happier, and Taking Charge!

Since 1985, about 25 million Americans have started exercising for the first time. A 1987 Gallup survey commissioned by *American Health* found that 69 percent of all Americans now exercise regularly.

Exercise improves physical fitness, alleviates stress, anxiety, and mild depression and serves to motivate us in other areas of our lives. The Gallup survey found that 64 percent of exercisers also try to eat more healthful foods and that 43 percent have lost weight. Ninety-three percent of those who exercise believe they can stay healthy if they take the right actions. When we take charge of our lives in one area, we feel more in control of the rest of our lives. Exercisers are more confident. They *enjoy* their workouts and the lighter foods they eat. They take pleasure in their optimism and their new, trimmer looks.

The survey exposes an area that needs some work. Most of us should increase the frequency and intensity of our workouts. Too few (about 16 percent) engage in exercise vigorous and regular enough to improve cardiovascular fitness.

Our quest for fitness and sound nutrition gains momentum as scientific studies confirm the wisdom of living well. Coronary deaths have dropped 30 percent over the past 20 years, and the average cholesterol level of middle-aged Americans has fallen from 240 in 1970 to 215.

People who have cholesterol levels below 150 rarely have heart attacks. In the 38-year health survey of 6,000 residents in Framingham, Massachusetts, not one participant who had a cholesterol level lower than 150 had a heart attack. The National Heart, Lung and Blood Institute reports that for every one percent drop in cholesterol level, the likelihood of having a heart attack drops two percent.

The *Journal of the American Medical Association (JAMA)* reported in 1987 that 80 percent of middle-aged American men risk premature death from heart disease; their blood cholesterol levels are too high. The report is based on a six-year study of 350,000 men between the ages of 35 and 57 who were healthy when the project began. The study shows that the risk of these men dying from heart disease rose as the levels of blood cholesterol increased. It also refutes the idea that lowering cholesterol levels below 200 does little to decrease heart disease risk.

High levels of blood cholesterol often result from eating diets too rich in animal fats and cholesterol. The American Heart Association (AHA) suggests limiting intake of cholesterol to 100 milligrams for every thousand calories consumed. In addition, we can control two other major risk factors for coronary disease—smoking and blood pressure. According to Dr. Las Ekelund of Duke University, cigarette smokers are almost three times as likely to die of heart attacks or strokes as nonsmokers.

Bad Marks for America's Youth

The move to improve vitality and longevity—in full force among the country's adults—has not yet hit the general ranks of younger Americans. While adults have concerned themselves with becoming fit, children have become flaccid.

Physicians and registered dieticians share a growing belief that what children eat and how much they exercise affect their well-being as adults. The President's Council on Physical Fitness reported in 1987 that the risk of children developing heart disease is actually increasing. During the last two decades, obesity increased from 18 to 27 percent among children ages six to eleven, from 16 to 22 percent among children ages twelve to seventeen. Forty percent of children ages five to eight have elevated blood pressure, high blood cholesterol, or do not exercise, the Council reported.

What the Council calls "major problems" includes lack of stamina and strength. Physical education teachers say students lack stamina because of poor nutrition and exercise habits. Children spend an average of 24 hours a week in front of the television, often eating the same sugary, fat-laden snacks advertised on the screen. Twenty-one percent of high school girls and 18 percent of high school boys smoke one or more cigarettes a day, even though the most recent figures from the Department of Health and Human Services show that lung cancer is the number one cause of cancer deaths.

Changes are underway. Twenty-four million children fed by the federal school lunch program are now, thanks to revised menus, eating foods with less fat, sugar, and salt. Physical education teachers are encouraging games, such as running and swimming, that are more likely to improve cardiovascular fitness over games such as baseball and basketball, which require more skill and fewer participants. Local school systems and concerned parents are working to readopt the bygone standard of requiring all children from kindergarten through twelfth grade to participate in one hour of physical education each day.

Living Well and Living On

Today, Americans live longer and healthier lives. This increase in life expectancy is linked to better overall nutrition, improved medical care, and changes in lifestyle (renouncing tobacco, controlling weight).

Being thin may help us live longer, according to researchers reporting in *JAMA*. The death rate is lower for people who are at least 10 percent thinner than the U.S. national average for their age and sex. The 1959 Metropolitan Life Insurance Height and Weight Tables are a better guide to ideal weight than the 1983 tables, which indicates that people can safely weigh more.

Exercise also may lengthen our lives. A study of Harvard alumni conducted by Ralph Paffenbarger, M.D. shows that men who expend 2,000 calories per week or more in physical activity are far more likely to see their 80th birthday than those who are less active. According to Dr. Las Ekelund of Duke University, men who are not physically fit are four times more likely to die of a heart attack than men who are fit.

Cancer: Is It A Lifestyle Disease?

Sophisticated tests can measure how much an altered diet, weight loss, and abstinence from smoking benefit the heart, but there are no comparable tests to show how lifestyle affects cancer. Most of what we know about cancer and lifestyle comes from scientific studies that try to isolate factors which increase or

decrease the risk of developing the disease.

Alcohol consumption has been linked to several kinds of cancer risks. Two recent studies show that alcohol may increase women's risk of developing breast cancer. A Harvard study found that women who drink three drinks per week have a 30 percent greater chance of developing breast cancer than women who seldom, if ever, drink. A National Cancer Institute study reported a 50 percent higher risk for women who drink any alcohol. For comparison, having a mother, sister, or daughter with breast cancer increases a woman's risk 300 percent. It is possible that another factor common to people who drink alcohol is what increases the risk and that alcohol may not be the culprit. More studies are needed.

Exercise may decrease the risk of some cancers. Research at the University of Southern California shows that physically active men have a lower incidence of colon cancer than their sedentary peers. Another study of 54,000 women found that former athletes who continued to exercise had fewer breast and reproductive system cancers than nonathletes. One reason may be that the athletes were slightly leaner; fat tissue converts hormones into potent estrogens that increase risk of breast cancer.

Researchers are gaining insight into how diet affects tumor development and growth. High-fat diets appear to increase risk of developing breast and colon cancers. A number of research studies suggest that people who eat more yellow and orange vegetables containing beta-carotene decrease their risk of cancer. Vitamins C and E along with the mineral selenium may control cell damage caused by substances called free radicals and possibly cut down on the risk of cancer. This year, studies suggest that cells deficient in the B vitamin folic acid are extra sensitive to cancer-causing

agents in the environment. Astounding preliminary results suggest that folic acid reverses precancerous changes in the cervix and lungs.

Guidelines for Health

What's wrong with the average American diet? We consume too much fat, cholesterol, and salt; too many calories; and not enough complex carbohydrates.

Cutting fat from the average 40 percent to 30 percent of daily calories lowers risk of heart disease, according to new American Heart Association guidelines. Moreover, the American Cancer Society says reducing fat in the diet may lower risk of breast and colon cancer.

New guidelines for women from the American Dietetic Association (ADA) advocate more calcium and iron-rich foods and emphasize maintaining normal body weight. They encourage the 10-calorie rule for safe weight loss and maintenance: Eat 10 calories daily for each pound of weight.

Losing Only to Gain

One out of every three American adults is currently dieting "with good intentions." Frequently, people try to lose weight by drastically reducing food intake, only to regain the lost weight more rapidly when they stop dieting. Such yo-yo dieting makes it harder to lose and maintain a desired weight. Current research indicates that repeated crash dieting triggers the body's protective mechanisms, making it burn calories more sparingly. As a result, with each new attempt to diet, weight comes off more slowly. Poor diet regimens can also mean swapping muscle for fat. When calorie intake is excessively low, muscle and organ tissue and large amounts of fluid are lost. After a crash diet is over, that weight returns primarily as fat.

How the Evidence Now Stands

The Latest on Caffeine

In 1982 Harvard professors struck fear in the hearts of coffee lovers by announcing that people who drank one or two cups of coffee a day increased their risk of developing cancer of the pancreas. Much to everyone's relief, a repeat study by the same researchers found no association for those who drank less than five cups of coffee a day and only a small increased risk for those who drank more than five cups a day. Two other studies, each lasting over 10 years, found no greater incidence of pancreatic cancer among coffee drinkers, even among those who drank many cups each day.

According to the Framingham heart study, drinking coffee does not appear to increase risk of heart disease. This data refutes a 1985 Johns Hopkins study suggesting that men who drink more than five cups of coffee a day increase their risk of heart disease almost three times over those who drink less. But the study did not consider the smoking, eating, and exercise habits of the participants. These factors may have influenced the increased risk more than coffee habits.

Although research fails to confirm most coffee-disease links for healthy people, moderation is always a good idea. Most people in the Framingham heart study consumed only one to two cups a day.

Calcium in Perspective

Consumers spent $18 million on calcium supplements in 1980. Last year the figure jumped to $240 million. Manufacturers now add calcium to everything from flour to milk. The increased interest in calcium stems from the 1984 National Institutes of Health (NIH) conference on osteo-porosis, the bone-thinning disease that affects some 20 million Americans and increases in frequency with age. Women were advised to increase daily calcium intake to 1,000 milligrams a day and to 1,500 milligrams after menopause. In more recent studies, the role of calcium in preventing loss of bone substance, especially after menopause, is far from clear. Eight studies show that extra calcium, even up to 3,000 milligrams a day, has little effect on the rate at which bone substance is lost in postmenopausal women.

On the other hand, estrogen does slow the loss of bone density that occurs after menopause. According to a 1987 study reported in the *Annals of Internal Medicine*, calcium combined with estrogen may be the best solution. This study of 73 women concurred that calcium alone fails to slow bone loss. But combining 1,500 milligrams of calcium daily with half the typical dose of estrogen appears to prevent loss of bone substance while it minimizes estrogen-related side effects.

What remains clear about calcium is that girls and young women *do* benefit from consuming ample amounts. Bones grow stronger until about age thirty-five. Then they slowly begin to lose mineral content. Building up as much bone density as possible before normal loss begins cuts down on the risk of developing osteoporosis years later.

Reconvening in 1987, the National Institutes of Health panel concurred that calcium alone will not retard bone loss after menopause. Estrogen will. Even so, the panel concluded that it is a good idea for the entire population to consume at least 1,000 milligrams of calcium a day. The best way to meet this requirement is through calcium-rich food sources that offer other valuable nutrients as well.

Safe Cholesterol Levels

There's more to the cholesterol picture than diet and lifestyle. The latest evidence confirms heredity's important role in how we respond to cholesterol-rich foods. People in one study ate three eggs a day (more than twice the recommended daily intake of cholesterol) for 10 weeks. This high-cholesterol diet elevated some people's cholesterol levels, but not others. When the participants stopped eating eggs, levels went down in some cases, but remained the same in others. The reason appears to be related to a difference in genetic makeup. In determining dietary requirements, the genetic profile of an individual should be considered, since the "average" person does not exist.

Lovastatin, a cholesterol-lowering "wonder drug," was approved by the Federal Drug Administration (FDA) in 1987. It can lower blood cholesterol levels by as much as 40 percent by blocking the formation of cholesterol by the liver. Primarily, it will be used to lower high cholesterol levels when diet, exercise, and weight loss fail. More research is needed on the long-term effects.

Other experimental programs for lowering cholesterol include Metamucil, a familiar laxative, and high doses of the B vitamin niacin, used in conjunction with diet and the prescription drug colestipol.

The most important self-help strategy for lowering blood cholesterol is diet; everyone—regardless of genes—responds somewhat to a low-fat, low-cholesterol diet.

Fish or Fish Oil?

Health-conscious people are trying to eat more fish that contain a beneficial fat called omega-3 fatty acids.

Research on Eskimos whose diet consisted largely of fatty fish containing omega-3s notes beneficial effects on the heart. These fats appear to lower blood cholesterol and triglyceride levels and interfere with the stickiness of platelets in the blood—a factor critical to the formation of blood clots. Preliminary studies also suggest that omega-3 fatty acids help relieve inflamation and cut down on pain associated with rheumatoid arthritis.

While encouraging, this data does not mean that adopting a regimen of fish oil pills will provide the same benefits. Little is known about how fish oil works, how much is needed, and what the long-term effects might be.

Sulfites Are Still Out There

Sulfites (preservatives added to foods) can cause severe allergic reactions and attacks of wheezing, usually in people with asthma. Even though the FDA banned the use of sulfites on fresh fruits and vegetables in 1986, many people did not realize that the ban excluded potatoes, wine, canned and frozen shellfish, canned and frozen fruit juices, dried fruits, and pickled foods and condiments. Many baked goods (including pizza crust and cookies) also contain sulfites.

As of January 1987, foods that contain 10 parts per million or more of sulfites must list the sulfiting agent on the label. Severe allergic reactions to foods containing less than this amount are rare. The names to look for on labels include *sodium sulfite, sodium or potassium bisulfite, sulfur dioxide, and potassium or sodium metabisulfite.*

Assessing Sweeteners

A no-calorie sweetener called sucralose (a sugar derivative, but 600 times sweeter) is under FDA review. Sucralose is especially attractive to cooks because, unlike aspartame, it is stable at high temperatures, making it suitable for baking. But it may take as long as ten years for FDA approval.

The FDA is also examining acesulfame-K, 130 times sweeter than sugar. A stable compound, it also can be used for baked goods and beverages.

In the meantime, aspartame and saccharin remain the only artificial sweeteners approved for a variety of food products. The FDA just recently announced its decision to approve aspartame's use in various fruit and fruit-flavored drinks, fruit and dairy bars, chilled ice tea drinks, and breath mints.

Vitamin C

Vitamin C is being studied for its cancer-preventing properties. According to a Mayo Clinic study, vitamin C does not cure colon cancer as some predicted it would. It may, however, play some role in decreasing the risk of developing stomach and colon cancer. According to a 20-year Swiss study of 6,000 men, those who ate diets low in vitamins A, C, and E were more likely to develop these cancers than the men who ate diets high in these nutrients. Vitamin C may interact with the other vitamins to interfere with the action of destructive chemicals called free radicals. Much work remains to be done to sort out the effects of single nutrients on cancer risks.

Although vitamin C intake does not affect the actual blood cholesterol level, it may increase the amount of cholesterol attached to high density lipoproteins (HDLs) that carry cholesterol away from blood vessels to the liver. Once HDLs reach the liver, vitamin C helps convert cholesterol into bile salts, which the body can then eliminate. Whether these effects are significant enough to decrease risk of heart disease remains unknown.

The Consensus Is Still Out

The U. S. Department of Agriculture's Human Nutrition Research Center is tackling one of the hottest nutrition issues around—body composition and what we can do to improve it for a healthier life. The researchers want to determine whether people can alter their ratio of fat to lean tissue by altering the percentage of fat in their diets while maintaining the same calorie intake.

Also on the horizon are answers to the question whether or not the damaged blood vessels of atherosclerosis victims can be reversed. We know it is possible to retard the advance of heart disease by changing our lifestyle and habits, but it is unclear if we can reverse the process that leads to heart and vascular disease. Early evidence suggests that a reversal may be possible by drastically reducing fat and cholesterol in the diet, increasing exercise, and reducing stress.

Sucrose polyester, a big gun in the fat-fighting battle is under study by the FDA. Because it is not absorbed from the intestine, it is essentially a calorie-free, cholesterol-free fat substitute that looks and tastes like fat. It will be several years, however, before the FDA gives us its verdict.

Regarding exercise, the Public Health Service has developed objectives for Americans to achieve by 1990. But unless unexpected changes occur in the next three years, it is unlikely that 90 percent of adolescents between ages 10 and 17, 60 percent of adults, or 50 percent of older people will be engaging in regular aerobic physical activities.

However, several goals are ''on track'' if present trends continue: The public is becoming more aware of the criteria for cardiovascular fitness; physicians are learning more about the importance of exercise; and more employers are encouraging fitness activities.

The Food and Fitness Connection

Throughout 1987, leading medical groups have touted the benefits of heart-healthy diets and improved nutrition to reduce the risk of disease. We have heard and read of the multiple benefits of exercise, most notably increased longevity. No question. Reasonable incentive exists to cut down on fats and cholesterol, remove the saltshaker from the table, put aside time for routine brisk walks.

But it's the prospect of a livelier and more rewarding life that really makes "taking control" an exciting venture. Exciting because you alone can make changes in the way you feel today and, more remarkably, the way you will feel ten years from now.

Making positive lifestyle changes requires a sensible approach based on sound information, and finding a way to get started often presents the biggest challenge. But the basic principles of food and fitness are easily applied when accompanied by practical strategies.

This chapter provides the nutritional and culinary know-how, the ingredients and the tools with which to create truly exciting ways of eating right and cooking light. It clarifies information on fitness so that you can design a safe, effective workout that fits into your real-world schedule. You will find no quick, easy steps to lose weight, reverse aging, cure cancer, or prevent heart disease. Instead, you will find recommendations based on sound scientific studies that, in the long run, will increase your chances for living a healthier, more vital life and, ideally, put you out of the market for the next "quick" cure, because you won't need one.

The right amount of aerobic exercise combined with a balanced diet is the key to feeling great and looking good. It's a winning combination!

Nutrition Basics for *Cooking Light*

Nutrition research in the '80s still gives credence to the familiar standard of well-balanced, regular meals with the right amount of vitamins and minerals, but new data has assigned more significance to certain nutrients. Research on the healthiest balance of nutrients has evolved into our modern-day diet, generous in complex carbohydrates, moderate in protein, low in fat. The "meat and potatoes" of yesteryear are now potatoes with a side order of meat. Fatty foods are out of favor because they make it easy to gain weight, contribute to heart disease, and may play a role in certain cancers. Fiber guidelines urge us to switch from white bread and other highly processed wheat products to more whole-grain breads and cereals, to eat more fresh fruits and vegetables. Sources of vitamins A, C, E, and folic acid take on new interest as scientists investigate their connection with cancer prevention. People are consuming dairy products for their therapeutic and preventive value in the treatment of osteoporosis, and the consumption of red meat is yielding to the benefits of fish such as salmon and mackerel, whose omega-3 fatty acids are thought to reduce blood cholesterol levels.

As for calories, emphasis is as much on a healthy balance of calorie sources as it is on the quantity of calories consumed. Calories have been characterized as the enemy to such an extent that their real importance is often forgotten. In simple terms, they are units of fuel derived from three nutrients: carbohydrates, proteins, and fats. These nutrients are turned into two basic energy sources: glucose (from the first two categories) and fatty acids (from the third). Carbohydrates and protein supply about 4 calories per gram; fat supplies more than twice that amount, about 9 calories per gram. (Some calories come from a non-nutrient source, alcohol, which supplies about 7 calories per gram.)

We can manipulate calories to our best advantage by avoiding excesses and eating a healthy balance of the energy nutrients.

All excess calories, regardless of the source, that are not expended as energy are stored as fat. One pound of fat represents 3,500 excess calories. Fifty excess calories per day would result in 5 pounds of stored body fat at the end of a year. Balancing energy input (food and beverages) with energy output (structured exercise and daily activity) keeps body weight stable.

When nutrients are properly balanced, we are likely to be more alert, have more control over our weight, and enjoy the many benefits associated

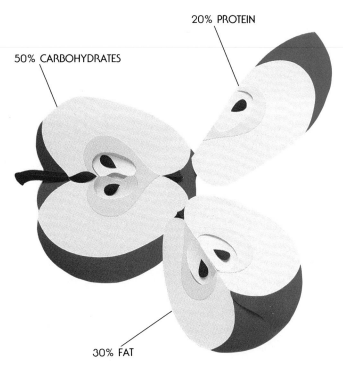

50% CARBOHYDRATES

20% PROTEIN

30% FAT

with abundant energy. By decreasing the amount of one nutrient (fat) in our diet and increasing another (complex carbohydrates), we can reduce the risk of heart disease and cancer and, in the process, chisel away at total calories because, gram for gram, fat is more fattening. *Cooking Light*'s guideline for a healthy balance of the three major nutrients is 50 percent carbohydrates, 30 percent fat, 20 percent protein.

Calories derived from carbohydrates should provide at least 50 percent of total daily calories, whereas fat and protein should be limited to no more than 30 percent and 20 percent, respectively. This means that for someone consuming 2,000 calories a day, at least 1,000 of those calories should

Computing Nutrition

Every Recipe Analyzed

Calories per serving and a nutrient breakdown accompany each of the recipes in this book. You will find grams of carbohydrates, fat, and protein per serving. Included also are milligrams of cholesterol, calcium, iron, and sodium per serving.

What You Need

When planning your meals, refer to these daily requirements to help you make the most of the nutrient values that follow *Cooking Light* recipes:

Calories	2,000
Protein	44 grams
Fat	67 grams
Carbohydrates	305 grams
Cholesterol	300 milligrams or less
Iron	18 milligrams
Sodium	1,100 to 3,300 milligrams
Calcium	800 to 1,200 milligrams

Men, teenagers, and pregnant women will need more of certain nutrients. If you're not sure of your ideal calorie intake, here is a rough guide: 2,000 calories is the *average* suggested for women 23 to 50, and 2,700 calories is the *average* for men. These levels vary somewhat according to age, body size, and level of activity.

Converting Dietary Guidelines to Grams

To convert the *Cooking Light* 50-30-20 guidelines (page 8) to grams of fat, carbohydrates, and protein, figure the calorie percentages based on your daily calorie intake, and divide by the number of calories per gram (9 calories per gram of fat and 4 calories per gram of carbohydrate or protein). For example, if you eat 2,000 calories per day, 600 calories represents 30 percent of your total calories. That means you should eat no more than 67 grams of fat per day in order to keep the caloric contribution to less than 30 percent total calories.

30% of 2,000 = 600 ÷ 9 = 67 grams

In addition, you would need at least 250 grams of carbohydrates and no more than 100 grams of protein.

50% of 2,000 = 1,000 ÷ 4 = 250 grams

20% of 2,000 = 400 ÷ 4 = 100 grams

Determining Calorie Percentages Per Serving

You can use *Cooking Light* nutrient breakdowns to calculate the percentage of calories contributed by fat, carbohydrates, and protein for an individual serving. Let's say you are looking at the recipe for Brown Rice Bread (complete recipe on page 108), and you want to determine how many of the calories are contributed by fat per serving (one ½-inch slice).

First, find grams of fat per serving. These are calculated in the analysis above to be 1.9. To find the percentage of calories from fat, multiply grams of fat by 9 (the number of calories per gram of fat) to get fat calories per serving. Then divide this quantity by the total calories. You'll find that fat contributes 13 percent of total calories in one slice of Brown Rice Bread.

1.9 x 9 = 17.1 ÷ 134 = .13 or 13% fat.

To calculate the calories contributed by carbohydrates and protein, multiply grams of carbohydrates or protein per serving by 4 (the number of calories per gram of protein or carbohydrate). Divide the quantity by total calories.

25.6 x 4 = 102.4 ÷ 134 = .76 or 76% carbohydrates

4.1 x 4 = 16.4 ÷ 134 = .12 or 12% protein

Menus and Menu Plans Meet 50-30-20 Guidelines

Each slice of Brown Rice Bread meets the recommended

BROWN RICE BREAD

PROTEIN 4.1 / FAT 1.9 / CARBOHYDRATE 25.6 / CHOLESTEROL 0 / IRON 0.9 / SODIUM 173 / CALCIUM 31

percentages: more than 50 percent carbohydrates; no more than 30 percent fat or 20 percent protein. All recipes will not fall so neatly within the guidelines. The goal is to achieve the recommended balance of nutrients on a daily basis, taking into consideration three meals and a snack. Use "Healthy American Meals" (page 27) and "*Cooking Light '88* Menu Plans" (pages 252-253) to create meals that meet the 50-30-20 guidelines.

How the Recipes are Analyzed

The calorie count and nutrient breakdown of each recipe are derived from a computer analysis, based primarily on information from the U.S. Department of Agriculture. The values are as accurate as possible and reflect certain standards:
• The recipes are developed for people who are interested in lowering their intake of calories, sodium, fat and/or cholesterol to maintain healthy eating patterns. The levels of these restricted nutrients in some recipes may be higher than those prescribed by a physician for specific health problems.
• All nutrient breakdowns are listed per serving.
• All meats are trimmed of fat and skin before cooking.
• When a range is given for an ingredient (e.g., 3 to 3½ cups flour), the lesser amount is calculated.
• Alcohol calories evaporate when heated, and this reduction is reflected in the calculations.
• When a marinade is used, the total amount of the marinade is calculated.
• Garnishes and other optional ingredients are not calculated.
• All fruit and vegetables listed in the ingredients are not peeled unless otherwise specified.

come from carbohydrates, no more than 600 from fat or 400 from protein.

Yet, determining the percentages of nutrients in food is often difficult because dietary recommendations from health authorities are usually expressed in grams and milligrams. The nutrition breakdown following *Cooking Light* recipes is expressed in weight values, as are food labels. To make the most out of the grams and milligrams of nutrition lingo, refer to "Computing Nutrition" on the preceding page.

Nutrition guidelines make it clear that simply eating nutritious foods will not deliver sound nutrition. There must be an appropriate balance of the energy nutrients. Even though foods contain combinations of carbohydrates, fat, and protein, certain foods supply greater quantities of one nutrient over another. The role these nutrients play in running the body "machine" determines how much of each nutrient is needed in relation to the others.

SPECIAL KUDOS GIVEN TO CARBOHYDRATES

Carbohydrates, especially complex carbohydrates, are making it big in the '80s. In fact, they're so important nutritionally that it's a good idea to plan meals around them. As the body's basic fuel, they are necessary for all the vital functions. Natural, unrefined carbohydrates are the only food category not linked to life-threatening diseases.

Complex carbohydrates (starches) are more than an energy source. They are economical, relatively low in calories and fat; rich in vitamins and minerals; and often a good source of fiber and protein.

American diets often lack enough complex carbohydrates. To make up more than 50 percent of 2,000 calories a day, all of these high-carbohydrate foods could be included: 4 slices whole wheat bread, 2 apples, ½ cup cooked brown rice, 1 baked potato, 1 banana, 1 cup cooked rolled oats, ½ cup cooked lima beans, and ½ cup cooked corn. In general terms, more complex carbohydrates mean meals with more foods such as legumes, fruits and vegetables, enriched and whole-grain breads, cereals, and pasta.

Simple carbohydrates can be low in nutrients. Simple carbohydrates (sugars) include brown and granulated sugar, honey, and syrups. These foods supply "empty" calories (calories low in nutrients). We find these simple sugars in regular sodas (11 teaspoons per 12-ounce can), candy, cakes, and other sweets. Better choices are the natural sugars in fruits, milk, and some vegetables because, calorie for calorie, they offer more nutrients. A glass of skim milk supplies 86 calories. In addition to the lactose (milk sugar), it also supplies high-quality protein, riboflavin, calcium, and a small amount of fat. Most soft drinks, which may have 150 calories, offer none of these.

To increase carbohydrates, select more foods from the complex category. An excess of simple carbohydrates can provide too much too soon. Since they are easily absorbed, they often act as a false energy booster, making blood sugar peak quickly and then dip lower than normal. This can cause weakness and irritability.

Dietary fiber is a carbohydrate bonus. Increasing consumption of certain carbohydrates helps increase dietary fiber. Fiber is found in the skin and pulp of fruits and vegetables and in the outer coating of grains, nuts, and seeds. Fiber-rich foods provide roughage to help the digestive tract function more efficiently and may have a beneficial role in reducing the risk of cardiovascular disease and some forms of cancer. Research shows that certain soluble fibers found in oat bran and legumes, such as dried beans and lentils, effectively lower blood cholesterol and may help stabilize the blood sugar in diabetics. Other studies reveal that the fiber in many fruits and vegetables, called pectin, may also help reduce blood cholesterol.

The average dietary fiber intake, estimated to be about 15 grams a day, is inadequate. Eating five servings of fiber-rich foods daily will measure up to the recommended 25 to 35 grams.

DIETARY FAT—A MATTER OF MANAGEMENT

Besides being a major source of energy, fat serves as transport and storage for fat-soluble vitamins (A, D, E, and K). Fat supplies the essential fatty acids, particularly linoleic acid, necessary for proper growth and healthy skin. But diets too high in fats and cholesterol are implicated in heart disease and certain cancers. Too much fat also contributes to obesity, a condition linked to other chronic health problems.

Even though only 2 teaspoons (10 grams) of fat a day are essential, most Americans consume the equivalent of 24 teaspoons (½ cup) each day. Just 2 teaspoons would be difficult to manage and is not even desirable. The American Heart Association's recommendation to cut fat calories to no more than 30 percent is a more realistic goal. Depending on the calorie goal, this translates into 8 to 16 teaspoons (40 to 80 grams) daily. Accomplishing this goal would involve eating more complex carbohydrates, which have less fat and no cholesterol, but it also means making decisions about which fats to eat.

Cholesterol is a fat-like substance found in all foods of animal origin (meat and dairy products), but not in foods from plants. Some cholesterol is needed by the body, but too much can build up in arteries and lead to heart disease, heart attack, or stroke. Diets rich in saturated fats tend to raise the level of blood cholesterol, whereas unsaturated fats work at lowering it. When planning meals, limit saturated fats, and strive to increase the ratio of unsaturated fats to saturated fats in the diet. It's important to remember, too, that all fats are high in calories.

Some "cholesterol-free" vegetable products such as coconut and palm oils can be more saturated than the fats found in meats. The following ingredients on labels can help uncover hidden fats and cholesterol in packaged foods: egg and egg-yolk solids; whole-milk solids; imitation or milk chocolate; lard; suet and animal by-products; butter; coconut oil; cream; hydrogenated fat or oil; cocoa butter; palm or palm kernel oil; shortening and bacon; beef or chicken fat. Be sure to check labels on snack items. Coconut and palm oils are widely used in making everything from crackers and chips to cookies, cake mixes, and granola bars.

Unsaturated fats, on the other hand, can actually lower cholesterol levels. These fats may be polyunsaturated, such as corn, safflower, soybean, and sunflower oils, or monounsaturated—olive, peanut, and canola oils. Unsaturated vegetable oil is often saturated to increase shelf life. The process, which makes the oil more solid, is called hydrogenation. Products such as the soft tub margarines that are

the least solid at room temperature are also the least saturated.

To live the low-fat, low-cholesterol life, incorporate strategies from "The *Cooking Light* Kitchen" to reduce the amount of fat in foods.

PROTEIN—MOST EFFICIENT WHEN BALANCED WITH OTHER NUTRIENTS

For protein to function efficiently, there must first be a healthy balance of carbohydrates and fat. Carbohydrates are the the body's most economical energy source; protein, the least. Adequate amounts of carbohydrates in the diet enable the body to burn primarily carbohydrates and fat for energy so that protein can build and repair tissue, its key function.

Since muscles are primarily made of protein, athletes in pursuit of extra strength and muscle size often increase their consumption to two or three times the recommended amount. But more protein does not result in more muscle. A balanced diet will insure that enough protein will be available for building muscle. Excess protein, like any other excess calories, will ultimately turn into fat. Exercise is the only way to make a particular muscle bigger.

No one, not even an athlete, requires more than 20 percent of daily calories from protein. Six ounces of meat, two servings of milk or a milk product, four servings of bread or cereal, and a starchy vegetable quickly add up to a day's worth of protein.

Reduce the fat in protein sources. Rely more on legumes and grains rather than animal sources for daily protein. Cutting back on animal protein helps reduce excess fat and cholesterol in the diet and at the same time increases fiber. Because grains and legumes are incomplete protein, serve them with each other or with a milk product. One cup of cooked dried beans has plenty of fiber and protein and only a trace of fat. Also, think of meat as a condiment, rather than as the centerpeice of each meal. Use small amounts in stir-fried combination dishes, soups, stews, and casseroles. Rely on *Cooking Light* recipes for ways to turn grains, legumes, pasta, and dairy products into complete protein cuisine with low-fat, high-carbohydrate benefits.

VITAMINS AND MINERALS FROM FOOD SOURCES

Vitamins and minerals are essential to good health. Small amounts of a wide variety are required each day. Ideally, a single "health" food would provide them all, but unfortunately no such food exists. Eating different kinds of foods from each of the Basic Four Food Groups is the best way to include adequate amounts of all the essential nutrients.

Supplements are not the answer. Sometimes the quest for nutritional insurance leads Americans to rely on supplements for their supply of vitamins and minerals. In fact, the practice is so widespread that in April 1987, a coalition of health agencies, including the American Medical Association and the American Dietetic Association, released a consensus statement outlining the importance of obtaining nutrients from food and pointed out the hazards of supplement abuse. While megadoses of a fat-soluble vitamin such as Vitamin A can be deadly, megadoses of even water-soluble vitamins such as Vitamin C and the B complex, once thought nontoxic, can have unpleasant or serious side effects. Excesses can be as undesirable as deficiencies. The basis of good health is good nutrition, adequate exercise, blood pressure and weight control, and no smoking or substance abuse. Good health is not achieved by taking supplements.

Certain vitamins may be linked to cancer prevention. The attention-getting vitamins of the '80s are vitamins A, C, E, and folic acid because of their possible role in preventing cancer. More studies are needed, however, to substantiate and sort out what the data mean. In any case, foods rich in these vitamins are desirable for general good health.

When it comes to minerals, Americans often consume too little or too much: not enough calcium and iron and too much sodium. Use the following basic guidelines to help determine daily needs:

● **Calcium** deficiency may be associated with osteoporosis, a severe loss of bone density that threatens older adults. The recommended daily allowance for calcium is 800 milligrams a day for men and women. Pregnant and lactating women are advised to consume 1,200 milligrams daily. A National Institutes of Health consensus panel recommends that postmenopausal women consume 1,200 to 1,500 milligrams of calcium daily. Foods rich in calcium include milk and milk products; sardines and canned salmon (eaten with bones); dark green, leafy vegetables; dried beans and peas.

● **Iron** is vital for oxygen transport. Insufficient iron can result in tiredness, lethargy, and irritability. During growth periods, it is important for the development of new muscle tissue and increased hemoglobin, the blood pigment that carries oxygen to body tissues. Once menstruation begins, women need to replace the iron lost in the menstrual flow. The recommended daily allowance for women in their childbearing years is 18 milligrams; for men and postmenopausal women, 10 milligrams. Foods rich in iron include liver; red meats; egg yolk; green leafy vegetables; dried beans and peas; enriched and whole-grain cereals; molasses; raisins.

● **Sodium** intake is associated with high blood pressure. Most adults should restrict sodium intake to between 1,100 to 3,300 milligrams daily or 1,000 milligrams for every 1,000 calories consumed. Most Americans consume 7,000 milligrams a day or the sodium equivalent found in one tablespoon of salt. Besides sodium chloride (salt) on labels, look for other sodium compounds, such as monosodium glutamate, sodium sulfite, and sodium bisulfite. Don't rely on your taste buds; these compounds don't always taste salty.

Values for each of these important minerals follow *Cooking Light* recipes.

BEST SOURCES OF PREVENTION-LINKED VITAMINS	
Vitamin A:	Liver; eggs; cheese; butter; fortified margarine and milk; fruits and yellow, orange, and dark green vegetables (e.g., carrots, broccoli, spinach, cantaloupe).
Vitamin C:	Citrus fruits and juices; tomatoes; strawberries; melons; green peppers; potatoes; dark green vegetables.
Vitamin E:	Vegetable oils; margarine; wheat germ; whole-grain cereals and breads; liver; dried beans; green leafy vegetables.
Folic Acid:	Liver; dark green, leafy vegetables; wheat germ; dried beans and peas; orange juice; cantaloupe.

HOW TO MANAGE IT ALL

Translating nutrient needs into food choices that achieve a balanced diet—adequate in protein, high in complex carbohydrates, and low in fat, with all the essential vitamins and minerals—is a tall order. The best way to manage it all is to choose a wide variety of foods in moderate amounts from each of the Basic Four Food Groups: meat, vegetable and fruit, bread and cereal, and milk and milk products.

Select from each group the foods with the most nutrients and the least amount of calories—the nutrient-dense foods. To keep total fat intake under 30 percent of total calories, select the low-fat foods from each group. For most people, over half of the total fat in the diet comes from the meat group. Minimize fat by choosing lean cuts of meat, removing skin from poultry and fish, eating more meatless meals, and selecting recipes and cooking methods that significantly limit or restrict the use of fats.

Most important of all, watch portion sizes. Three ounces of meat supply the protein needed at any one meal. That's equivalent to ½ cup of cooked, chopped meat or one skinless, boneless cooked chicken breast.

Moderate portion sizes apply to the other food groups. Even a diet balanced according to the Basic Four can be fattening if you eat too much.

To boost daily supplies of vitamins and minerals and increase complex carbohydrates and dietary fiber, choose fresh fruits and vegetables along with whole-grain breads and cereals. For extra calcium, low-fat milk is the best source.

BASIC FOUR FOOD GROUPS			
Food Group	Daily Servings	Serving Size	Principal Nutrients
Meat, Fish, Poultry, Legumes, Nuts & Seeds	2 (Vegetable protein without animal protein must be balanced.)	2 to 3 oz. cooked lean meat, fish, or poultry (not including fat or bone) 1 cup legumes ½ cup nuts or seeds	Protein Iron
Vegetable & Fruit	4 (1 Vitamin C source daily; 1 Vitamin A source every other day)	½ cup fruit juice 1 medium-sized fruit ½ cup cooked vegetable 1 cup raw vegetable	Vitamin A Vitamin C Fiber Water
Bread & Cereal (enriched or whole grain)	4	½ cup cooked cereal ¾ cup ready-to-eat cereal 1 slice bread	Thiamin Riboflavin Niacin Iron
Milk & Milk Products	2-4*	1 glass (8 oz.)	Calcium

*Note: Calcium needs for children, teenagers, and women are greater.

The servings suggested by the Basic Four are the minimum number. If your normal intake demands more, choose additional servings from the Basic Four and/or foods from the Fifth Food Group.

Choose from the Fifth Food Group judiciously. Foods such as margarine, mayonnaise, oils, candy, soft drinks, rich desserts, and liquor make up the Fifth Food Group. They supply calories but contribute little or no protein, vitamins, or minerals to the diet. They are not "bad" foods. Rather they are best enjoyed after the Basic Four guidelines are met. Just remember, at a cocktail party two or three drinks, a handful of peanuts, and some chips with dip can easily add up to 1,000 calories.

The *Cooking Light* Kitchen

Become a *Cooking Light* cook. Translate dietary guidelines into menus for yourself and your family. The goal of the *Cooking Light* cook is to become adept at reducing the excesses discussed in "Nutrition Basics." Learning to cut fat, sodium, and sugar

from recipes gives meals lighter, healthier appeal. The techniques used to develop *Cooking Light* recipes make it possible for even the most inexperienced cook to modify family favorites without sacrificing one morsel of enjoyment.

KEY LIME PIE BY A MORE NUTRITIOUS RECIPE

In *Cooking Light*'s Key Lime Meringue Pie (complete recipe on page 241), lighter ingredients replace "heavier" counterparts to save 215 calories per serving. Each serving contains 61 percent less fat, 59 percent less cholesterol, and 73 percent less sodium than the traditional version.

The amount of saturated fat in the traditional recipe makes each serving excessively high in calories and cholesterol. The *Cooking Light* version reduces fat in the crust from ⅓ cup to 3 tablespoons, eliminates the tablespoon of butter (102 calories) in the filling, and replaces sweetened condensed milk (1,365 calories) with a lighter, lime juice and cornstarch-based filling that contains 2 egg yolks instead of 4 (a 125-calorie savings).

By eliminating sweetened condensed milk and using only ¼ cup sugar for sweetener, calories from simple carbohydrates are reduced by almost half. And by reducing salt in the crust and filling, sodium is all but eliminated.

What about the flavor? The flavor remains. In fact, the more nutritious filling lets the tangy flavor of lime take the limelight in this wonderfully "light lime" dessert. And for a tropical accent—the flavor of coconut is in the crust.

COOKING LIGHT RECIPES TESTED FOR NUTRITION AND PLEASURE FACTORS

The *Cooking Light* cook wants to make nutritious eating a pleasant experience. That's why you will enjoy the recipes in this book. Each is developed

KEY LIME MERINGUE PIE

Cooking Light	Traditional
1 cup all-purpose flour	1 cup all-purpose flour
1 tablespoon flaked coconut	½ teaspoon salt
Dash of salt	⅓ cup lard
3 tablespoons shortening	1 tablespoon butter
3 tablespoons cold water	2 tablespoons water
¼ cup cornstarch	1 (15-ounce) can sweetened condensed milk
¼ cup sugar	½ cup Key lime juice
⅛ teaspoon salt	1 tablespoon grated lime rind
2 cups water	¼ teaspoon salt
2 egg yolks	4 eggs, separated
¼ cup Key lime juice	¼ cup plus 2 tablespoons sugar
2 teaspoons margarine	⅛ teaspoon cream of tartar
2 teaspoons grated lime rind	
3 egg whites	Yield: 8 servings
⅛ teaspoon cream of tartar	Calories: 403 per serving
2 tablespoons plus 1½ teaspoons sugar	

Yield: 8 servings
Calories: 188 per serving

PROTEIN 3.8 / FAT 6.9 / CARBOHYDRATE 27.7 / CHOLESTEROL 68 /
IRON 0.8 / SODIUM 91 / CALCIUM 13

PROTEIN 9.2 / FAT 17.5 / CARBOHYDRATE 53.1 / CHOLESTEROL 167 /
IRON 1.1 / SODIUM 340 / CALCIUM 172

and tested to meet strict standards for sound nutrition, excellent flavor, and visual appeal.

Featured below are just a few ways of applying Cooking Light's test kitchen techniques to maximize nutrition in other recipes.

You'll find more tips on the following pages.

KEEP IT LIGHT AND KEEP THE FLAVOR

MAPLE OAT BRAN COFFEE CAKE

In most recipes calling for 2 eggs, 1 egg yolk can be removed to cut 272 milligrams of cholesterol. This procedure and fiber-rich oat bran make Maple Oat Bran Coffee Cake (page 104) a wholesome bread to serve for breakfast or brunch.

FRESH STRAWBERRY TART

Using luscious fruits and low-fat yogurt to create desserts or modify old favorites can result in something as tempting as Fresh Strawberry Tart (page 242). Elegant fare can indeed be tops in flavor and tops in nutrition.

BEEF AND SPINACH STIR-FRY

Lean cuts of meat cooked with minimal fat keep fat percentages low. To make Beef and Spinach Stir-Fry (page 143), a flank steak is cut across the grain into thin strips and stir-fried in a wok coated with cooking spray.

MOCK SOUR CREAM

Low-fat dairy products offer all the nourishing benefits of whole-milk dairy products. Mock Sour Cream (page 200) is made with 1 part nonfat buttermilk and 4 parts pureed low-fat cottage cheese. This calcium-rich condiment has 90 percent less fat than the real thing.

CRUNCHY TUNA POCKETS

Rinsing canned foods such as tuna fish and vegetables under cold tap water for 1 minute can reduce sodium by as much as 80 percent. This method is used in preparing Crunchy Tuna Pockets (page 194), a lunchtime way to keep dietary excesses low.

CRANBERRY-GRAPEFRUIT FIZZ

Adding club soda or mineral water to fruit juices and alcoholic beverages helps dilute both calories and alcohol. In non-alcoholic Cranberry-Grapefruit Fizz (page 99), 2 parts club soda are added to 3 parts fruit juice to create a bubbly, quenching drink.

NUTRITION-ENHANCING TECHNIQUES

Many recipes in this book will become regulars in your meal planning, but you will still want to prepare your traditional favorites. *Cooking Light* recipes are developed with a variety of nutrition-enhancing techniques that you can refer to when you re-examine your recipe files to determine how to cut unwholesome excesses. It's not necessary to attack them all at once to be successful. Most cooks rely on about ten standard recipes. Why not tackle them one at a time, assessing each for its nutritional benefits? Even people who think they love only rich foods will find their list of favorites includes many dishes that can be made more nutritious with changes that leave the flavor, texture, and appearance intact.

- **Add Procedures**

  Remove skin from chicken and fish, and trim fat from meat before cooking. Skim, drain, and blot or wipe excess fat from foods and utensils when possible. Rinse tuna, canned vegetables, and feta cheese to reduce sodium. Use cooking bags or parchment paper to allow foods to cook in their own juices. Chill stocks and remove solidified fat to save 120 calories per tablespoon. Add carbonated water to juices and alcoholic beverages to dilute calories and alcohol.

- **Omit Procedures**

  Don't sauté vegetables in oil if they are going to be cooked at length in a stew or casserole. Don't automatically butter or grease cookware; use nonstick cookware coated with vegetable cooking spray. To lighten calories in fruit pies and cobblers, leave off the top or bottom crust.

- **Use Alternate Cooking Methods**

  Foods do not have to be fried to be tasty. You can cut fat by broiling, grilling, stir-frying, steaming, poaching, baking, or roasting. The shorter the cooking time for fruits and vegetables, the fewer nutrients you will lose. Stir-frying and steaming are extra quick methods that seal in vitamins and minerals rather than let them escape into cooking liquids.

- **Eliminate Ingredients**

  Cook rice, pasta, and vegetables without salt or fat, especially if you plan to add sauces or other seasonings.

- **Reduce Amount of Ingredients**

  Try reducing the amount of sugar by one-third or more and cutting the amount of salt in half. Use less meat in combination dishes, and add more vegetables or grain products to get the same number of servings. Try removing 1 egg yolk for every 2 eggs in a recipe.

- **Use Lighter Ingredients**

  Replace fatty cuts of meat with lean cuts, ground beef with ground turkey or tofu.

  Use no-salt-added tomato products and unsalted margarine instead of the regular products. (Even if you add ⅛ teaspoon salt to your recipe, you can eliminate more than 70 percent of the sodium by using these no-salt products.)

  Use reduced-calorie mayonnaise and salad dressings and low-sodium soy sauce.

  Replace the flavor of salt and fat with one or more of the following: wine, jalapeño peppers, fresh herbs, spices, Dijon mustard, or flavored vinegars.

  Dip fillets in lemon juice or skim milk instead of egg before breading.

  Sweeten with spices, flavorings, liqueurs, low-calorie maple syrup, and fruit juices. Try low-sugar spreads to replace jams and jellies. Use unsweetened cocoa instead of chocolate (¼ cup cocoa + 2 teaspoons vegetable oil = 1 square baking chocolate).

  Replace whole-milk dairy products with their low-fat counterparts. Replace sour cream with yogurt or low-fat commercial sour cream, or use substitute recipes such as Mock Sour Cream (page 200). Replace cream cheese with Neufchâtel cheese or Sweet Yogurt-Cheese Spread (page 199). Replace whipped cream or commercial toppings with whipped evaporated skim milk, low-fat yogurt, or tofu.

  Use pureed vegetables, low-fat yogurt, and skim milk to "cream" soups; use unflavored gelatin and Dijon mustard to thicken and emulsify salad dressings.

  Use water-packed tuna instead of oil-packed; juice-packed canned fruit instead of syrup-packed; vegetable oil and soft tub margarines instead of the more solid fats like butter and shortening.

Equipment that accommodates *Cooking Light* techniques (clockwise from front): poultry shears, parchment paper, vegetable steamer rack, mini food processor, gravy skimmer, broiler pan, blender, wire grilling basket, wok, frozen dessert maker, loafpan with drain holes, and nonstick skillet.

- **Use** *Cooking Light* **Counterparts**

     As an alternative to modifying your old recipes, you may want to consider replacing some of them with *Cooking Light* counterparts. Whether it's a Waldorf salad, Baked Alaska, or cornbread, be sure to look to the menu and recipe sections for a new, lighter perspective on old standards.

EQUIPMENT PUTS *COOKING LIGHT* INTO ACTION

Certain equipment is particularly well suited for the *Cooking Light* kitchen. The following items are by no means "must haves," especially for the resourceful cook who can modify equipment as well as recipes. But these items offer valuable assistance when it comes to preparing recipes that are calorie- and fat-conservative. Items you are missing might be good candidates for a holiday or birthday gift list.

- **Blender**—for pureeing fruit to make a refreshing treat such as Four Fruit Shake (page 99) or pureeing vegetables to thicken mock cream soups.
- **Broiler Pan**—for low-fat cooking of meats, poultry, and fish.

- **Frozen Dessert Maker**—for making low-calorie frozen treats such as Peach-Yogurt Freeze (page 232) and Strawberry-Rosé Ice (page 232). It requires no salt, ice, electricity, or cranking and delivers ice-cold creations in 20 minutes.
- **Gravy Skimmer**—for separating excess fat from gravy.
- **Loafpan with Drain Holes**—for use in baking meats. Its special inner rack with holes allows grease to drain into the outer pan.
- **Mini Food Processor**—for slicing, mincing, shredding, chopping, and pureeing. A space-saver compared to bulkier predecessors, it can process up to four cups of dry ingredients, depending on the brand.
- **Nonstick Skillets**—for avoiding excess butter and oil when sautéing and browning. Use with vegetable cooking spray.
- **Parchment Paper**—for baking without adding extra fat. Orange Flounder in Papillote (page 118) is prepared in this fashion.
- **Poultry Shears**—for skinning poultry to reduce about 50 percent of fat (method for skinning poultry on page 171).
- **Vegetable Steamer Rack or Pot**—for a quick, low-fat, nutrient-saving method of cooking fruits and vegetables. It can also serve as a poacher for small fish.
- **Wire Grilling Basket**—for added convenience in grilling fish. Simply spray rack with vegetable cooking spray; place fish in basket, and flip to grill on both sides.
- **Wok or Wok Skillet**—for stir-frying meats and vegetables with minimal fat. You'll find a variety of tasty stir-fry recipes in the menu and recipe sections.

Exercise—The Perfect Partner

The balanced diet's perfect partner is exercise. An adequate amount of weekly exercise is no less beneficial to our health than a weekly plan of nutritious eating. Since any excess of nutritive energy is stored as fat, energy intake should be balanced with energy expenditure in order to maintain body weight. People who want to lose weight often use a single strategy—eating fewer calories. A dual strategy—cutting calories and increasing exercise—makes weight loss easier and more permanent. A workout burns extra calories, and the increased metabolism may even allow the body to burn calories at a higher rate for several hours afterwards.

Exercise does more than burn up calories; a physically fit person is able to sustain vigorous activity with less fatigue and generally feels better, sleeps better, and is more energetic. Fitness becomes a state of mind that carries over to all areas of life—career, self-esteem, productivity, and relationships. The well-conditioned body tempers reactions to stress; it invites an overall sense of well-being. Feeling fit means feeling great.

Exercise builds muscles for more strength. Muscles burn calories; fat does not. The most obvious reward of toned muscles is a sleeker and slimmer look. Looking fit means looking good.

EXERCISING FOR THE HEALTH OF IT

The long-term incentive for becoming fit is just for the health of it. Consider the high marketability of a pill that when taken would help lower the risk of hypertension, coronary disease, erratic blood sugar levels, lower back pain, stress, and osteoporosis—with a possible side effect of increased longevity. Lines at the drug stores would trail for miles. Yet, a prescription for adequate exercise is often met with a "ho-hum" reaction, even though studies demonstrate that those who are physically active throughout their lives have better chances of avoiding ill health and that those who are physically fit and develop an illness have a better chance of surviving and recovering.

Don't wait until you need a cure before you start

Just What the Doctor Ordered

For _____

Address _____ Age _____

R _____ Date _____

Exercise Rx: *Take regularly for a lifetime*

Type: *The Aerobic Workout* *

Frequency: *3-4 times per week*

Duration: *30 minutes minimum*

Intensity: *70-85% maximum heart rate*

*Note: If you are over 35 years old and have not been exercising regularly, you should consult your physician before beginning any exercise program.

prevention. Above is a prescription for a more vital, healthier lifestyle. You can fill it yourself.

WHY AN AEROBIC WORKOUT?

People who reach peak physical fitness do so with a combination of three kinds of exercise: *aerobic, strength,* and *flexibility.* Aerobic exercise brings heart and lung performance to a level that increases endurance; strength exercise strengthens and tones muscle; and flexibility exercise improves range of motion of joints, prevents stiffness, and stretches muscles.

The most crucial of these exercises is aerobic. Aerobic conditioning provides increased oxygen supplies to the tissues, making it possible for the body to use energy more efficiently. Activities such as brisk walking, jogging, cycling, and swimming are aerobic; they call for an increased intake and delivery of oxygen over an extended period of time. Strength workouts that include activities such as sprinting, weight lifting, and calisthenics are generally short, intense activities which the body cannot sustain for extended periods because the oxygen demand exceeds the oxygen supply.

HOW TO FILL YOUR EXERCISE PRESCRIPTION

To achieve and maintain aerobic fitness, your workout should include four basic phases: warm-up, stretching, aerobic workout, and cool-down.

Ease into and out of vigorous exercise with a warm-up and cool-down. Whatever your fitness level, a warm-up before exercise and a cool-down afterwards are vital phases of the workout. A 5-minute warm-up prepares the body for vigorous activity. Muscles lose their injury-prone stiffness, and the cardiovascular system has a chance to gear up. A less intense form of the aerobic activity is usually best because it provides a "rehearsal." For instance, a runner may begin by walking; a swimmer, by wading through the water.

After you complete the aerobic phase of your workout, cool down by slowing down until your breathing returns to normal. This prevents a sudden drop in blood pressure and keeps blood flowing through working muscles to prevent it from "pooling" in the legs.

Stretch warm muscles. Follow your warm-up and cool-down with moderate stretching of the major muscle groups used in the aerobic phase.

This will further reduce risk of injury and increase flexibility. (Many people like to stretch before the warm-up, but studies now show that stretching a warm muscle is safer and more effective than stretching a cold muscle.) Most aerobic activities involve the following muscles: lower leg, quadriceps, hamstring, groin, lower back, upper body, and neck. Avoid injurious bouncing and bobbing when you stretch these muscles. Instead, slowly move into the stretch until you feel mild tension. Hold the position for 10 to 30 seconds without forcing the muscles. Relax after each stretch and repeat 2 to 6 times. While you are stretching one muscle group, pay attention to form and be careful not to overtax other muscles or tendons and ligaments in the process. (See pages 22-23.)

Monitor the frequency, duration, and intensity of your aerobic workout. For maximum aerobic fitness, work up to three or four weekly workouts of 40 minutes each: a 5-minute warm-up, a 30-minute aerobic phase, and a 5-minute cool-down. To remain flexible, you can change the length of the aerobic phase during the week—a minimum of 20 minutes on some days, 45 on others.

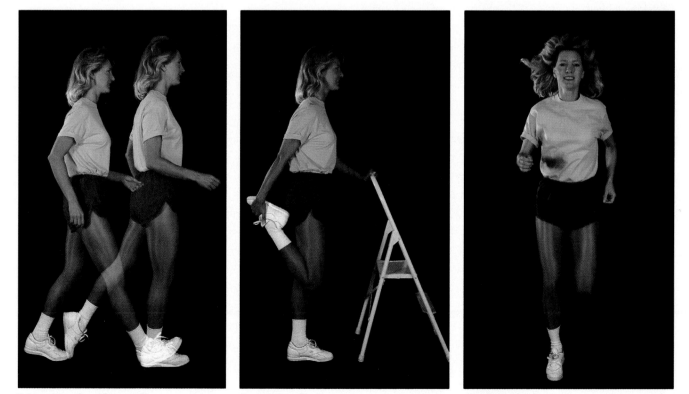

Warm-Up, Cool-Down Phases   *Stretching Phase*   *Aerobic Phase*

As you progress, some benefits will be more and more measurable: a drop in your resting heart rate (your heart will be pumping more blood with fewer beats); increased muscle mass; loss of fat tissue; and improved levels of blood fats.

The duration and intensity of the aerobic activity determine to what extent the body shifts its fat stores to supply energy to the muscles.

THE LONGER YOU EXERCISE, THE MORE FAT YOUR BODY BURNS

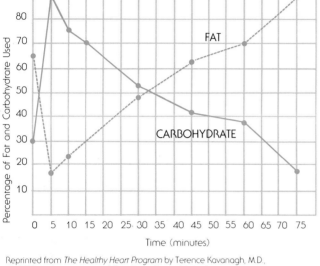

Reprinted from *The Healthy Heart Program* by Terence Kavanagh, M.D., © 1985, with permission of Key Porter Books Limited.

Working up to a level of exercising beyond 30 minutes allows the body to switch from carbohydrate stores to fat stores so that the greater percentage of the calories burned will come from fat stores. If it's weight loss you're after, consider increasing the duration of your aerobic activity beyond 30 minutes.

Don't confuse body fat and dietary fat; body fat is the stored form of excess dietary protein, carbohydrates, and fats. Even lean people have more than enough fat stores for energy production.

Let your target heart rate monitor the intensity of your workout. The easiest way to build up endurance is to repeat the same activity, but you can increase the challenge and add fun and interest to the workout if you cross-train (train in more than one aerobic activity).

Whatever the activity, exercise until your heart rate reaches a predetermined target heart rate (THR), which should fall within the zone of 70 to

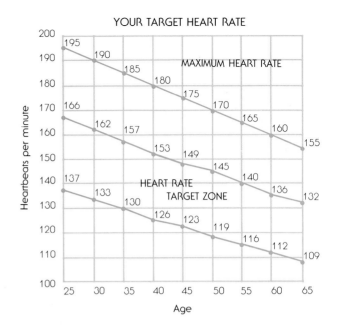

YOUR TARGET HEART RATE

85 percent of your maximum heart rate (MHR). To determine your target heart rate zone, subtract your age from 220; multiply by 70 percent and 85 percent.

MHR = 220 minus age
THR = MHR x 70% and 85%

During the aerobic phase, your heart rate per minute should remain within the target zone. If you are older than 35, in poor health, or on medication, check with your physician before determining your training goals.

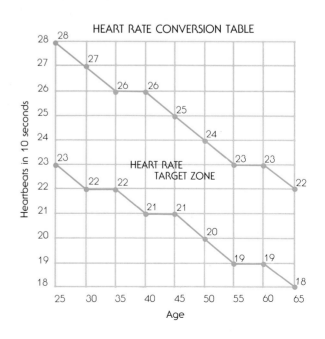

HEART RATE CONVERSION TABLE

AEROBIC CHOICES

Activity	Progression		Considerations
Brisk Walking	To Begin:	15 to 20 minutes	Excellent choice for most people, especially the elderly and beginners. Risk of injury is low. Tones leg muscles.
	To Increase:	20 to 30 minutes	
	To Maintain:	30 to 45 minutes	
Running	To Begin:	Alternate walk-jog for 15 to 20 minutes	Good choice for the well-conditioned individual who can walk 2 miles in 30 minutes. Tones leg muscles.
	To Increase:	20 minutes of continuous running	
	To Maintain:	30 minutes or more of continuous running	
Cycling	To Begin:	10 minutes with no resistance 5 to 10 minutes with light resistance	Good choice for most people. Especially helpful for those with leg injuries, arthritis, or minor back problems. This nonweight-bearing activity tones the front muscles of the legs.
	To Increase:	5 to 10 minutes with no resistance 15 to 25 minutes with moderate resistance	
	To Maintain:	5 minutes with moderate resistance 30 minutes or more with moderate resistance	
Swimming	To Begin:	Swim 1 length; rest 30 to 60 seconds; continue for 15 to 20 minutes.	Excellent choice for most people. Especially good for people with circulatory or orthopedic problems. Tones the muscles of the entire body.
	To Increase:	Swim 1 length; rest 30 to 60 seconds; continue for 20 to 30 minutes.	
	To Maintain:	Swim continuously for 30 minutes or more; rest only as needed.	
Aerobic Dancing	To Begin:	Select a class or video that stresses gradual progression and proper exercise techniques. Exercise at your own pace and rest as needed.	Good choice for those who enjoy group activity and music. Low-impact aerobic dance may reduce risk of injury. Most classes are designed to tone the entire body.
	To Increase:	Exercise on a regular basis to improve endurance. Reduce rest time and increase time of continuous movement.	
	To Maintain:	Dance vigorously for 20 to 30 minutes.	
Rowing	To Begin:	15 minutes with almost no resistance	Good for most people, but not for individuals with lower back problems. Risk of injury is low. Tones muscles of the legs, arms, and abdominal area.
	To Increase:	15 to 20 minutes with light resistance	
	To Maintain:	20 to 30 minutes with moderate resistance	

To quickly determine if you are exercising within your target zone, place two fingers on the thumb-side of your wrist. Count the pulse beats during a 10-second period; multiply by 6 or check the heart rate conversion chart (opposite page). Do this about every ten minutes until you learn to judge when you are in the target zone. Then check it only in the middle of the aerobic phase and immediately afterwards. If you are below your target zone and experiencing no discomfort, increase the intensity of your workout. Increasing the intensity of

exercise beyond the target zone will not increase benefits, but it will invite health hazards and injury.

You can't rush fitness. A common mistake is for beginners to approach the workout too aggressively. They become overtired and often drop out, sometimes because of injury. Work through the beginning levels before increasing the duration and intensity of the aerobic phase of your workout. When added exertion is not too strenuous, you will have proof of the most basic benefit of aerobic conditioning—increased endurance and energy.

Don't Let Exercise Cause a Pain in the Back

A number of exercises can be done to strengthen and stretch the abdomen, back, arms, legs, thighs, buttocks, and chest. Since back problems associated with weak muscles are common, it is particularly important to improve abdominal and back strength. But keep in mind that the back is also an area easily strained during exercise. The exercises on these pages demonstrate how attention to technique and body movement can put minimal stress on the back and other areas of the body while you stretch, strengthen, and tone your muscles. To avoid undue strain and pain, avoid the techniques shown in the boxes.

Abdominal Crunch vs. Straight-Leg Raise: Crunches strengthen the abdomen without straining the back. Cross right leg over bent knee and raise left elbow toward knee; repeat 8 to 12 times and switch to other side. Lifting and lowering straight legs causes the back to arch, putting undue stress on the lower back muscles.

Bent-Knee Curl-Up vs. Straight-Leg Sit-Up: Bent-knee curl-ups strengthen the abdominal muscles. Cross hands on chest, keeping back flat against floor; curl up, raising shoulder blades off floor 30 degrees. Repeat 8 to 12 times. Pulling up with legs straight works the hip flexors more than the abdomen and puts strain on the lower back.

Bent-Knee Leg Lift vs. Straight-Leg Lift: Leg lifts performed with the bottom leg bent strengthen the outer-thigh and buttocks. Support body with both hands; slowly lift and lower top leg, keeping it aligned with body. Repeat 8 to 12 times, and switch to other side. When both legs are straight, the body is easily thrown out of alignment.

Bent-Leg Lift vs. Donkey Kick: Bent-leg lifts strengthen the hamstring muscles and buttocks. Support body with hands and one knee; slightly lower and raise thigh no higher than hip level, keeping knee bent at 90-degree angle. Repeat 8 to 12 times and switch to other side. Kicking your leg with the supporting knee locked is hard on the back and leg muscles.

Back Stretch vs. Plow: To stretch the back muscles, push lower back to floor for support and pull leg to chest; hold for 10 to 30 seconds; relax and repeat 2 to 6 times. Switch to other side. The plow can cause serious injury when shifted weight puts undue strain on the spine.

Hamstring Stretch vs. Hurdle Stretch: To stretch the hamstring, inner thigh, and lower back, sit with one leg outstretched, the other leg tucked in. Keeping back straight, slowly stretch forward from the hip; bring chest towards knee while looking forward. Hold for 10 to 30 seconds; relax and repeat 2 to 6 times. Switch to other side. The hurdle position and a rounded back place undue stress on the knee and lower back. Grabbing toes and pulling forward may overstretch the hamstring muscle.

180-Degree Neck Stretch vs. 360-Degree Neck Roll: To loosen neck muscles, roll neck slowly from side to side; relax and repeat 2 to 6 times. Rolling your head backwards may injure the spine.

Supplement your aerobic program with strength training to tone your muscles. You will increase overall strength, thereby decreasing risk of injury from sudden and sustained exertion. Lower back problems, for example, are often avoided by strengthening the abdominal muscles.

Weight training and calisthenics build muscular strength. Correct form, proper breathing, and stepped increases are key factors. It is best undertaken with a partner trained in technique and safety precautions.

Push-ups, leg-raises, and abdominal crunches are good examples of calisthenics. When beginning a strength exercise, try to complete 8 to 12 repetitions. Keep in mind that you will want to add increments of 8 to 12 repetitions as your fitness level improves.

Follow these no-strain, no-pain strategies:
• Don't hold your breath. This increases blood pressure and puts unnatural strain on the heart. Exhale when exerting effort; inhale when easing up.
• Do exercises slowly, in controlled movements to build maximum strength. Focus on technique, not speed. Good technique and proper movements help to avoid making excessive demands on muscles and joints. (See pages 22-23.)
• Practice moderation. Exercising too hard, too often, and too long weakens muscles—a common cause of injury. Stop or take a break if you experience sharp or consistent pain.

Set Yourself Up for Success

While changing lifetime habits makes good health sense, it is never an overnight proposition. Even the most intelligent and motivated people have difficulty unlearning bad health habits and adopting new ones. Beyond knowledge and know-how, you've got to start slowly with realistic expectations, and put your heart into the matter.

TAKE INITIATIVE

Once you are convinced that making positive lifestyle changes is what you want, don't "tomorrow" away your chances for success. The secret to overcoming inertia is *today*. Begin to take charge; the changes will follow.

TAKE CHARGE MENTALLY

Studies show that people who believe in their ability to succeed are more likely to do it; they will try harder to master the challenges, whereas, those who doubt their capabilities tend to slacken their efforts or give up altogether. If you believe in your power to take charge of your own vitality and health, you'll be more likely to succeed. Nurture the belief in your ability to succeed by concentrating on similar goals you've already achieved. Maybe you gave up cigarettes, gained control over your drinking, or mastered some other difficult task. What is it you're trying to do now? Begin an exercise program? Cut calories? Realistically assess your chances of accomplishing each goal. If you believe your chances are good, you're on your way.

TAKE IT EASY

As you begin, don't undertake too much at one time. Instead of saying, "I'm going to get in shape," you might put on some comfortable shoes, head out the door, and walk briskly for five minutes. In the time it takes to get back, you've put in ten minutes, which will give you, as a beginner, more energy than an hour's workout. Fatigue and anticipated exertion often kill motivation and encourage burnout. Begin with a week of ten-minute workouts, and increase the time to fifteen minutes. Continue until you've progressed to thirty-minute workouts. Be consistent about when you exercise; don't let other interests sabotage your efforts.

Small changes count. The *New England Journal of Medicine* reported that the mortality rate is 28 percent lower for men expending more than 2,000 calories per week than for those expending less energy. Walking 5 to 10 miles weekly increases your chances of outliving sedentary peers.

To improve nutrition, tackle the obvious habits first. Becoming aware of what you eat and why you eat it is half the battle. A daily food journal checked against the Basic Four and tallied for calories might reveal some habits that can be turned into strategies: Turn "nibbling" into a planned snack (fruit instead of a candy bar). Eat only on the cue of hunger; the more you pay attention to physical signs of hunger, the less you need to rely on psychological willpower. Say "yes" to smaller portions and "no thanks" to seconds.

When weight loss is the goal, patience and perseverance yield the highest dividends. Remember, it probably took years to acquire the excess pounds, so don't put pressure on yourself to lose them in a few weeks. The key is to cut back on daily calories on a consistent basis. For example, cutting 250 calories a day will result in a loss of 26 pounds over a year. How so? The reason is as simple as it is foolproof. In two weeks, 250 fewer calories a day add up to 3,500 fewer calories, the amount needed to lose one pound of body fat. Since there are 26 sets of two-week periods in a year, 26 is the number of pounds you would lose. Studies show that this pound-shedding pace, when compared to quick-loss strategies, is safer and more likely to be permanent. A person who loses seven pounds in 10 days is likely to lose more water and lean muscle tissue than fat. If you think about it, you wouldn't want to starve for a week and a half because you're too muscular!

Of course, the way each person's metabolism responds to reduced calorie intake is unique; moreover, a precise determination of calories consumed is difficult. But, give or take a couple of pounds, this method works.

Happily, 250 calories a day are easily dropped when you limit foods high in fat. A little less butter on the toast, reduced-calorie mayonnaise on the sandwich, and an extra light dressing on the salad will help get you there.

Giving up a small portion of high-fat food will cut as many calories as a larger portion of food that is mostly protein or carbohydrate. Two bites of chocolate cake (65 calories, of which about 30 are fat) don't even weigh an ounce. An orange with the same amount of calories weighs about five ounces. Your stomach will feel fuller if you eat the orange and let the cake go. The nutritive gain? Instead of fat and sugar, you'll be getting a day's worth of vitamin C and a serving of fiber.

TAKE MORE RESPONSIBILITY

Don't relegate responsibility for your health to your doctor. Doctors themselves are convinced that eliminating certain foods and emphasizing others can be an important preventive measure, especially against heart disease and cancer. They are further convinced that exercise is a multi-benefit proposition. But the one person who can best manage these lifestyle traits is you, not your doctor.

Stay informed about risk factors such as smoking, hypertension, obesity, cholesterol, and stress. Become familiar with factors that promote wellness, and integrate them into your lifestyle. Read food labels to expose hidden grams of fat and milligrams of sodium; seek out reliable data on preventive health maintenance. Start by reading *Cooking Light* nutrition and fitness facts flagged by the following symbols:

NUTRITION   FITNESS

TAKE PLEASURE

To live happier as well as longer, take pleasure in whatever it is you're doing right. When you approach your workout, know that you are burning the calories; don't worry about feeling the burn. Moderation is a much-touted word in exercise this year. The fact that more strenuous exercise does not equate with superior fitness sheds a new light on workouts. Feel free to concentrate on pleasant thoughts while you pursue your favorite activity (walking, aerobic dance, etc.). Concentrating on pain is no way to become fit.

Admit it. You're not going to eat tasteless, unappealing food, even with the promise of good health. Certainly you eat for pleasure and not for a miracle cure. Yet, you do know there's wisdom in eating defensively. Take pleasure in eating health-conscious foods that are delicious and appealing. Take pleasure in *Cooking Light* menus and recipes. They're delightfully culinary—not medical.

Healthy American Meals

The menus in this chapter celebrate the "light" revolution in American cuisine, a merger of our growing interest in nutrition and health with our national affinity for freshness and simple elegance. Regional and ethnic flavor add the adventure. Whether it's a morning meal plantation-style or an attractive salad buffet Mediterranean-style, these menus will satisfy the eclectic American palate.

At times, you may choose to follow each menu as it is presented, using the full-color photographs to glean ideas for subtleties of presentation—table settings, centerpieces, garnishes—the touches that will make your meals superlatively appealing as well as healthful. When time is a key factor, this approach means you can start with deciding what to buy at the marketplace instead of what to serve for the meal. Useful also are the time-efficient preparation tips that accompany the menus.

Sometimes you will have enough leisure time to bring your own experience, creativity, and family preferences to the meal. You may want to use *Cooking Light* menus to get started, as suggestions for planning balanced meals. Each menu was developed specifically to accommodate *Cooking Light*'s dietary guidelines. Of the total calories in each menu, more than 50 percent are provided by carbohydrates, less than 30 percent by fat, and less than 20 percent by protein. When you want to substitute a particular dish in a menu, draw from the hundreds of flavorful dishes in the recipe section of this book. To keep the meals balanced, it is best to substitute foods comparable in calories and nutrients.

Even if you don't live on the sunny, West Coast, you can make your guests feel a part of the healthy, California cuisine: Grilled Herbed Chicken, Spaghetti Vegetables, and Baked Sonoma Goat Cheese Salad accompanied by white wine (California Dreamin' menu begins on page 75).

Four sections cover almost any opportunity to dine American-style, from tempting family fare to elegant special occasions:

Breakfast and Brunch. Early or late morning, you will find a suitable menu to provide that first mental and physical boost of the day. Pamper someone with Breakfast in Bed, or put the Kids in the Kitchen to prepare Grilled Peanut Butter-Banana Sandwiches. Have a pregame brunch, and make it Mexican, complete with margaritas, tortillas, and Pinto Bean Salad. Or nestle in for Brunch, Plantation-Style with Deep-South know-how. Keep New Year's Day Brunch simple this year, but don't forget to add the luck—Black-Eyed Pea Soup.

Quick and Easy. Making short work of savory, wholesome meals is a lifestyle given in the '80s. An easy-to-bake omelet flavored with cinnamon and apple makes Sunday Night Supper what it should be—a time of family fellowship and comfort. Chicken Dinner from the Grill speaks for itself; grilling makes quick work of any entrée. Traditional Southern dishes are modified for modern schedules and sophisticated tastes in Slightly Southern Supper. Celebrate Father's Day Dinner with an incredible chocolate cake drenched in Kahlúa. Why incredible? There are only 138 calories per serving. Shrimp in Garlic Sauce and Fruit Mélange are two dishes that make the Mardi Gras Celebration Dinner quick and easy, but ever so tasty.

Microwave It Light. Good-tasting, attractive meals don't have to compete with daily obligations, especially when the microwave oven is employed to cut preparation time and lock in nutrients. If you're not around and the kids are, delegate the Pronto Kid's Menu, which features easy-to-make tacos and Jicama Chips. The Continental Take-Out Lunch is a portable meal. All the foods can be served cold or at room temperature. Salads, ideal time-savers, can be made early and chilled until needed. A Mediterranean Salad Buffet affords just that kind of head start. And you won't waste a microwave minute when preparing the Oriental Menu. It's synchronized to move from one food to another. Rely on the African Menu for culinary adventure and Elegant Company Fare for elegance with ease.

That's Entertaining. Americans love to entertain, and generally they prefer to keep it casual. No one enjoys the pleasures of casual entertaining more than Californians. Settle in for some California Dreamin' with easy-to-grill chicken and garden-fresh gazpacho. Every bit as casual, but more Texan in flavor is the Southwestern Patio Buffet, featuring Turkey Chili. White Bean Salad and Eggplant Lasagna make the Mediterranean Vegetarian Dinner as economical as it is nutritious. When thoughts turn to more exotic fare, present an Indian Tandoori Feast with saffron-flavored rice and yogurt-marinated cornish hens. On easy-living summer days, cool off along with your guests with a colorful Summer Salad Buffet.

Pamper yourself with a light Breakfast in Bed (menu begins on page 30)—Breakfast Bagels, Fresh Fruit Cups with Nutmeg, Champagne Spritzers, and coffee. Fluff up the pillows and relax!

Breakfast & Brunch

Start the weekend off right with breakfast in bed and a Tropical Spritzer—a refreshing blend of guava juice and club soda.

Breakfast In Bed

There is no better way to pamper yourself than to have breakfast in bed. When Saturday rolls around, a leisurely breakfast, the morning paper, and a soft pillow at your back will renew spirits and energy after a hectic week. To insure that relaxed atmosphere, everything but the beverages in this menu can be made ahead. In fact, the ham-and-egg spread for the bagels will keep for several days in the refrigerator. And you won't spend a min-

Breakfast Bagels
Fresh Fruit Cups with
Nutmeg
Champagne Spritzers
or
Tropical Spritzers
Coffee

Serves 2
Total calories per serving: 305

ute of your precious weekend worrying about calories. Low-fat cottage cheese and lean ham help keep fat and calories low. Start the Fresh Fruit Cups with Nutmeg the night before, or prepare them from start to finish in five minutes in the morning. For a special touch, try using freshly ground nutmeg.

Adding club soda to champagne or guava juice cuts the spritzers' alcohol calories in half. Be sure to highlight the mood by serving the spritzers in tall, graceful champagne flutes.

BREAKFAST BAGELS

¼ cup low-fat cottage cheese
1 teaspoon reduced-calorie mayonnaise
½ teaspoon prepared mustard
Dash of hot sauce
½ hard-cooked egg, chopped
2 tablespoons minced lean cooked ham
1 teaspoon diced pimiento
1 whole wheat bagel, split and toasted

Combine first 4 ingredients in container of an electric blender or food processor; process until smooth. Stir in egg, ham, and pimiento. Spread 3 tablespoons cottage cheese mixture onto each bagel half. Yield: 2 servings (161 calories per serving).

PROTEIN 10.8 / FAT 4.1 / CARBOHYDRATE 19.8 / CHOLESTEROL 76 / IRON 1.4 / SODIUM 387 / CALCIUM 42

FRESH FRUIT CUPS WITH NUTMEG

1 medium peach, peeled, pitted, and chopped
1 medium plum, pitted and chopped
½ cup chopped fresh pineapple
2 teaspoons lime juice
¼ teaspoon ground nutmeg
1 tablespoon plus 1½ teaspoons chopped pecans, toasted
Fresh mint sprigs (optional)

Combine first 5 ingredients in a medium bowl; toss gently. Spoon fruit mixture evenly into 2 individual dessert dishes. Top with pecans. Garnish with mint sprigs, if desired. Yield: 2 servings (94 calories per serving).

PROTEIN 1.1 / FAT 4.2 / CARBOHYDRATE 15.3 / CHOLESTEROL 0 / IRON 0.4 / SODIUM 1 / CALCIUM 9

BREAKING THE FAST

Some health-conscious families forego breakfast, thinking they're ahead of the game if they avoid bacon, eggs, and buttered bread. True, breakfasts can easily be loaded up with fat, cholesterol, and sodium. But skipping breakfast is not the solution. Everyone in the family should be encouraged to "break the fast" after a night of sleep. A meal in the morning brings blood sugar to required levels, providing energy needed for high performance.

Even on rushed weekdays there are quick breakfast options that avoid undesirable excesses. Quick-cooking oatmeal makes a great fix-your-own kind of breakfast. Freeze-ahead oat or bran muffins with raisins are favorites and provide good sources of fiber and B vitamins. Served along with a glass of low-fat milk for protein and calcium and a glass of orange juice for vitamin C and potassium, oatmeal or muffins make a satisfying breakfast.

For more leisurely weekend breakfasts, whole wheat pancakes with a glass of skim milk or vegetable omelets, made with more egg whites and fewer yolks, make a ready meal plan. When you or someone special is presented with the opportunity to treat yourself to breakfast in bed, set the stage for the do-ahead Breakfast in Bed menu by first presenting a Champagne Spritzer. This low-calorie, low-alcohol beverage will add sparkle to the day.

CHAMPAGNE SPRITZERS

½ cup club soda, chilled
½ cup pink champagne, chilled
Fresh whole strawberries (optional)

Combine club soda and champagne; stir lightly. Pour into 2 champagne glasses. Garnish with strawberries, if desired. Serve immediately. Yield: 2 servings (45 calories per 1-cup serving).

PROTEIN 0.2 / FAT 0.0 / CARBOHYDRATE 0.7 / CHOLESTEROL 0 / IRON 0.3 / SODIUM 15 / CALCIUM 5

TROPICAL SPRITZERS

½ cup club soda, chilled
½ cup guava fruit juice, chilled
Fresh whole strawberries (optional)

Combine club soda and guava juice; stir lightly. Pour into 2 champagne glasses. Garnish with strawberries, if desired. Serve immediately. Yield: 2 servings (34 calories per 1-cup serving).

PROTEIN 0.0 / FAT 0.0 / CARBOHYDRATE 8.0 / CHOLESTEROL 0 / IRON 0.0 / SODIUM 16 / CALCIUM 3

Wholesome foods abound in this fun-to-make children's menu.

Kids In The Kitchen

When your children ask to help in the kitchen, let this brunch menu be their first lesson. It's quick, easy, and everyone can get involved. Someone can mix the peanut butter filling and spread it on the bread while another dips sandwiches in the egg wash. The children may need supervision with the grilling at first, but they'll soon catch on.

The granola-topped parfaits can be adapted to include your family's favorite fruit flavors.

Yogurt Crunch Parfaits
Grilled Peanut
Butter-Banana Sandwiches
Raspberry-Cinnamon Tea

Serves 4
Total calories per serving: 484

Tempting combinations of fresh fruit and low-fat yogurts are almost endless. Brightly colored Raspberry-Cinnamon Tea will get the day off to a cheerful start.

Try experimenting with the many different flavors of herbal tea and spices to create unique decaffeinated beverages.

This kid-pleasing menu earns high marks in nutrition. Naturally wholesome peanut butter is fortified with the goodness of toasted wheat germ. But this peanut butter sandwich won't look ordinary. Not after it is dipped in egg, grilled like French toast, and topped with banana slices. It's an old standard with new appeal.

YOGURT CRUNCH PARFAITS

¾ cup fresh blueberries
2 (8-ounce) cartons lemon low-fat
  yogurt
¼ cup granola cereal

Spoon 3 tablespoons fresh blueberries into each of four 6-ounce parfait glasses; top berries with ½ carton lemon yogurt. Sprinkle 1 tablespoon granola over yogurt in each parfait glass. Serve immediately. Yield: 4 servings (200 calories per serving).

PROTEIN 5.1 / FAT 2.2 / CARBOHYDRATE 41.4 / CHOLESTEROL 0 /
IRON 0.3 / SODIUM 90 / CALCIUM 150

GRILLED PEANUT BUTTER-BANANA SANDWICHES

⅓ cup crunchy peanut butter
3 tablespoons wheat germ, toasted
3 tablespoons reduced-calorie
  maple syrup
¼ teaspoon ground cinnamon
⅛ teaspoon ground nutmeg
8 slices thinly sliced whole wheat
  bread
1 egg, lightly beaten
¼ cup skim milk
1 medium banana, cut into 16 slices

Combine peanut butter, wheat germ, syrup, cinnamon, and nutmeg in a small bowl, stirring until well blended. Spread peanut butter mixture evenly over 4 slices whole wheat bread. Top with remaining 4 bread slices.

Combine egg and milk in a shallow bowl, beating well.

Place a non-stick skillet over medium heat until hot. Dip one sandwich at a time into egg mixture, coating well. Drain off excess egg mixture. Place sandwiches in skillet, and cook over medium heat 1 to 2 minutes on each side or until lightly browned. Cut each sandwich into 4 triangles. Top each triangle with 1 slice banana. Serve immediately. Yield: 4 servings (252 calories per serving).

PROTEIN 12.3 / FAT 13.5 / CARBOHYDRATE 25.1 / CHOLESTEROL 71 /
IRON 1.7 / SODIUM 241 / CALCIUM 60

RASPBERRY-CINNAMON TEA

4 raspberry herbal tea bags
2 tablespoons firmly packed brown sugar
½ teaspoon whole cloves
2 (3-inch) sticks cinnamon
4 cups boiling water
Additional sticks cinnamon (optional)

Place tea bags, sugar, cloves, and 2 sticks cinnamon in a 1-quart glass measure; slowly pour boiling water over tea bags. Cover and steep 15 minutes. Strain liquid; discard tea bags and spices. Serve tea over ice; garnish with cinnamon sticks, if desired. Yield: 4 cups (32 calories per 1-cup serving).

PROTEIN 0.1 / FAT 0.1 / CARBOHYDRATE 8.7 / CHOLESTEROL 0 /
IRON 0.7 / SODIUM 3 / CALCIUM 22

 EARLY EATING HABITS SET LIFETIME PATTERNS

In the same fashion as busy adults, children and adolescents frequently skip meals or resort to fast foods and convenience foods for regular meals. National surveys show that young people's diets contain too much fat and sodium but not enough vital minerals such as iron and calcium. Moreover, eating disorders are on the rise.

One way to combat poor nutrition practices among children is to set the stage early. Eating patterns and attitudes toward foods established during early childhood are likely to follow a person throughout life. Help children get off to a healthy start by offering a wide variety of nutrient-dense foods from the Basic Four, and include each food group at every meal. Have nutritious snacks such as fresh fruit and fruit juices. Encourage sensible attitudes toward food, and avoid the pitfalls of past generations. Disband the "clean-plate club," and avoid offering food as a reward for good behavior.

Discourage skipping meals. Recognize breakfast as a key meal of the day. Although not all studies agree, some show that children who have a good breakfast before school fare better and score higher on tests than those who skip breakfast. Above all, set an example for children. If variety, moderation, and balance are integral to the parents' eating patterns, children will more than likely follow suit.

Mexican Brunch

Morning Margaritas
Brunch Tortillas
Pinto Bean Salad
Strawberry-Mango
Compote
Orange-Cinnamon Coffee

Serves 8
Total calories per serving: 575

Brunch Tortillas make a satisfying entrée that will carry you through the day.

Mexican fare doesn't have to be calorie laden with fried tortillas, refried beans, and such. At least, not in this brunch, which includes the basic favorites—even tart margaritas! (Freshly squeezed orange juice and club soda help reduce calories.) Scrambled eggs and chicken flavored with green chiles and picante sauce and then wrapped in flour tortillas, make an *olé* entrée. Colorful pinto beans highlight the salad and contribute plenty of carbohydrates and fiber to the meal. Toss in lots of extra flavor with a fresh cilantro-flavored dressing. For dessert? A typically Mexican fruit combination: fresh mangos and strawberries, dolloped with cinnamon-spiced low-fat yogurt.

MORNING MARGARITAS

1 cup frozen limeade concentrate, undiluted
1⅔ cups freshly squeezed orange juice
⅔ cup tequila
4 cups ice cubes
2 cups club soda
Lime slices (optional)
Orange slices (optional)

Combine limeade concentrate, orange juice, and tequila in container of an electric blender; process until smooth. Add ice and process until tequila mixture is slushy. Transfer to a large pitcher; lightly stir in club soda. Pour into 8 serving glasses; garnish with lime slices and orange slices, if desired. Serve immediately. Yield: 8 cups (137 calories per 1-cup serving).

PROTEIN 0.4 / FAT 0.1 / CARBOHYDRATE 23.6 / CHOLESTEROL 0 / IRON 0.2 / SODIUM 13 / CALCIUM 9

BRUNCH TORTILLAS

8 (6-inch) flour tortillas
Vegetable cooking spray
1 teaspoon vegetable oil
½ cup peeled, shredded potato
3 green onions with tops, chopped
1 clove garlic, minced
1 medium tomato, seeded and chopped
1 tablespoon plus 1½ teaspoons chopped green chiles
1 tablespoon chopped green pepper
1 tablespoon chopped sweet red pepper
7 eggs, beaten
2 cups chopped cooked chicken breast (skinned before cooking and cooked without salt)
¼ teaspoon salt
⅛ teaspoon pepper
½ cup picante sauce
2 green onions (optional)

Wrap tortillas in aluminum foil; bake at 350° for 10 minutes or until thoroughly heated. Set aside and keep warm.

Coat a large skillet with cooking spray; add oil, and place over medium heat until hot. Add potato, chopped green onions, and garlic; sauté vegetables 3 minutes. Add tomato, chiles, green pepper, and sweet red pepper; sauté vegetables 2 minutes or until tender. Add eggs, chicken, salt, and pepper. Cook, stirring occasionally, until eggs are firm but still moist.

Spoon ½ cup egg mixture onto each warm tortilla. Roll tortillas, and place seam side up on a serving platter. Spoon 1 tablespoon picante sauce over each tortilla. Garnish with green onions, if desired. Serve immediately. Yield: 8 servings (260 calories per serving).

PROTEIN 19.3 / FAT 9.1 / CARBOHYDRATE 26.6 / CHOLESTEROL 269 / IRON 2.4 / SODIUM 270 / CALCIUM 64

PINTO BEAN SALAD

2 (16-ounce) cans pinto beans
1 cup shredded Romaine lettuce
½ cup chopped celery
⅓ cup chopped purple onion
¼ cup chopped sweet red pepper
3 tablespoons red wine vinegar
2 tablespoons vegetable oil
2 teaspoons minced fresh cilantro
¼ teaspoon garlic salt
Lettuce leaves
½ cup (2 ounces) shredded Cheddar
    cheese

Place beans in a colander, and rinse under cold water 1 minute; set colander aside to let beans drain 1 minute.

Combine beans and next 4 ingredients in a large bowl; set aside. Combine vinegar, oil, cilantro, and garlic salt in a jar; cover tightly, and shake vigorously. Pour vinegar mixture over reserved bean mixture; toss gently to coat well. Cover and chill thoroughly.

To serve, spoon bean mixture into a lettuce-lined salad bowl; sprinkle with cheese. Yield: 8 servings (123 calories per serving).

PROTEIN 4.9 / FAT 6.3 / CARBOHYDRATE 11.7 / CHOLESTEROL 7 / IRON 0.9 / SODIUM 117 / CALCIUM 82

STRAWBERRY-MANGO COMPOTE

2 cups chopped ripe mango
2 cups sliced fresh strawberries
½ cup vanilla low-fat yogurt
⅛ teaspoon ground cinnamon
Dash of ground nutmeg

Combine mango and strawberries in a medium bowl; toss gently. Cover and chill thoroughly. Combine yogurt, cinnamon, and nutmeg; stir well.

Spoon fruit mixture evenly into 8 compotes; top each serving with 1 tablespoon yogurt mixture. Yield: 8 servings (50 calories per serving).

PROTEIN 1.1 / FAT 0.4 / CARBOHYDRATE 11.6 / CHOLESTEROL 1 / IRON 0.2 / SODIUM 11 / CALCIUM 34

ORANGE-CINNAMON COFFEE

2 quarts strong, hot coffee
2 medium oranges, thinly sliced
3 (3-inch) sticks cinnamon

Combine all ingredients in a large Dutch oven. Cover; let stand 30 minutes. Strain, discarding oranges and cinnamon. Serve hot. Yield: 8 cups (5 calories per ¾-cup serving).

PROTEIN 0.2 / FAT 0.0 / CARBOHYDRATE 1.0 / CHOLESTEROL 0 / IRON 1.0 / SODIUM 5 / CALCIUM 5

 ## MUSCLES AND BONE DENSITY

Building strong muscles is a way to build strong bones and decrease risk of developing osteoporosis, the bone-thinning disease. Studies show that exercises, such as brisk walking or jogging, which require the skeleton to bear some weight, help preserve and may even increase bone density and strength.

Research conducted by a group of physicians at the Mayo Clinic reveals a possible link between strength of back muscles and density of the vertebrae (bones that make up the spinal column). The stronger the back muscles, the denser the bones. The same researchers now want to determine if specific exercises designed to strengthen back muscles and support the spine can stop or reverse the loss of spinal bone density.

Turkey Hash on Cornbread Cakes, Tomato Wedges with Basil Dressing, Ambrosia, and Mock Mint Juleps.

Brunch, Plantation-Style

Deep South knows how to ... morning meal. When ... nestled in a rocker on a spra... ng veranda with a mint julep in hand, plantation life never looked so good. Hearty fare was the order of the day on nineteenth-century plantations. Here are some old Southern favorites, lightened to keep pace with twentieth-century tastes.

No cream in the sauce for the Turkey Hash. It's made with skim milk. And the vegetables are sautéed in a skillet coated with

cooking spray (not tablespoons of butter) before being added to the hash. Diluting the bourbon with unsweetened apple cider and heating the Mock Mint Julep cut the alcohol content and calories by more than half.

This is an ideal company menu, for almost everything can be prepared early. However, do make the Cornbread Cakes close to serving time in order to have them at their finest.

Turkey Hash
Cornbread Cakes
Tomato Wedges with
Basil Dressing
Ambrosia
Mock Mint Juleps

Serves 8
Total calories per serving: 580

TURKEY HASH

Vegetable cooking spray
⅔ cup sliced fresh mushrooms
2 tablespoons chopped onion
2 tablespoons chopped green pepper
2 tablespoons chopped sweet red pepper
3 tablespoons margarine
¼ cup plus 1 tablespoon all-purpose flour
1½ teaspoons chicken-flavored bouillon granules
1½ cups skim milk
1½ cups water
½ teaspoon pepper
¼ teaspoon paprika
5 cups chopped, cooked turkey breast (skinned before cooking and cooked without salt)
Fresh parsley sprigs

Coat a large skillet with cooking spray. Place

over medium heat until hot. Add mushrooms, onion, green pepper, and sweet red pepper; cook until vegetables are tender. Remove vegetables from skillet, and set aside.

Melt margarine in skillet over low heat. Add flour and bouillon granules, stirring until smooth. Cook 1 minute, stirring constantly (mixture will be dry). Gradually add milk and water; cook over medium heat, stirring constantly with a wire whisk, until smooth and thickened. Stir in pepper, paprika, turkey, and reserved vegetables. Cook until thoroughly heated. Garnish with parsley sprigs. Yield: 8 servings (216 calories per serving).

PROTEIN 28.4 / FAT 7.4 / CARBOHYDRATE 7.3 / CHOLESTEROL 61 / IRON 1.6 / SODIUM 202 / CALCIUM 78

CORNBREAD CAKES

2 cups cornmeal
2 cups skim milk
2 eggs, lightly beaten
¼ teaspoon salt
¼ teaspoon garlic powder
Vegetable cooking spray

Combine cornmeal and milk in a large bowl; stir well. Let stand 5 minutes. Stir in eggs, salt, and garlic powder.

Heat a griddle or skillet coated with cooking spray over medium heat until hot. For each cake, pour 1 tablespoon batter into skillet. Turn cakes when tops are bubbly and edges are slightly dry. Repeat procedure until all batter is used. Yield: 24 cakes (149 calories per 3-cake serving).

PROTEIN 5.8 / FAT 1.9 / CARBOHYDRATE 26.2 / CHOLESTEROL 69 / IRON 1.3 / SODIUM 115 / CALCIUM 66

TOMATO WEDGES WITH BASIL DRESSING

⅓ cup plain low-fat yogurt
3 tablespoons reduced-calorie mayonnaise
1½ teaspoons malt vinegar
¾ teaspoon chopped fresh basil
⅛ teaspoon dry mustard
4 medium tomatoes, cut into 32 wedges
Curly leaf lettuce leaves

Combine yogurt, mayonnaise, vinegar, basil, and mustard in a small bowl; mix well. Cover and chill thoroughly.

To serve, arrange tomato wedges on a lettuce-lined platter. Spoon yogurt mixture over tomato wedges. Yield: 8 servings (35 calories per serving).

PROTEIN 1.2 / FAT 1.8 / CARBOHYDRATE 4.2 / CHOLESTEROL 2 / IRON 0.3 / SODIUM 54 / CALCIUM 23

AMBROSIA

4 large navel oranges, peeled
1 (20-ounce) can unsweetened pineapple chunks, undrained
2 large bananas, sliced
⅓ cup unsweetened grated coconut

Section oranges over a bowl, reserving juice. Drain pineapple chunks, reserving juice. Layer pineapple chunks, orange sections, and banana slices in a bowl. Pour reserved orange and pineapple juices over layered fruit mixture. Cover and chill thoroughly. To serve, arrange chilled fruit mixture on a serving dish. Sprinkle with grated coconut. Yield: 8 servings (119 calories per serving).

PROTEIN 1.6 / FAT 2.5 / CARBOHYDRATE 25.2 / CHOLESTEROL 0 / IRON 0.8 / SODIUM 3 / CALCIUM 46

MOCK MINT JULEPS

1 cup loosely packed fresh mint leaves
3½ cups water
½ cup bourbon
4 cups unsweetened apple cider
Fresh mint sprigs

Place mint leaves in a 2-quart glass measure. Using the back of a spoon, gently bruise the leaves; set leaves aside. Combine water and bourbon in a large saucepan; bring mixture to a boil. Pour bourbon mixture over reserved mint leaves; cover, and let stand 5 minutes. Strain mixture, discarding mint leaves. Stir in apple cider. Serve over crushed ice, and garnish with fresh mint sprigs. Yield: 8 cups (61 calories per 1-cup serving).

PROTEIN 0.2 / FAT 0.1 / CARBOHYDRATE 15.0 / CHOLESTEROL 0 / IRON 0.9 / SODIUM 7 / CALCIUM 18

 WEIGHT TRAINING IMPROVES SELF-ESTEEM

A recent study conducted with both young and middle-aged women who participated in a 12-week weight-training program showed both groups of women to be not only stronger, but significantly more satisfied with their lives than a similar group of women who didn't lift weights. The stronger women, happy with their new-found strength, also demonstrated higher self-esteem on psychological tests. The researchers conclude: Participation in a weight-training program is effective for increasing strength and self-esteem in young and middle-aged women.

New Year's Day Brunch

The day after the most festive night of the year is a time for simplified entertaining. This New Year's Day Brunch has what it takes to pull it off: foods that are easily prepared and require very little last-minute fussing. The day before, whip up a batch of Chilled Orange Cappuccino, flavored with coffee low-fat yogurt.

Black-Eyed Pea Soup is a tasty way to get all that good luck in, along with an impressive supply of protein and fiber. It can either

Black-Eyed Pea Soup
Lettuce Wedges with
Warm Mustard Dressing
Cheddar Cheese Biscuits
Fudge-Nut Parfaits
Chilled Orange
Cappuccino

Serves 12
Total calories per serving: 464

be mixed the day before or quickly put together before

the guests arrive.

No ordinary Cheddar Cheese Biscuits are these! They have the distinctive taste of masa harina, the main ingredient in tortillas. The biscuits can be made several days ahead and frozen. Reheat just before serving.

After weeks of what might be heavier than holiday eating, your guests will appreciate the fact that Fudge-Nut Parfaits are made with low-fat ice milk and are a light 146 calories per serving.

BLACK-EYED PEA SOUP

1 (28-ounce) can whole tomatoes, undrained
2 (10-ounce) packages frozen black-eyed peas
1 cup chopped onion
2 quarts water
1 tablespoon chicken-flavored bouillon granules
1½ teaspoons Worcestershire sauce
½ teaspoon dried whole oregano
½ teaspoon pepper
¼ teaspoon dried whole thyme
¼ teaspoon red pepper
1 clove garlic, minced
1 cup sliced carrots
1 cup sliced celery
½ cup chopped green pepper
¼ cup chopped fresh parsley
2 cups chopped, cooked turkey breast (skinned before cooking and cooked without salt)

Combine first 11 ingredients in a large Dutch oven. Bring to a boil. Reduce heat, and simmer, uncovered, 30 minutes. Stir in carrots, celery, green pepper, and parsley; simmer 30 minutes. Add turkey; simmer 30 minutes or until vegetables are tender. Ladle into serving bowls. Yield: 3 quarts (131 calories per 1-cup serving).

PROTEIN 12.3 / FAT 1.4 / CARBOHYDRATE 17.8 / CHOLESTEROL 16 / IRON 2.2 / SODIUM 240 / CALCIUM 49

The New Year begins with Black-Eyed Pea Soup for luck.

LETTUCE WEDGES WITH WARM MUSTARD DRESSING

1 (2-pound) head iceberg lettuce
2 tablespoons unsalted margarine
2 tablespoons all-purpose flour
2 tablespoons plus 1 teaspoon Dijon
   mustard
1 tablespoon honey
2 teaspoons white wine Worcestershire
   sauce
1 cup skim milk
¼ cup unsweetened orange juice
2 teaspoons grated orange rind

Wash lettuce, and remove core. Slice lettuce into 12 wedges. Place wedges on a serving platter. Cover and chill thoroughly.

Melt margarine in a medium saucepan over medium heat. Stir in flour, mustard, honey, and Worcestershire sauce; cook 1 minute, stirring constantly. Gradually stir in milk; cook, stirring constantly, until thickened and bubbly. Stir in orange juice and rind; cook until thoroughly heated. Pour warm mustard mixture over lettuce wedges. Serve immediately. Yield: 12 servings (48 calories per serving).

PROTEIN 1.5 / FAT 2.2 / CARBOHYDRATE 5.7 / CHOLESTEROL 0 /
IRON 0.3 / SODIUM 112 / CALCIUM 38

CHEDDAR CHEESE BISCUITS

¾ cup all-purpose flour
¼ cup masa harina
2 teaspoons baking powder
¼ teaspoon salt
2 tablespoons unsalted margarine
¼ cup plus 2 tablespoons skim milk
¼ cup (1 ounce) shredded sharp Cheddar
   cheese
Vegetable cooking spray

Combine first 4 ingredients in a medium bowl, stirring well. Cut in margarine with a pastry blender until mixture resembles coarse meal. Add milk and cheese, stirring with a fork just until dry ingredients are moistened.

Turn dough out onto a lightly floured surface;

knead 4 to 5 times. Roll dough to ½-inch thickness; cut with a 2-inch biscuit cutter. Place biscuits on a baking sheet coated with cooking spray. Bake at 425° for 12 minutes or until golden brown. Serve immediately. Yield: 12 biscuits (69 calories each).

PROTEIN 2.0 / FAT 2.9 / CARBOHYDRATE 8.8 / CHOLESTEROL 3 /
IRON 0.5 / SODIUM 118 / CALCIUM 65

FUDGE-NUT PARFAITS

6 cups vanilla-fudge ice milk
½ cup crème de cacao
⅓ cup finely chopped pecans, toasted

Scoop ¼ cup vanilla-fudge ice milk into 12 individual parfait glasses. Top each with 1 teaspoon crème de cacao. Repeat layers. Sprinkle evenly with toasted pecans. Serve parfaits immediately. Yield: 12 servings (146 calories per serving).

PROTEIN 2.3 / FAT 4.2 / CARBOHYDRATE 22.4 / CHOLESTEROL 0 /
IRON 0.1 / SODIUM 65 / CALCIUM 2

CHILLED ORANGE CAPPUCCINO

1 tablespoon instant coffee granules
2 tablespoons boiling water
3 (8-ounce) cartons coffee low-fat yogurt
2⅔ cups skim milk
¼ cup unsweetened orange juice
¼ teaspoon ground cinnamon
Orange rind strips (optional)

Dissolve coffee granules in boiling water. Combine coffee, yogurt, milk, orange juice, and cinnamon in container of an electric blender or food processor; process until smooth. Cover and chill thoroughly.

To serve, pour chilled yogurt mixture into cups. Garnish each serving with a strip of orange rind, if desired. Yield: 12 servings (70 calories per ½-cup serving).

PROTEIN 4.7 / FAT 0.8 / CARBOHYDRATE 11.0 / CHOLESTEROL 4 /
IRON 0.1 / SODIUM 66 / CALCIUM 165

A dressed-for-success lunch: Chicken Chow Mein Salad, Tomato-Lime Bouillon, and High-Energy Prune Bars.

Balanced Brown Bag Menu

Career people know the advantages of the brown-bag lunch. Besides the convenience of having lunch ready when they are, the food can be fresher and more economical than lunch-counter fare. Best of all is the satisfaction that comes with eating right.

This brown-bag menu is a giant step away from the ubiquitous sandwich. Chicken Chow Mein Salad starts with a crisp combination of spinach, water chestnuts, and bamboo shoots.

Chicken Chow Mein Salad
High-Energy Prune Bars
Tomato-Lime Bouillon

Serves 1
Total calories per serving: 368

Add chicken, mandarin oranges, and top with a lemon low-fat yogurt dressing spiced with ground ginger. You might want to use an insulated nylon bag to keep the chill on the salad during the morning. (An empty snap-top pill bottle makes an ideal salad

dressing holder.) Be sure to pack the chow mein noodles in a separate container to keep them crunchy, and add them to the salad just before eating.

To ease the time squeeze in the morning, prepare the whole menu the night before. Keep in mind that the calorie count includes two High-Energy Prune Bars per serving. Made from fiber-rich prunes and low-fat yogurt, extra bars can be frozen for a perfect on-the-go breakfast addition later in the week.

CHICKEN CHOW MEIN SALAD

1 tablespoon plus 1½ teaspoons lemon low-fat
  yogurt
¼ teaspoon reduced-sodium soy sauce
⅛ teaspoon ground ginger
2 large cabbage leaves
1 cup torn fresh spinach
1½ ounces chopped cooked chicken breast (skinned
  before cooking and cooked without salt)
1 tablespoon sliced water chestnuts
1 tablespoon sliced bamboo shoots
1 tablespoon shredded carrot
½ (11-ounce) can unsweetened mandarin oranges,
  drained
¼ cup chow mein noodles

Combine yogurt, soy sauce, and ginger; stir
until well blended. Cover and chill thoroughly.
Place cabbage leaves in a small bowl. Combine spinach and next 5 ingredients, tossing
gently. Spoon chicken mixture onto cabbage
leaves. Pour reserved yogurt mixture over salad.
Top with chow mein noodles. Yield: 1 serving
(208 calories per serving).

PROTEIN 17.9 / FAT 4.7 / CARBOHYDRATE 23.7 / CHOLESTEROL 38 /
IRON 2.6 / SODIUM 267 / CALCIUM 112

HIGH-ENERGY PRUNE BARS

¼ cup margarine, softened
½ cup firmly packed brown sugar
1 teaspoon vanilla extract
2 eggs
2 cups all-purpose flour
1 teaspoon baking powder
1 teaspoon baking soda
¼ teaspoon salt
1½ teaspoons ground allspice
1 teaspoon ground cinnamon
½ cup plain low-fat yogurt
1 tablespoon lemon juice
12 large dried, pitted prunes, cooked and chopped
Vegetable cooking spray
1 tablespoon sifted powdered sugar

Cream margarine in a medium bowl; gradually add brown sugar, beating until light and
fluffy. Stir in vanilla. Add eggs one at a time,
beating well after each addition. Combine flour
and next 5 ingredients; add to creamed mixture
alternately with yogurt, mixing just until
blended. Combine lemon juice and prunes; fold
into batter. Spread batter into a 13- x 9- x 2-inch
baking pan coated with cooking spray. Bake at
350° for 15 minutes or until a wooden pick inserted in center comes out clean. Remove from
oven, and let cool completely on a wire rack.
Sprinkle with powdered sugar, and cut into bars.
Yield: 40 bars. Serving size: 2 bars (119 calories
per serving).

PROTEIN 2.5 / FAT 3.1 / CARBOHYDRATE 20.5 / CHOLESTEROL 28 /
IRON 0.9 / SODIUM 125 / CALCIUM 45

TOMATO-LIME BOUILLON

¼ teaspoon beef-flavored bouillon granules
¼ cup boiling water
¾ cup no-salt-added tomato juice
1½ teaspoons lime juice
¼ teaspoon Worcestershire sauce
Lime slice (optional)

Dissolve bouillon granules in boiling water.
Add tomato juice, lime juice, and Worcestershire sauce; stir well. Cover and chill thoroughly.
Garnish with a lime slice, if desired. Yield: 1
serving (41 calories per 1-cup serving).

PROTEIN 1.9 / FAT 0.1 / CARBOHYDRATE 10.0 / CHOLESTEROL 0 /
IRON 0.0 / SODIUM 147 / CALCIUM 2

*Prepare Pork Loin Chops with
Tarragon Sauce, Steamed Broccoli
Stems, corn-on-the-cob, and Summer
Waldorf Salad for a quick and easy,
we-think-you're-special kind of meal
to celebrate Father's Day (menu
begins on page 52).*

Sunday Night Supper

American families traditionally have enjoyed a large meal at noon on Sundays. Yet, the less formal Sunday night supper is preferred in some families because it is anticipated as a time of quiet, homey comfort.

A Sunday evening meal is usually lighter and more easily prepared. Here, apple slices sprinkled with cinnamon adorn the Baked Apple Omelet, which bakes up light and fluffy for picture perfection every time. Of course, both tart apples and fresh eggs go well with ham, so place

Baked Apple Omelet
Ham Slice
Marinated Tomato,
Cucumber and
Onion Slices
Hearty Whole Wheat
Muffins
Raspberry-Pear Sorbet

Serves 6
Total calories per serving: 500

a 3-ounce portion of lean ham next to each serving of omelet. The balance of nutrients

and color on each plate is completed with a marinated tomato, cucumber, and onion salad and a Hearty Whole Wheat Muffin. Freeze extra muffins for a quick, nutritious breakfast bread to serve later in the week.

Whip up a refreshingly light Raspberry-Pear Sorbet in the electric blender or food processor. Made with convenient, unsweetened canned pears and frozen raspberries, this sorbet makes a light, satisfying conclusion to a mealtime memory of family fellowship on Sunday evening.

BAKED APPLE OMELET

¼ cup plus 1 tablespoon all-purpose flour
½ teaspoon baking powder
⅛ teaspoon salt
3 eggs, separated
2 tablespoons sugar, divided
¼ cup skim milk
1 tablespoon plus 1½ teaspoons lemon juice
Vegetable cooking spray
1 medium-size cooking apple, cored and cut into thin wedges
¼ teaspoon ground cinnamon

Combine flour, baking powder, and salt in a large bowl; set aside. Beat egg whites (at room temperature) until soft peaks form; gradually add 1 tablespoon sugar, beating until stiff peaks form. Set aside. Combine egg yolks and milk; mix well. Add egg yolk mixture to reserved flour mixture, stirring just until dry ingredients are moistened. Fold reserved egg white mixture into flour mixture. Stir in lemon juice.

Place a 10-inch ovenproof skillet coated with cooking spray in a 375° oven for 10 minutes. Remove from oven. Pour egg mixture into skillet; arrange apple wedges in a circle on top of egg mixture. Combine remaining 1 tablespoon

sugar and cinnamon; sprinkle over apple slices. Bake at 375° for 15 minutes or until set. Yield: 6 servings (100 calories per serving).

PROTEIN 4.2 / FAT 3.0 / CARBOHYDRATE 14.2 / CHOLESTEROL 137 / IRON 0.8 / SODIUM 114 / CALCIUM 47

MARINATED TOMATO, CUCUMBER AND ONION SLICES

3 medium tomatoes, cut into wedges
1 large cucumber, scored and sliced
1 small purple onion, cut into rings
Lettuce leaves
⅔ cup red wine vinegar
2 tablespoons Worcestershire sauce
½ teaspoon coarsely ground pepper
2 tablespoons sugar
1 tablespoon dried whole basil
½ teaspoon dried whole thyme

Combine tomatoes, cucumber, and onion; place on a lettuce-lined serving platter. Combine vinegar and remaining ingredients in a jar; cover tightly, and shake vigorously. Pour vinegar mixture over vegetables. Yield: 6 servings (50 calories per serving).

PROTEIN 1.3 / FAT 0.3 / CARBOHYDRATE 10.8 / CHOLESTEROL 0 / IRON 0.9 / SODIUM 59 / CALCIUM 31

HEARTY WHOLE WHEAT MUFFINS

1 cup whole wheat flour
1 cup all-purpose flour
2 teaspoons baking powder
½ teaspoon salt
1 cup skim milk
¼ cup molasses
¼ cup unsalted margarine, melted and cooled
1 egg, beaten
Vegetable cooking spray

Combine first 4 ingredients in a large bowl, stirring well. Make a well in center of flour mixture. Combine milk, molasses, margarine, and egg; add to dry ingredients, stirring just until dry ingredients are moistened.

Spoon batter into muffin pans coated with cooking spray, filling two-thirds full. Bake at 400° for 20 minutes or until lightly browned. Yield: 1 dozen muffins (139 calories each).

PROTEIN 3.8 / FAT 4.6 / CARBOHYDRATE 21.1 / CHOLESTEROL 23 / IRON 1.2 / SODIUM 167 / CALCIUM 86

Heart-warming, healthy eating—Baked Apple Omelet, Hearty Whole Wheat Muffins, and ham.

MAKE WAY FOR MUFFINS

More than ever, muffins are rising across the country. In Boston, commuters grab "a meal in a muffin" before boarding the subway. Chocolate chip cookie counters in malls are newly ordained muffin marts. Doughnut shops do more muffin business. Manufacturers display new muffin products on grocery shelves and in frozen food bins.

Tasty and portable, muffins appeal to today's on-the-go families. Suit your fancy: 2-ounce or 10-ounce high-crown apple-coconut, ham' n cheese, or favorite blueberry and bran muffins.

Muffins can be more nutritious than cookies, doughnuts, croissants, or Danish pastries if the wholesomeness is not diminished by the use of too much fat, sodium, and sugar. For optimum quality control, make your own muffins. Enhance sweetness with fruit or raisins; add fiber with whole wheat flour, oats, cornmeal, or bran; and use vegetable oil instead of shortening or margarine. For more flavor options, consider adding dillweed, Dijon mustard, or jalapeño peppers.

RASPBERRY-PEAR SORBET

1 (10-ounce) package frozen raspberries in light syrup, thawed and undrained
1 (16-ounce) can unsweetened pear halves, undrained
3 tablespoons lime juice

Place raspberries in container of an electric blender or food processor; process until smooth. Strain and discard seeds.

Return strained raspberry puree to container of electric blender or food processor. Add pears and lime juice; process until smooth.

Pour raspberry mixture into an 8-inch loafpan; cover and freeze until slushy. Return to container of electric blender or food processor; process until smooth. Return raspberry mixture to loafpan; freeze until firm. Scoop sorbet into individual dessert dishes. Serve immediately. Yield: 3 cups (89 calories per ½-cup serving).

PROTEIN 0.6 / FAT 0.1 / CARBOHYDRATE 22.8 / CHOLESTEROL 0 / IRON 0.5 / SODIUM 4 / CALCIUM 15

Cranberry-Crowned Meringues are sure to impress with only 176 calories per serving.

Chicken Dinner From The Grill

Chicken is an American-menu superstar, and for good reason. One of the most versatile of all meats, it can be mixed with other foods and seasonings to create new and exciting flavor combinations. For this reason alone, chicken is praiseworthy. That's even before identifying it as an economical source of low-fat protein.

This menu features time-saving cooking methods for busy cooks. Grilling turns wine-marinated chicken into a quick and easy entrée. Varieties of fresh and

Grilled Chablis Chicken
Mixed Vegetables with
Piquant Sauce
Fruit Salad with
Citrus Dressing
Wheat Germ Cornbread
Cranberry-Crowned
Meringues

Serves 6
Total calories per serving: 624

frozen vegetables are quickly steamed to lock in their

valuable nutrients before adding tangy, low-calorie Piquant Sauce.

Toss fresh apple, banana, and strawberries with a cooked citrus dressing to bring fiber and an impressive amount of vitamins A and C to the meal. Wheat Germ Cornbread packs the nutritional bonus of vitamin E. This cornbread recipe makes nine serving-size pieces. Save extras for a head start on a nutritious lunch. The regal finale: crisp Cranberry-Crowned Meringues, filled with ice milk and set off by sprigs of fresh mint.

GRILLED CHABLIS CHICKEN

6 boneless chicken breast halves (1½ pounds), skinned
⅓ cup Chablis or other dry white wine
⅓ cup white wine vinegar
4 green onions with tops, chopped
½ teaspoon dried whole basil
¼ teaspoon pepper
Vegetable cooking spray

Trim excess fat from chicken. Rinse chicken with cold water, and pat dry. Place in a 12- x 8- x 2-inch baking dish. Combine wine, vinegar, green onions, basil, and pepper; stir well. Pour wine mixture over chicken. Cover and marinate in refrigerator 4 hours.

Remove chicken from marinade; discard green onions and reserve marinade. Arrange chicken on a grill coated with cooking spray. Grill 6 inches over hot coals 10 minutes or until chicken is tender, turning and basting with reserved marinade every 3 minutes. Yield: 6 servings (142 calories per serving).

PROTEIN 25.8 / FAT 3.0 / CARBOHYDRATE 0.8 / CHOLESTEROL 70 / IRON 1.0 / SODIUM 64 / CALCIUM 19

MIXED VEGETABLES WITH PIQUANT SAUCE

3 cups cauliflower flowerets (1 pound)
1 pound baby carrots, scraped
1 (10-ounce) package frozen brussels sprouts
1 cup water
1 tablespoon cornstarch
½ teaspoon chicken-flavored bouillon granules
1 (2-ounce) jar diced pimiento, drained
1 tablespoon chopped fresh parsley
2 teaspoons lemon juice
1 teaspoon prepared mustard

Arrange cauliflower and carrots in a vegetable steamer. Place over boiling water; cover and steam 8 minutes or until crisp-tender. Drain; set aside, and keep warm.

Cook brussels sprouts according to package directions, omitting salt. Drain, and add to reserved cauliflower-carrot mixture.

Combine water, cornstarch, and bouillon granules in a medium saucepan, stirring until well blended. Bring to a boil. Reduce heat to medium; cook, stirring constantly, until mixture is thickened and bubbly. Remove from heat. Stir in pimiento, parsley, lemon juice, and mustard. Pour pimiento mixture over vegetables; toss gently. Transfer mixture to a serving platter, and serve immediately. Yield: 6 servings (72 calories per serving).

PROTEIN 3.8 / FAT 0.4 / CARBOHYDRATE 15.7 / CHOLESTEROL 0 / IRON 1.2 / SODIUM 93 / CALCIUM 69

FRUIT SALAD WITH CITRUS DRESSING

1 large Red Delicious apple, cored and diced
1 medium banana, diagonally sliced
¼ cup plus 1 tablespoon lemon juice, divided
1½ cups sliced fresh strawberries
¼ cup unsweetened orange juice
1½ teaspoons cornstarch
2 tablespoons sugar
6 curly leaf lettuce leaves

Combine apple and banana in a medium bowl. Sprinkle with 1 tablespoon lemon juice. Add strawberry slices; toss gently, and set aside.
Combine orange juice, remaining ¼ cup lemon juice, and cornstarch in a small saucepan; stir until smooth. Add sugar, stirring well to combine. Bring mixture to a boil. Reduce heat to medium; cook, stirring constantly, until thickened and bubbly. Remove from heat, and let cool. Pour orange juice mixture over reserved fruit mixture. Toss gently to coat well.

Place lettuce leaves on 6 individual salad plates. Spoon ½ cup fruit mixture onto each lettuce leaf. Serve immediately. Yield: 6 servings (85 calories per serving).

PROTEIN 0.9 / FAT 0.5 / CARBOHYDRATE 21.5 / CHOLESTEROL 0 / IRON 0.4 / SODIUM 3 / CALCIUM 14

WHEAT GERM CORNBREAD

¾ cup all-purpose flour
½ cup yellow cornmeal
2 tablespoons sugar
1 tablespoon baking powder
1 egg, beaten
½ cup skim milk
¼ cup vegetable oil
Vegetable cooking spray
1 tablespoon plus 1 teaspoon wheat germ

Combine first 4 ingredients in a medium bowl, stirring until well blended. Combine egg, milk, and oil; add to cornmeal mixture, stirring just until dry ingredients are moistened. Pour batter into an 8-inch square baking pan coated with cooking spray. Sprinkle with wheat germ. Bake at 425° for 20 minutes or until lightly browned. To serve, cut into 3-inch squares. Yield: 9 servings (149 calories per serving).

PROTEIN 3.3 / FAT 7.0 / CARBOHYDRATE 18.1 / CHOLESTEROL 31 / IRON 0.8 / SODIUM 115 / CALCIUM 86

CRANBERRY-CROWNED MERINGUES

3 egg whites
1 teaspoon vanilla extract
¼ teaspoon cream of tartar
⅛ teaspoon salt
¾ cup sugar, divided
¾ cup cranberry juice cocktail
2 teaspoons cornstarch
2 teaspoons lemon juice
¼ teaspoon almond extract
1½ cups vanilla ice milk
Fresh mint sprigs (optional)

Line a baking sheet with unglazed brown paper. Draw six 4-inch circles on paper-lined baking sheet. Set aside.

Beat egg whites (at room temperature) in a large bowl at high speed of an electric mixer until foamy. Sprinkle vanilla, cream of tartar, and salt over egg whites; continue beating until soft peaks form. Gradually add ½ cup plus 2 tablespoons sugar, 1 tablespoon at a time, beating until stiff peaks form and sugar dissolves.

Spoon meringue mixture in 6 equal portions onto circles on paper-lined baking sheet. Using the back of a spoon, shape meringues into 4-inch circles; shape each circle into a shell. (Sides should be about 1½ inches high.) Bake at 225° for 1 hour. Turn oven off, and cool meringues in oven at least 1 hour. Carefully peel paper from meringues, and cool meringues completely on wire racks.

Combine remaining 2 tablespoons sugar, cranberry juice cocktail, cornstarch, and lemon juice in a medium saucepan; stir until well blended. Cook over medium heat, stirring constantly, until mixture thickens. Remove from heat, and stir in almond extract. Let cool.

To serve, scoop ¼ cup ice milk into each meringue shell. Top with 2 tablespoons cranberry juice mixture. Garnish with mint sprigs, if desired. Serve immediately. Yield: 6 servings (176 calories per serving).

PROTEIN 3.0 / FAT 1.4 / CARBOHYDRATE 38.3 / CHOLESTEROL 5 / IRON 0.1 / SODIUM 110 / CALCIUM 47

OUTDOOR WORKOUTS

Workouts in the great outdoors revitalize spirits as well as bodies—if you safely accommodate the weather. Hot or cold temperatures challenge the body's internal thermostat and can lead to serious problems. To be on the safe side, follow these simple guidelines:
● Dress comfortably. In hot weather, wear loose-fitting, lightweight clothes. In cold weather, rely on layered clothing with an outer wind-resistant layer. To avoid losing body heat from head and hands, wear a cap and gloves.
● Cold temperatures make the beginning warm-up especially important; don't neglect this critical phase of your workout to prevent problems later on.
● Jogging on snow requires about twice the energy as jogging on a hard surface; adjust the intensity and duration of your workout accordingly.
● In hot weather, reduce the intensity and duration of your workout to guard against overheating.
● Exercise during the coolest times of day—early morning or late afternoon.
● Always drink plenty of fluids before and after the workout, even if you're not feeling thirsty. You can't depend on thirst to indicate your body's need for replenishing fluids.
● In any weather, avoid rubberized suits. When body heat can't escape, the heart becomes overstressed.

Slightly Southern Supper

Mimosas
or
Hawaiian Coolers
Fillet of Catfish in Wine
Savory Carrots
Apple-Cabbage Slaw
Mint Julep Sundaes

Serves 6
Total calories per serving: 634

Set the stage for this genteel but modern Southern meal with a refreshingly light Mimosa or Hawaiian Cooler.

Catfish never tasted so good as it does when it is seasoned with herbs and simmered in wine. The culinary trend towards chic catfish dishes is picking up momentum, primarily because this citizen from Southern ponds is an economical, low-calorie source of high quality protein.

Savory Carrots provide plenty of flavor and vitamin A. Slim chance that the slaw will add many calories, but count on the apple to add fiber and crunch. Prepare the sauce for the Mint Julep Sundaes earlier in the day to allow flavors to mellow. Don't forget to add a sprig of fresh mint to the sundaes before you go looking for the porch swing.

A lighter version of popular Southern foods can be found in this satisfying meal: Fillet of Catfish in Wine, Savory Carrots, Apple-Cabbage Slaw, and Mint Julep Sundaes.

MIMOSAS

2¾ cups unsweetened orange juice
1 (25.4-ounce) bottle champagne
Fresh mint leaves

Combine orange juice and champagne in a large pitcher; stir lightly. Pour over ice into 6 champagne glasses. Garnish with mint leaves. Serve immediately. Yield: 6 servings (147 calories per 1-cup serving).

PROTEIN 1.2 / FAT 0.1 / CARBOHYDRATE 13.8 / CHOLESTEROL 0 / IRON 0.7 / SODIUM 6 / CALCIUM 14

HAWAIIAN COOLERS

2 cups unsweetened pineapple juice, chilled
1½ cups sparkling mineral water, chilled
2 tablespoons sifted powdered sugar
2½ cups Chablis or other dry white wine, chilled
Orange rind strips (optional)
Fresh mint sprigs (optional)

Combine pineapple juice, mineral water, and sugar in a large pitcher. Stir gently until sugar dissolves. Add wine. Pour into serving glasses. Garnish with orange rind strips and mint sprigs, if desired. Serve immediately. Yield: 6 cups (140 calories per 1-cup serving).

PROTEIN 0.4 / FAT 0.1 / CARBOHYDRATE 18.0 / CHOLESTEROL 0 / IRON 0.6 / SODIUM 18 / CALCIUM 23

FILLET OF CATFISH IN WINE

⅓ cup golden raisins
6 catfish fillets (1½ pounds)
¼ cup all-purpose flour
½ teaspoon dried whole sage
½ teaspoon pepper
Vegetable cooking spray
1 tablespoon margarine
3 tablespoons lemon juice
¼ cup Chablis or other dry white wine
¼ cup dry sherry
1 tablespoon reduced-sodium soy sauce
Fresh sage leaves (optional)

Place raisins in a small bowl; add enough water to cover. Let stand 10 minutes. Drain, and set aside.

Rinse fillets with cold water, and pat dry. Combine flour, sage, and pepper in a shallow dish; dredge fillets in flour mixture to coat well.

Coat a skillet with cooking spray; add margarine, and place over medium heat until margarine melts. Add fillets, lemon juice, and reserved raisins. Cover; reduce heat, and simmer 10 minutes. Remove cover, and turn fillets. Add wine, sherry, and soy sauce to skillet. Bring to a boil; reduce heat, and simmer 5 minutes or until wine mixture is slightly thickened. Carefully transfer fillets and wine mixture to a serving platter. Garnish with sage leaves, if desired. Yield: 6 servings (191 calories per serving).

PROTEIN 21.1 / FAT 5.4 / CARBOHYDRATE 13.9 / CHOLESTEROL 62 / IRON 0.9 / SODIUM 193 / CALCIUM 37

SAVORY CARROTS

¾ cup water
1 pound carrots, scraped and
    sliced
Vegetable cooking spray
1 tablespoon margarine
4 green onions with tops, sliced
¼ cup finely chopped lean
    cooked ham
1 tablespoon firmly packed
    brown sugar
¼ teaspoon pepper

Bring water to a boil in a medium saucepan. Add carrots. Cover; cook over medium heat 8 minutes or until crisp-tender. Remove from heat; drain, and set aside.

Coat medium saucepan with cooking spray; add margarine, and place over medium heat until margarine melts. Add onions and sauté 3 minutes or until tender. Add reserved carrots, ham, brown sugar, and pepper. Cover; cook over medium heat 5 minutes or until vegetables are thoroughly heated. Yield: 6 servings (72 calories per serving).

PROTEIN 2.5 / FAT 2.5 / CARBOHYDRATE 10.7 / CHOLESTEROL 3 / IRON 0.9 / SODIUM 122 / CALCIUM 39

APPLE-CABBAGE SLAW

3 tablespoons all-purpose flour
3 tablespoons sugar
1 teaspoon dry mustard
½ teaspoon celery seeds
1 cup skim milk
¼ cup vinegar
3 tablespoons lemon juice
5 cups shredded cabbage
1 medium-size Red Delicious apple, cored and cubed

Combine flour, sugar, mustard, and celery seeds in a small saucepan; gradually stir in milk. Cook over medium heat, stirring constantly, until mixture thickens. Remove from heat; stir in vinegar and lemon juice. Cool to room temperature.

Combine cabbage and apple in a large bowl. Pour vinegar mixture over cabbage mixture, tossing to coat well. Cover and chill thoroughly. Yield: 6 servings (86 calories per serving).

PROTEIN 2.7 / FAT 0.4 / CARBOHYDRATE 19.2 / CHOLESTEROL 1 / IRON 0.6 / SODIUM 32 / CALCIUM 84

MINT JULEP SUNDAES

1 (8-ounce) can unsweetened crushed pineapple, undrained
2 teaspoons lemon juice
1 tablespoon cornstarch
2 tablespoons crème de menthe
3 cups vanilla ice milk
Fresh mint leaves

Combine pineapple, lemon juice, and cornstarch in a non-aluminum saucepan; stir until cornstarch is dissolved. Bring to a boil; reduce heat, and cook, stirring constantly, until thickened. Remove from heat; stir in crème de menthe. Scoop ½ cup ice milk into 6 individual dessert dishes. Top each serving with 2 tablespoons pineapple mixture. Garnish with fresh mint leaves. Serve immediately. Yield: 6 servings (138 calories per serving).

PROTEIN 2.7 / FAT 2.9 / CARBOHYDRATE 23.8 / CHOLESTEROL 9 / IRON 0.2 / SODIUM 53 / CALCIUM 93

BURNING CALORIES

Body weight is largely the result of how much we eat, how active we are, and how efficiently our basal metabolism functions.

Basal metabolic rate (BMR) refers to the minimum amount of energy needed to carry out involuntary functions of the body, such as breathing, maintaining muscle tone, heartbeat, and liver and kidney functions. BMR accounts for well over half our calorie needs. The average man burns about 1,500 to 1,800 calories a day to maintain his body at rest. The average woman burns 10 to 20 percent fewer calories. One advantage of regular exercise, particularly aerobic exercise, is that it may increase the BMR, which causes calories to be burned at a higher rate than normal, long after the workout is over.

Additional calories are burned during voluntary activities. Depending on lifestyle, a person actively burns anywhere from 1,000 to 5,000 calories per day. Exactly how many depends on body weight, level of daily activity (at work and at home), and amount of exercise.

CALORIES BURNED PER HALF HOUR

	130 lbs. Body Weight	190 lbs. Body Weight
Job:		
Office Work	63	81
Nursing	96	138
Retail Work	102	138
Housework	114	168
Light Machine Operator	156	228
Exercise:		
Playing Golf (cart)	99	135
Walking (3 mph)	135	189
Swimming (20 yds. per minute)	135	189
Weight training	135	189
General Calisthenics	135	189
Hiking (20-lb. backpack at 3.5 mph)	171	234
Stationary Biking	189	258
Singles Tennis	189	258
Jogging (5.5 mph)	294	402
High-Intensity Aerobic Dancing	294	402
Other:		
Sleeping	30	39
Watching Television	36	54
Eating or Driving (automatic shift)	42	51
Cooking a Meal or Washing Dishes	60	82
Housecleaning or Grocery Shopping	111	159
Mowing the Lawn	198	288

Father's Day Dinner

On Father's Day, show Dad how much you care by preparing his favorite foods—*Cooking Light*-style. What Father wouldn't smile when a pork chop smothered in a deceptively light tarragon sauce appears simultaneously with his very special gift.

Steamed Broccoli Stems are an inviting departure from the familiar presentation of spears or flowerets. High in vitamins A and C, broccoli also supplies a significant amount of iron.

Pork Loin Chops with Tarragon Sauce
Steamed Broccoli Stems
Corn-on-the-Cob
Summer Waldorf Salad
Mocha-Drenched Chocolate Cake

Serves 6
Total calories per serving: 602

Prepare sweet corn in water flavored with black peppercorns

and onion slices, and Dad won't even think about adding butter and salt.

Summer Waldorf Salad is a lightened version of an old standard. Fat and calories are abandoned, but not the flavor.

You may have to convince Dad that a serving of Mocha-Drenched Chocolate Cake is only 138 calories. Be sure to refrigerate leftover cake servings to remind Dad of his special status throughout the week.

PORK LOIN CHOPS WITH TARRAGON SAUCE

6 (¾-inch-thick) lean center loin pork chops (2¼ pounds)
1 tablespoon Dijon mustard
1½ teaspoons coarsely ground pepper
Vegetable cooking spray
2 teaspoons margarine
2 medium carrots, scraped and diagonally sliced
½ cup chopped onion
¼ pound fresh mushrooms, sliced
1 cup Chablis or other dry white wine
¼ cup brandy
1 tablespoon dried whole tarragon
1 cup skim milk
1 tablespoon cornstarch

Trim excess fat from chops. Spread ¼ teaspoon mustard on each side of chops. Sprinkle each side with ⅛ teaspoon pepper.

Coat a large skillet with cooking spray. Add margarine, and place over medium-high heat until margarine melts. Add chops. Cook until browned on both sides. Remove chops, and drain on paper towels.

Add carrots and onion to skillet; sauté until tender. Return pork chops to skillet. Add sliced mushrooms, wine, brandy, and tarragon. Bring to a boil. Cover; reduce heat, and simmer 30

minutes or until chops are tender. Transfer chops to a serving platter, and keep warm.

Combine milk and cornstarch; stir well. Add to drippings in skillet; cook until thickened and bubbly. Pour over warm pork chops and serve. Yield: 6 servings (261 calories per serving).

PROTEIN 26.7 / FAT 9.6 / CARBOHYDRATE 9.9 / CHOLESTEROL 70 / IRON 1.7 / SODIUM 196 / CALCIUM 76

STEAMED BROCCOLI STEMS

3 pounds fresh broccoli
¼ teaspoon salt
⅛ teaspoon pepper
1 (2-ounce) jar sliced pimiento, drained

Trim off leaves and tough ends of lower stalks of broccoli. Wash broccoli. Remove flowerets; reserve for other uses. Peel stems, if desired; cut crosswise into ¼-inch-thick slices.

Arrange broccoli slices in a vegetable steamer. Place over boiling water; cover and steam 5 minutes or until crisp-tender. Transfer broccoli to a serving dish; sprinkle with salt and pepper. Garnish with pimiento. Yield: 6 servings (34 calories per serving).

PROTEIN 3.5 / FAT 0.4 / CARBOHYDRATE 6.5 / CHOLESTEROL 0 / IRON 1.1 / SODIUM 131 / CALCIUM 56

Low-fat chocolate milk and coffee-flavored liqueur make Mocha-Drenched Chocolate Cake something special.

SUMMER WALDORF SALAD

2 cups seedless red grapes, halved
1 cup sliced celery
¼ cup chopped pecans
2 tablespoons reduced-calorie mayonnaise
2 tablespoons plain non-fat yogurt
1 tablespoon unsweetened apple juice
Lettuce leaves

Combine grapes, celery, and pecans in a medium bowl. Combine mayonnaise, yogurt, and apple juice in a small bowl, stirring until well blended. Add mayonnaise mixture to fruit mixture; toss lightly to coat well. Cover and chill thoroughly. Spoon ½ cup fruit mixture onto each of 6 lettuce-lined salad plates. Yield: 6 servings (91 calories per serving).

PROTEIN 1.2 / FAT 5.0 / CARBOHYDRATE 12.1 / CHOLESTEROL 2 /
IRON 0.3 / SODIUM 59 / CALCIUM 25

MOCHA-DRENCHED CHOCOLATE CAKE

6 eggs, separated
¼ cup water
1 teaspoon vanilla extract
1¼ cups sugar, divided
⅛ teaspoon salt
1 cup all-purpose flour
¼ cup unsweetened cocoa
½ teaspoon baking powder
1 teaspoon cream of tartar
1 cup low-fat chocolate milk
2 tablespoons instant coffee granules
2 tablespoons Kahlúa or other coffee-flavored
   liqueur

Beat egg yolks in a medium bowl at high speed of an electric mixer 6 minutes or until thick and lemon colored. Add water and vanilla; beat 4 minutes or until mixture thickens. Gradually add ¾ cup sugar and salt; continue beating at high speed 5 minutes.

Combine flour, cocoa, and baking powder; gradually sprinkle over yolk mixture, folding in carefully.

Beat egg whites (at room temperature) in a large bowl until foamy; add cream of tartar, and continue beating until soft peaks form. Gradually add remaining ½ cup sugar, 1 tablespoon at a time, beating until stiff peaks form. Gently fold 1 cup of egg whites into egg yolk mixture. Fold yolk mixture into remaining egg whites.

Pour batter into an ungreased 10-inch tube pan, spreading evenly with a spatula. Bake at 350° for 45 minutes or until cake springs back when lightly touched. Remove from oven. Invert pan on funnel or bottle, and cool 40 minutes. Loosen cake from sides of pan using a small metal spatula. Remove cake from pan and cool completely on a wire rack.

Combine milk, coffee granules, and liqueur in a small saucepan. Place over low heat, and cook, stirring constantly, until coffee dissolves. Remove from heat, and cool completely. Punch holes in top of cake with a wooden skewer; slowly spoon coffee mixture over top of cake, allowing it to absorb into cake. Cover and refrigerate overnight. Yield: 16 servings (138 calories per serving).

PROTEIN 4.1 / FAT 2.5 / CARBOHYDRATE 24.8 / CHOLESTEROL 103 /
IRON 0.9 / SODIUM 76 / CALCIUM 38

Mardi Gras Celebration Dinner

Mardi Gras is an annual Southern celebration—one last fling preceding Lenten season, the forty days before Easter. It's a festive atmosphere of carnival spirits, magnificent costumes, and exciting foods.

This tempting culinary celebration of Mardi Gras begins with a glass of white wine (3½ ounces) and Chunky Primavera Soup, so chock full of fresh vegetables that you might want to call it a salad. Add Cheese Sticks flavored

Chunky Primavera Soup
Cheese Sticks
Shrimp in Garlic Sauce
Fruit Mélange
Chocolate-Almond
Meringues
White Wine

Serves 6
Total calories per serving: 681

with red pepper, Cheddar cheese, and Worcestershire sauce

for easy-to-fix accompaniments.

Large, fresh shrimp simmered in wine and garlic and served on spinach pasta is so simple to prepare, but it's so impressive as an entrée!

Fruit Mélange is a sweet contrast to the slightly bitter cocoa in the Chocolate-Almond Meringues. Quick and easy to prepare, any leftover meringues can be saved for several days in an airtight container. Don your mask, and let the festivities begin!

A tempting culinary celebration: Chunky Primavera Soup and Cheese Sticks.

CHUNKY PRIMAVERA SOUP

1 medium cucumber, peeled and chopped
2 small tomatoes, coarsely chopped
1 small green pepper, seeded and chopped
2 green onions with tops, chopped
1 cup cocktail vegetable juice
1 tablespoon red wine vinegar
⅛ teaspoon pepper

Combine cucumber, tomatoes, green pepper, green onions, vegetable juice, vinegar, and pepper in a medium bowl, stirring well. Cover and chill vegetable mixture at least 2 hours before serving. Yield: 6 servings (25 calories per ½-cup serving).

PROTEIN 1.1 / FAT 0.2 / CARBOHYDRATE 5.6 / CHOLESTEROL 0 / IRON 0.7 / SODIUM 154 / CALCIUM 17

CHEESE STICKS

¼ cup plus 2 tablespoons all-purpose flour
⅛ teaspoon red pepper
¼ cup (1 ounce) shredded extra-sharp Cheddar cheese
2 tablespoons margarine, softened
2 teaspoons white wine Worcestershire sauce
½ teaspoon water

Combine flour and red pepper in a small bowl. Cut in cheese and margarine with a pastry blender until mixture resembles coarse meal. Combine white wine Worcestershire sauce and

water; sprinkle evenly over flour mixture, stirring just until dry ingredients are moistened. Shape dough into a ball.

Roll dough out to ¼-inch thickness on a lightly floured surface. Cut into 3- x ½-inch strips. Place strips on an ungreased baking sheet. Bake at 450° for 6 minutes or until lightly browned. Remove from baking sheet, and cool on wire racks. Yield: 24 sticks. Serving size: 4 sticks (86 calories per serving).

PROTEIN 2.1 / FAT 5.5 / CARBOHYDRATE 6.9 / CHOLESTEROL 5 / IRON 0.3 / SODIUM 93 / CALCIUM 39

SHRIMP IN GARLIC SAUCE

4½ cups water
1½ pounds large fresh shrimp, peeled and deveined
1 tablespoon margarine
2 tablespoons olive oil
1 cup chopped onion
¼ cup chopped fresh parsley
3 cloves garlic, crushed
1 teaspoon dried whole oregano
1 cup Sauterne or other sweet white wine
½ cup reduced-calorie Italian salad dressing
½ cup water
¼ teaspoon freshly ground pepper
1 (8-ounce) package spinach fettuccine

Bring 4½ cups water to a boil; add shrimp, and cook 30 seconds. Drain; rinse with cold water, and drain again. Place shrimp in a shallow broiling pan; set aside.

Combine margarine and olive oil in a large

saucepan. Place over medium heat until margarine melts. Add onion, parsley, garlic, and oregano. Cook, stirring occasionally, until onion is tender. Add wine, dressing, ½ cup water, and pepper, stirring well. Reduce heat to medium-low, and cook 5 minutes. Remove from heat, and pour dressing mixture over reserved shrimp. Cover and marinate in refrigerator 2 hours.

Cook fettuccine according to package directions, omitting salt. Drain, and place in a large bowl. Keep warm.

Drain shrimp, reserving marinade. Broil shrimp 4 inches from heating element 3 to 5 minutes or until shrimp turn pink, turning shrimp after 2 minutes. Add shrimp and reserved marinade to fettuccine. Toss gently. Transfer to a serving platter. Serve immediately. Yield: 6 servings (311 calories per serving).

PROTEIN 20.5 / FAT 8.8 / CARBOHYDRATE 31.9 / CHOLESTEROL 128 / IRON 3.1 / SODIUM 330 / CALCIUM 92

FRUIT MÉLANGE

1 (8½-ounce) can pear halves in extra-light syrup, undrained and coarsely chopped
1 (8-ounce) can unsweetened pineapple chunks, undrained
1 large cooking apple, cored and chopped
1 medium banana, peeled and sliced
1 cup seedless green grapes
1 medium kiwifruit, peeled and sliced
3 tablespoons frozen orange juice concentrate, thawed and undiluted
1 tablespoon honey
2 tablespoons grated fresh coconut, toasted

Drain pears and pineapple, reserving juices in a small bowl. Combine pears, pineapple, apple, banana, grapes, and kiwifruit in a large bowl. Add orange juice concentrate and honey to reserved juices; stir well, and pour over fruit mixture. Toss gently to coat well. Cover and chill at least 2 hours.

Spoon fruit mixture evenly into 6 individual serving bowls; sprinkle with coconut. Yield: 6 servings (140 calories per serving).

PROTEIN 1.1 / FAT 1.6 / CARBOHYDRATE 32.5 / CHOLESTEROL 0 / IRON 0.6 / SODIUM 4 / CALCIUM 20

CHOCOLATE-ALMOND MERINGUES

2 egg whites
¾ cup plus 2 tablespoons sifted powdered sugar
2 tablespoons unsweetened cocoa
½ cup finely chopped blanched almonds, divided
½ teaspoon almond extract
Vegetable cooking spray

Beat egg whites (at room temperature) in a medium bowl until soft peaks form. Combine sugar and cocoa; gradually add sugar mixture to egg whites, 1 tablespoon at a time, beating until stiff peaks form. Fold in ¼ cup almonds and almond extract.

Drop almond mixture by teaspoonfuls, 1 inch apart, onto cookie sheets coated with cooking spray. Sprinkle with remaining almonds. Bake at 300° for 40 minutes or until set. Cool slightly on cookie sheets; gently remove to wire racks, and cool completely. Store in an airtight container. Yield: 3 dozen meringues. Serving size: 2 meringues (51 calories per serving).

PROTEIN 1.4 / FAT 2.2 / CARBOHYDRATE 6.9 / CHOLESTEROL 0 / IRON 0.3 / SODIUM 6 / CALCIUM 11

KIWIFRUIT: INORDINATELY COLORFUL, CHIC, AND NUTRITIOUS

Kiwifruit, now grown in bountiful supply in California, is no longer an esoteric import. The emerald green, black-seeded fruit gives light cuisine exotic color and flavor. Some people say the fruit tastes similar to strawberries; others compare it to watermelon. Any way you look at it, the taste is refreshingly different. Add it to fruit salads, as in Fruit Mélange. Feature it in a spectacular tart. Slice it over cereal. One kiwifruit has only 44 calories and a day's supply of vitamin C.

A bit of "kiwi-wisdom": Leave them out of congealed salads; the fruit contains an enzyme that keeps gelatin from gelling. At the supermarket, select kiwifruit that are slightly soft, or let firmer fruit soften a few days at room temperature before storing in the refrigerator.

Relax and eat in gourmet style with Continental Salmon Loaf, Asparagus-Yellow Squash Salad, Snappy Cucumber Pickles, and decaffeinated Spiced Cranberry Tea (menu begins on page 60).

Pronto Kid's Menu

Kids are sure to wonder what's for lunch when Mom takes out cookie cutters and an ice cream scoop! These tools and the microwave oven team up for a speedy, kid-pleasing menu. Use your favorite cookie cutters to turn slices of jicama into fun-shaped chips—a nutritious, crisp, low-fat alternative to potato chips. No one will know the

Mexicali Tacos
Jicama Chips
Fruit and Cheese Splits

Serves 4
Total calories per serving: 432

wholesomeness of the taco filling comes from ground turkey and wheat germ. No matter if they do; the taste will tempt even the

most skeptical. Warm the taco shells in the microwave for an extra burst of flavor.

A banana split that doesn't melt? Serve the ricotta cheese and fresh fruit mixture with an ice cream scoop; then make a guessing game out of this dessert by playing "guess the ingredients." See how many bites it takes for the winning answer!

Fun to make and healthy to eat: cutter-shaped Jicama Chips and yummy Mexicali Tacos.

MEXICALI TACOS

½ pound ground chuck
¼ (1-pound) package raw ground
  turkey, thawed
2 tablespoons wheat germ, toasted
3 tablespoons reduced-calorie chili
  sauce
½ teaspoon ground cumin
½ teaspoon dried whole oregano
4 taco shells
1 cup shredded iceberg lettuce
½ cup chopped tomato

Crumble ground chuck and turkey into a 2-quart casserole. Cover with wax paper, and microwave at HIGH for 5 to 6 minutes or until meat is no longer pink, stirring every 2 minutes. Drain meat well; pat with paper towels to remove excess grease. Wipe drippings from casserole. Return meat to casserole; stir in wheat germ, chili sauce, cumin, and oregano. Cover and microwave at MEDIUM (50% power) for 3 to 4 minutes or until meat mixture is thoroughly heated.

Place taco shells in a circle on a paper plate. Microwave at HIGH for 45 to 60 seconds or until taco shells are thoroughly heated. Divide meat mixture evenly among warm taco shells. Divide shredded lettuce and chopped tomato evenly among taco shells. Yield: 4 servings (219 calories per serving).

PROTEIN 19.7 / FAT 11.3 / CARBOHYDRATE 10.3 / CHOLESTEROL 51 /
IRON 2.6 / SODIUM 109 / CALCIUM 22

JICAMA CHIPS

1 (1-pound) jicama, peeled and cut into ¼-inch
  slices

Cut jicama slices with assorted (1-inch) cookie cutters. Store in an airtight container in refrigerator. Yield: 4 servings. Serving size: 8 chips (46 calories per serving).

PROTEIN 1.5 / FAT 0.2 / CARBOHYDRATE 9.9 / CHOLESTEROL 0 /
IRON 0.7 / SODIUM 7 / CALCIUM 17

FRUIT AND CHEESE SPLITS

2 medium bananas, split lengthwise and halved
1 cup fresh strawberries, washed, hulled, and sliced
½ cup part-skim ricotta cheese
2 tablespoons wheat germ, toasted
1 tablespoon sifted powdered sugar
⅛ teaspoon ground cinnamon
¼ cup raisins
¼ cup strawberry low-fat yogurt
Whole strawberries (optional)

Arrange banana halves on 4 individual dessert plates. Top with sliced strawberries. Combine cheese, wheat germ, sugar, and cinnamon; stir well. Fold in raisins. Scoop or spoon cheese mixture on top of strawberries. Top each serving with 1 tablespoon yogurt. Garnish with a strawberry, if desired. Yield: 4 servings (167 calories per serving).

PROTEIN 6.3 / FAT 3.5 / CARBOHYDRATE 31.1 / CHOLESTEROL 10 /
IRON 1.0 / SODIUM 48 / CALCIUM 119

 ## THE NEED TO INVOLVE AMERICA'S YOUTH IN THE FITNESS BOOM

The fitness boom, by and large, has skirted the involvement of American youth. Many are overweight and underconditioned. Sedentary lifestyles, poor eating habits, unenlightened parents, and inadequate physical education programs at school all share the blame.

Inactive children are likely to become sedentary, overweight adults, at high risk for heart disease and other physical problems. Most young people spend a minimum of three hours a day watching television. To alleviate boredom, they snack on foods with plenty of calories, but few nutrients. Adults drive children a few blocks to visit friends rather than encouraging them to walk or bicycle. More often than not, youngsters are spectators rather than participants at sports activities. Physical education in school curriculums has become expendable under tight budgets. Only 17 states have mandatory physical education programs. Many students get as little as one hour of this type of instruction per week.

What can parents do? Set a good example, and influence exercise and good eating habits early. Discourage television viewing and encourage family walking, hiking, biking, swimming, and outdoor play. Encourage and give support to physical education programs that promote cardiovascular fitness. Children are rarely as concerned about their health as you are, so make activities fun.

Continental Take-Out Lunch

Continental Salmon Loaf
Asparagus-Yellow Squash
Salad
Snappy Cucumber Pickles
Dilled New Potato Halves
Spiced Cranberry Tea

Serves 4
Total calories per serving: 515

The culinary trend of gourmet take-out restaurants and delis is the inspiration for this continental menu. All the foods are portable and can be served cold or at room temperature. No ordinary, run-of-the-mill picnic fare, the eclectic flavors represented here will add continental romance to any occasion.

An eye-catching meal accompaniment—Dilled New Potato Halves.

CONTINENTAL SALMON LOAF

2 (4-ounce) salmon steaks, about ¾-inch thick
½ cup thinly sliced green onions
1 tablespoon olive oil
1 tablespoon all-purpose flour
1 cup skim milk
2 eggs, beaten
½ teaspoon dried whole dillweed
¼ teaspoon salt
¼ teaspoon coarsely ground pepper
1 tablespoon finely chopped pistachio nuts
1 small onion, thinly sliced
1 lemon, cut into wedges
Fresh dill sprigs (optional)

Rinse salmon with cold water, and pat dry. Arrange in a 1-quart casserole; cover with heavy-duty plastic wrap, and vent. Microwave at HIGH 4 minutes or until fish flakes easily when

tested with a fork, turning steaks after 2 minutes. Let cool to room temperature. Remove skin, and flake fish from bones. Set aside.

Combine green onions and oil in casserole. Microwave, uncovered, at HIGH 1 to 1½ minutes or until onions are tender. Stir in flour. Gradually stir in milk. Microwave, uncovered, at MEDIUM (50% power) 9 to 12 minutes or until thickened, stirring every 2 minutes. Add reserved salmon, eggs, dillweed, salt, and pepper; stir gently. Cover casserole with wax paper, and place in oven on top of an inverted saucer. Microwave at MEDIUM-HIGH (70% power) 8 to 10 minutes or until set, rotating casserole a half-turn after 4 minutes. Let casserole stand, covered, 5 minutes. Chill thoroughly.

Invert chilled salmon mixture onto a serving

plate. Sprinkle with pistachio nuts. Separate onion slices into rings, and arrange with lemon wedges around salmon. Garnish with dill sprigs, if desired. To serve, cut into slices or wedges. Yield: 4 servings (239 calories per serving).

PROTEIN 18.5 / FAT 14.0 / CARBOHYDRATE 11.4 / CHOLESTEROL 157 / IRON 1.9 / SODIUM 242 / CALCIUM 228

ASPARAGUS-YELLOW SQUASH SALAD

1 pound fresh asparagus spears, diagonally sliced
2 tablespoons water
1 pound yellow squash, sliced
3 tablespoons freshly squeezed lemon juice
1 tablespoon finely chopped green onions
2 teaspoons olive oil
2 teaspoons Dijon mustard
½ teaspoon dried whole basil
¼ teaspoon pepper

Combine asparagus and water in a 2-quart casserole. Cover with heavy-duty plastic wrap and vent; microwave at HIGH 2 minutes. Add squash and microwave at HIGH 4 minutes or until vegetables are tender, stirring after 2 minutes. Let stand, covered, 2 minutes.
Combine lemon juice and remaining ingredients in a small bowl; stir until well blended. Pour lemon juice mixture over vegetables, and toss lightly to coat well. Cover and chill thoroughly. Stir well before serving. Yield: 4 servings (74 calories per serving).

PROTEIN 4.9 / FAT 2.9 / CARBOHYDRATE 10.4 / CHOLESTEROL 0 / IRON 1.4 / SODIUM 79 / CALCIUM 52

SNAPPY CUCUMBER PICKLES

½ pound small cucumbers
¼ cup cider vinegar
2 tablespoons water
2 teaspoons sugar
⅛ teaspoon red pepper

Wash cucumbers, and pat dry. Cut each cucumber lengthwise into 4 spears. Place spears, cut side down, in a shallow container; set aside.
Combine vinegar, water, sugar, and pepper in a 1-cup glass measure; stir well. Microwave, uncovered, at HIGH 2 to 3 minutes or until mixture boils. Pour over reserved cucumber spears. Cover

and refrigerate at least 8 hours. Serve, using a slotted spoon. Yield: 4 servings. Serving size: 4 spears (18 calories per serving).

PROTEIN 0.3 / FAT 0.1 / CARBOHYDRATE 4.6 / CHOLESTEROL 0 / IRON 0.3 / SODIUM 1 / CALCIUM 9

DILLED NEW POTATO HALVES

8 small new potatoes (1 pound)
½ cup plain low-fat yogurt
1 tablespoon prepared horseradish
⅛ teaspoon dried whole dillweed
2 tablespoons chopped fresh chives

Rinse potatoes and pat dry. Prick potatoes several times with a fork, and place in a ring on a paper towel in microwave oven. Microwave at HIGH 6 to 7 minutes, turning over after 3½ minutes. Let stand 5 minutes.
Cut potatoes in half lengthwise; set aside. Combine yogurt, horseradish, and dillweed in a small bowl; stir well. Spoon 1 teaspoon yogurt mixture onto each potato half. Sprinkle with chives. Serve at room temperature. Yield: 4 servings (104 calories per serving).

PROTEIN 4.1 / FAT 0.6 / CARBOHYDRATE 21.3 / CHOLESTEROL 2 / IRON 1.6 / SODIUM 32 / CALCIUM 71

SPICED CRANBERRY TEA

3 cups water
1½ teaspoons whole allspice
1 teaspoon whole cloves
2 (3-inch) sticks cinnamon
2 regular tea bags
1 cup cranberry juice cocktail
2 tablespoons honey
Orange slices (optional)

Place water in a 4-cup glass measure. Microwave, uncovered, at HIGH 10½ to 11½ minutes or until boiling. Tie allspice, cloves, and cinnamon in a cheesecloth bag; add to water with tea bags. Cover and steep 5 minutes. Strain liquid; discard spice bag and tea bags. Stir in cranberry juice cocktail and honey. Serve over ice; garnish with orange slices, if desired. Yield: 4 cups (80 calories per 1-cup serving).

PROTEIN 0.3 / FAT 0.3 / CARBOHYDRATE 21.0 / CHOLESTEROL 0 / IRON 0.9 / SODIUM 6 / CALCIUM 32

Mediterranean Salad Buffet

Put your microwave in sync with the ultimate in taste trends—a salad buffet featuring Mediterranean flavorings.

Brown rice prepared in the microwave oven will cook in about the same time as by conventional means, but the cleanup will be easier. Microwave spillovers are rare when rice is prepared in the right size container. The flavors of mint and orange blend together as Brown Rice with Pecans is chilling. When pre-

**Shredded Chicken Salad
Brown Rice with Pecans
Fresh Tomatoes with
Spinach Sauce
Berry Duo in Wine**

Serves 4
Total calories per serving: 395

sented, it is flavor perfect.

Cook the chicken in the microwave and shred it; arrange it with the remaining ingredients

on an attractive serving platter. Cover and refrigerate to serve with the freshly made dressing.

Spinach Sauce is reminiscent of pesto, but lower in calories. Its flavor will mellow wonderfully while chilling. Then it's a simple matter of slicing tomatoes. At mealtime, top the tomatoes with the nutrient-rich sauce. Voilà! A colorful addition to your buffet.

Wine-marinated strawberries and blueberries await the signal for dessert.

SHREDDED CHICKEN SALAD

2 boneless chicken breast halves (½ pound), skinned
4 large Romaine lettuce leaves
2 cups shredded iceberg lettuce
1 cup thinly sliced cucumber
½ cup shredded zucchini
1 tablespoon olive oil
1 clove garlic, minced
¼ teaspoon dried whole oregano
¼ cup red wine vinegar
3 tablespoons water
⅛ teaspoon pepper
1 tablespoon grated Parmesan cheese

Trim excess fat from chicken. Rinse chicken with cold water, and pat dry. Place in a 1-quart glass baking dish. Cover with heavy-duty plastic wrap and vent; microwave at HIGH for 4 to 6 minutes or until chicken is tender, turning chicken and rotating dish a half-turn after 2 minutes. Let cool to room temperature. Shred chicken into bite-size pieces, and set aside.

Arrange Romaine leaves on a serving platter. Top with shredded lettuce, cucumber slices, zucchini, and reserved chicken.

Place oil in a 1-cup glass measure. Microwave, uncovered, at HIGH for 30 seconds to 1 minute. Stir in garlic and oregano. Microwave at HIGH for 30 seconds. Stir in vinegar, water, and pepper.

Pour mixture over salad. Sprinkle with cheese. Yield: 4 servings (123 calories per serving).

PROTEIN 14.7 / FAT 5.4 / CARBOHYDRATE 3.3 / CHOLESTEROL 36 / IRON 1.2 / SODIUM 63 / CALCIUM 52

BROWN RICE WITH PECANS

1¾ cups hot water
¼ cup unsweetened orange juice
⅔ cup uncooked long grain brown rice
1 teaspoon chicken-flavored bouillon granules
1 tablespoon chopped fresh mint
1 tablespoon chopped fresh parsley
½ teaspoon grated orange rind
⅛ teaspoon pepper
2 tablespoons chopped pecans, toasted

Combine water and orange juice in a 2-quart casserole. Cover with lid and microwave at HIGH for 4 minutes or until boiling. Stir in rice and bouillon granules. Microwave, covered, at MEDIUM (50% power) for 45 minutes or until liquid is absorbed. Let stand, covered, 5 minutes. Add mint, parsley, orange rind, and pepper; stir well. Cover and chill thoroughly. Stir in pecans just before serving. Yield: 4 servings (145 calories per serving).

PROTEIN 2.8 / FAT 3.2 / CARBOHYDRATE 26.5 / CHOLESTEROL 0 / IRON 0.7 / SODIUM 99 / CALCIUM 16

Cool, crisp Shredded Chicken Salad composed of chicken breast, cucumber, lettuce, and zucchini is dressed in a red wine vinaigrette and sprinkled with Parmesan cheese—a lot of flavor and style for a mere 123 calories per serving.

FRESH TOMATOES WITH SPINACH SAUCE

¾ cup torn fresh spinach
¼ cup loosely packed fresh basil leaves
¼ cup low-fat buttermilk
2 tablespoons chopped green onions
1 tablespoon reduced-calorie mayonnaise
1 clove garlic, minced
3 medium tomatoes, cut into ¼-inch slices

Place spinach in a 1-quart casserole. Cover with heavy-duty plastic wrap and vent; microwave at HIGH for 30 seconds to 1 minute. Drain spinach well. Combine spinach, basil, and next 4 ingredients in container of an electric blender or food processor. Process until smooth. Cover and chill thoroughly.

Arrange tomato slices on a serving platter. Top with chilled spinach mixture. Yield: 4 servings (43 calories per serving).

PROTEIN 2.0 / FAT 1.5 / CARBOHYDRATE 6.5 / CHOLESTEROL 1 / IRON 0.9 / SODIUM 53 / CALCIUM 42

BERRY DUO IN WINE

¼ cup Chablis or other dry white wine
3 tablespoons sugar
1 tablespoon lemon juice
½ teaspoon grated lemon rind
1 pint fresh strawberries, washed, hulled, and halved
½ cup fresh or frozen blueberries, thawed
1 tablespoon Triple Sec or other orange-flavored liqueur

Combine wine and sugar in a 1-quart casserole. Microwave, uncovered, at HIGH for 2½ to 3 minutes or until sugar dissolves. Stir in lemon juice, rind, strawberries, and blueberries. Microwave, uncovered, at HIGH for 1 to 2 minutes. Sprinkle fruit mixture with liqueur. Cover and chill thoroughly. Spoon chilled fruit mixture into 4 individual dessert dishes. Yield: 4 servings (84 calories per serving).

PROTEIN 0.6 / FAT 0.4 / CARBOHYDRATE 19.1 / CHOLESTEROL 0 / IRON 0.4 / SODIUM 3 / CALCIUM 13

Shrimp in Oyster Sauce, Sesame-Ginger Rice, and Spinach Salad with Yogurt-Poppy Seed Dressing.

Oriental Menu

The serenity of an oriental garden is yours with the ease of microwave sequential cooking. This Oriental Menu is synchronized to move gracefully from one food to another, culminating in a peaceful repast that delights all the senses.

Start with the marinated items. Marinating is a frequently used technique in oriental cookery that creates maximum flavor in foods prepared by quick-cook methods such as the wok and microwave oven. The warmed liqueur-flavored marinade will

Shrimp in Oyster Sauce
Sesame-Ginger Rice
Spinach Salad with
Yogurt-Poppy Seed
Dressing
Marinated Pineapple
Wedges
Tea

Serves 4
Total calories per serving: 468

quickly penetrate the pineapple, but the flavors will be even more developed after refrigeration.

Next, marinate the shrimp.

Not a microwave moment is wasted! Now the time is perfect to prepare the Sesame-Ginger Rice. Toast the sesame seeds to coax extra flavor. Wash and assemble the fresh salad ingredients while the rice is cooking. Attractive and chock-full of nutrients, the Spinach Salad with Yogurt-Poppy Seed Dressing is harmony in flavor. Complete the Shrimp in Oyster Sauce preparation; set the table. Add the final serene touch—a soothing cup of tea. May you find good fortune!

SHRIMP IN OYSTER SAUCE

1 tablespoon dry sherry
1 tablespoon water
2 teaspoons vegetable oil, divided
1 pound medium-size fresh shrimp, peeled and deveined
1 (8-ounce) can sliced water chestnuts, drained
1 cup sliced celery
1 medium-size sweet red pepper, seeded and cut into strips
2 cloves garlic, minced
1 teaspoon minced fresh gingerroot
½ cup water
1 tablespoon cornstarch
1 tablespoon oyster sauce
1 teaspoon sugar
1 teaspoon reduced-sodium soy sauce
½ teaspoon chicken-flavored bouillon granules
½ cup diagonally sliced green onions
Green onion fan (optional)

Combine sherry, 1 tablespoon water, and 1 teaspoon oil in a shallow dish. Add shrimp; toss gently. Let stand 20 minutes.

Combine remaining 1 teaspoon oil, water chestnuts, celery, sweet red pepper, garlic, and gingerroot in a 2-quart casserole. Microwave, uncovered, at HIGH 2 to 3 minutes. Drain shrimp,

discarding liquid. Add shrimp to casserole; stir well. Microwave, uncovered, at HIGH 3 to 4 minutes or until shrimp are no longer pink, stirring after 2 minutes. Cover, and set aside.

Combine ½ cup water and next 5 ingredients in a 2-cup glass measure, stirring well. Microwave, uncovered, at HIGH 2 minutes, stirring after 1 minute. Add to reserved shrimp mixture. Stir in sliced green onions. Microwave, uncovered, at HIGH 1 to 2 minutes or until thoroughly heated. Garnish with green onion fan, if desired. Yield: 4 servings (149 calories per serving).

PROTEIN 16.6 / FAT 3.2 / CARBOHYDRATE 12.4 / CHOLESTEROL 128 / IRON 2.5 / SODIUM 395 / CALCIUM 80

 BUYING AND STORING GINGERROOT

Fresh gingerroot is a staple in Oriental cuisine. Look for it in the produce department of a supermarket or Oriental grocery store. (Ground ginger is not a substitute.) Knobby in appearance, the freshest gingerroot has even-colored light brown skin, a firm texture, and pleasant aroma. Slice only what you need and peel each slice; store the remainder in the refrigerator unwrapped.

SESAME-GINGER RICE

2 cups hot water
¼ teaspoon salt
⅔ cup uncooked long grain rice
½ cup diced carrots
¾ teaspoon minced fresh gingerroot
2½ teaspoons sesame oil

Place water and salt in a 2-quart casserole. Microwave at HIGH for 3 to 3½ minutes or until boiling. Add rice, carrots, and gingerroot; stir well. Cover with lid, and microwave at HIGH for 5 minutes. Reduce to MEDIUM (50% power), and microwave 14 minutes or until liquid is absorbed. Stir in oil; let stand 5 minutes. Fluff with a fork, and serve immediately. Yield: 4 servings (143 calories per serving).

PROTEIN 2.2 / FAT 3.0 / CARBOHYDRATE 26.2 / CHOLESTEROL 0 / IRON 1.0 / SODIUM 153 / CALCIUM 12

SPINACH SALAD WITH YOGURT-POPPY SEED DRESSING

1 medium orange
¼ pound spinach leaves, washed and trimmed
½ cup sliced water chestnuts
2 tablespoons thinly sliced green onions
Yogurt-Poppy Seed Dressing

Grate ½ teaspoon orange rind; reserve for use in Yogurt-Poppy Seed Dressing. Peel, seed, and section orange.

Place spinach leaves on a serving platter. Arrange orange sections in a circular pattern on spinach, overlapping sections.

Combine water chestnuts and green onions; place in center of salad. Top with dressing.

Yield: 4 servings (90 calories per serving).

Yogurt-Poppy Seed Dressing:

3 tablespoons plain low-fat yogurt
3 tablespoons reduced-calorie mayonnaise
2 teaspoons honey
½ teaspoon grated orange rind
1 teaspoon poppy seeds

Combine all ingredients; stir with a wire whisk until smooth. Cover; chill. Yield: ⅓ cup.

PROTEIN 2.2 / FAT 3.7 / CARBOHYDRATE 13.4 / CHOLESTEROL 4 / IRON 1.0 / SODIUM 116 / CALCIUM 76

MARINATED PINEAPPLE WEDGES

¼ cup water
¼ cup unsweetened frozen apple juice concentrate, thawed and undiluted
1 tablespoon freshly squeezed lime juice
½ teaspoon grated lime rind
¼ teaspoon ground allspice
1 tablespoon Triple Sec or other orange-flavored liqueur
1 small fresh pineapple

Combine first 5 ingredients in a 2-cup glass measure. Microwave, uncovered, at HIGH for 2½ to 3 minutes or until boiling. Let mixture cool slightly. Stir in liqueur, and set aside.

Peel and trim eyes from pineapple, removing core and reserving leaves. Cut pineapple lengthwise into four 3-ounce wedges. Place wedges in a shallow container. Reserve remaining pineapple for other uses. Pour reserved liqueur mixture over pineapple wedges. Cover and marinate in refrigerator 4 hours or overnight, turning wedges occasionally. Drain wedges, discarding marinade. Garnish with pineapple leaves. Yield: 4 servings (84 calories per serving).

PROTEIN 0.4 / FAT 0.5 / CARBOHYDRATE 19.3 / CHOLESTEROL 0 / IRON 0.5 / SODIUM 5 / CALCIUM 11

African Menu

Safari Chicken Stew
Couscous with Parsley
Sweet Potato Salad
Glazed Bananas
Pineapple-Mint Coolers

Serves 4
Total calories per serving: 645

Plan an exciting flavor safari with this African Menu. The microwave oven makes it easy to capture the cuisine of the Dark Continent. Begin your dining adventure with Safari Chicken Stew and couscous, the versatile wheat-grain product, North African in origin. Sweet Potato Salad will be a welcome encounter.

Don't forget the Pineapple-Mint Coolers! Just before serving, add the "sparkle" of mineral water. Last on your itinerary of flavors: Glazed Bananas topped with peanuts.

A nutritious flavor safari into African cuisine.

SAFARI CHICKEN STEW

1 (2-pound) broiler fryer, cut up and skinned
1 tablespoon olive oil
1 clove garlic, minced
2 medium onions, sliced
2 medium carrots, scraped and sliced
2 small zucchini, sliced
¾ cup cubed turnips
2 tablespoons raisins
½ cup water
½ teaspoon chicken-flavored bouillon granules
½ teaspoon lemon juice
½ teaspoon ground cinnamon
½ teaspoon ground cumin
⅛ teaspoon crushed red pepper

Trim excess fat from chicken. Rinse chicken with cold water, and pat dry. Arrange chicken pieces on a 12-inch round glass platter, placing meatier portions to outside of dish. Combine olive oil and garlic in a small bowl; sprinkle over chicken. Cover with heavy-duty plastic wrap and vent; microwave at HIGH for 7 to 8 minutes, rotating platter a half-turn after 3 minutes.

Transfer chicken to a 3-quart casserole. Add onions and next 4 ingredients; set aside. Combine water and bouillon granules; stir in remaining ingredients. Pour bouillon mixture over reserved chicken and vegetables. Cover with lid; microwave at HIGH for 14 to 15 minutes or until chicken and vegetables are tender, rotating dish after 7 minutes. Let stand, covered, 5 minutes. Yield: 4 servings (249 calories per serving).

PROTEIN 25.4 / FAT 9.8 / CARBOHYDRATE 15.0 / CHOLESTEROL 72 / IRON 2.0 / SODIUM 150 / CALCIUM 60

COOKING LIGHT THE EASY WAY

Thanks to the microwave oven, cooking light is a cooking-easy proposition. Nutritious foods can be made in minutes with fewer vitamins and minerals cooked away. Microwaves do especially well on high-water, low-fat foods like fish, poultry, vegetables, and fruit.

Microwaving enhances flavors and keeps foods moist without adding oil. One U.S. Department of Agriculture (USDA) study found that microwaved meats had less fat and fewer calories than meat cooked by electric broiling, charbroiling, roasting, convection heating, or frying.

COUSCOUS WITH PARSLEY

½ cup water
3 ounces couscous
1 tablespoon olive oil
¼ teaspoon ground turmeric
2 tablespoons chopped fresh parsley

Place water in a 4-cup glass measure. Microwave at HIGH for 1½ minutes or until water boils; stir in remaining ingredients. Cover with heavy-duty plastic wrap, and vent; microwave at HIGH for 1½ to 2 minutes or until liquid is absorbed. Let stand 2 to 3 minutes. Fluff couscous with a fork before serving. Yield: 4 servings (51 calories per serving).

PROTEIN 0.8 / FAT 3.4 / CARBOHYDRATE 4.5 / CHOLESTEROL 0 / IRON 0.3 / SODIUM 1 / CALCIUM 5

SWEET POTATO SALAD

¾ pound sweet potatoes, peeled and cubed
3 tablespoons water
1 tablespoon vegetable oil
1 tablespoon lemon juice
½ teaspoon sugar
Curly leaf lettuce leaves

Place sweet potatoes and water in a 1-quart casserole. Cover with lid, and microwave at HIGH for 6 to 7 minutes, stirring after 3 minutes. Let stand 2 minutes. Drain potatoes well, and set aside.

Combine vegetable oil, lemon juice, and sugar; pour over reserved potatoes. Toss gently to coat. Serve at room temperature on curly leaf lettuce leaves. Yield: 4 servings (122 calories per serving).

PROTEIN 1.4 / FAT 3.7 / CARBOHYDRATE 21.5 / CHOLESTEROL 0 / IRON 0.5 / SODIUM 11 / CALCIUM 19

GLAZED BANANAS

1 tablespoon margarine
1 tablespoon firmly packed brown sugar
⅛ teaspoon ground cinnamon
⅛ teaspoon ground ginger
⅛ teaspoon ground nutmeg
⅓ cup unsweetened orange juice
2 medium bananas, split lengthwise and halved
2 tablespoons chopped unsalted peanuts

Place margarine in a 2-quart casserole. Microwave at HIGH for 30 seconds or until margarine melts. Add brown sugar, cinnamon, ginger, nutmeg, and orange juice; mix well. Microwave at HIGH for 5½ to 6 minutes, stirring after 3 minutes. Add bananas, turning to coat well. Microwave at HIGH for 1 minute or until thoroughly heated. Sprinkle with peanuts. Serve immediately. Yield: 4 servings (129 calories per serving).

PROTEIN 2.0 / FAT 5.4 / CARBOHYDRATE 20.5 / CHOLESTEROL 0 / IRON 0.4 / SODIUM 36 / CALCIUM 14

PINEAPPLE-MINT COOLERS

1 (6-ounce) can frozen lemonade concentrate, thawed and diluted
2 tablespoons fresh mint leaves
2 cups unsweetened pineapple juice
1 (6½-ounce) bottle sparkling mineral water, chilled
Ice cubes
Fresh mint sprigs (optional)

Combine 1 cup prepared lemonade and mint leaves in a 4-cup glass measure. Reserve remaining lemonade for other uses. Microwave lemonade mixture, uncovered, at HIGH 2 to 3 minutes or until thoroughly heated. Let stand 5 minutes. Stir in pineapple juice. Cover and chill at least 2 hours; strain. Lightly stir in sparkling mineral water. Serve over ice. Garnish with fresh mint sprigs, if desired. Yield: 4 cups (94 calories per 1-cup serving).

PROTEIN 0.5 / FAT 0.1 / CARBOHYDRATE 23.6 / CHOLESTEROL 0 / IRON 0.5 / SODIUM 14 / CALCIUM 25

Elegant Company Fare

Here is elegance with ease, the microwave way! This eye-catching menu tastes as good as it looks. An appealing assortment of flavors makes this meal a showstopper. Both the microwave oven and conventional stove-top are used to cut down on time spent in the kitchen.

From the opening act of the Asparagus-Escarole Soup, the stage is set for applause. Fresh basil adds just enough flavor to the pasta to attract attention, yet not enough to upstage the rest

Asparagus-Escarole Soup
Lemon Flounder
Summer Squash Medley
Basil-Scented Pasta
Maple Meringue Orange
Cups

Serves 4
Total calories per serving: 397

of the meal. The Lemon Flounder definitely commands the limelight when accompanied by colorful Summer Squash Medley.

Some preparation beforehand will leave more time for visiting, but don't overlook the opportunity to involve guests as part of the evening's entertainment! The Maple Meringue Orange Cups surely invite participation. Hidden talents will surface when a guest is coaxed into decorating the orange shells with orange-rind bows. The most fun is in the eating, of course. The maple-orange combination will be as much of a flavor surprise as the low calorie count.

ASPARAGUS-ESCAROLE SOUP

½ pound fresh asparagus spears
3 cups chopped escarole
1 teaspoon chicken-flavored bouillon granules
1 cup water
½ cup low-fat buttermilk
1 teaspoon chopped fresh parsley
¼ cup commercial croutons

Snap off tough ends of asparagus. Remove scales using a knife or vegetable peeler, if desired. Cut asparagus into 1-inch pieces. Combine asparagus, escarole, bouillon granules, and water in a 2-quart glass measure. Cover with heavy-duty plastic wrap, and vent. Microwave at HIGH for 8 to 9 minutes or until asparagus is tender. Let stand 1 minute.

Pour mixture into container of an electric blender or food processor. Add buttermilk and parsley; process until smooth. Ladle into serving bowls, and top each serving with 1 tablespoon croutons. Serve immediately. Yield: 3 cups (47 calories per ¾-cup serving).

PROTEIN 3.1 / FAT 1.4 / CARBOHYDRATE 6.3 / CHOLESTEROL 0 / IRON 0.6 / SODIUM 118 / CALCIUM 64

Maple Meringue Orange Cups—a simple microwave dessert that seals in the sweet flavor of oranges with a light maple-flavored meringue.

LEMON FLOUNDER

3 medium lemons, thinly sliced
4 (4-ounce) flounder fillets
1 tablespoon margarine

Arrange lemon slices on a 12-inch round glass platter. Rinse fish with cold water, and pat dry. Arrange fillets on lemon slices with thickest end of fillet at outer edges of platter. Place margarine in a 1-cup glass measure. Microwave at HIGH for 35 seconds or until melted. Drizzle margarine over fish.

Cover with heavy-duty plastic wrap, and vent. Microwave at HIGH for 6 to 8 minutes or until fish flakes easily when tested with a fork, rotating platter after 3 minutes. Let stand 1 minute. Drain off excess liquid. Serve immediately. Yield: 4 servings (131 calories per serving).

PROTEIN 19.9 / FAT 4.0 / CARBOHYDRATE 8.6 / CHOLESTEROL 57 / IRON 1.4 / SODIUM 124 / CALCIUM 64

SUMMER SQUASH MEDLEY

Vegetable cooking spray
1 tablespoon margarine
1 large clove garlic, minced
1 small sweet red pepper, seeded and
  cut into strips
2 small yellow squash, cut into ¼-inch
  diagonal slices
2 small zucchini, sliced
2 green onions, sliced
1 cup cherry tomatoes, halved
¼ teaspoon dried whole oregano
¼ teaspoon salt
⅛ teaspoon pepper

Coat a large skillet with cooking spray; add margarine and place over medium heat until margarine melts. Add garlic; cook 1 minute, stirring constantly. Add sweet red pepper, yellow squash, and zucchini; cover and cook 4 minutes. Stir in onions, tomatoes, oregano, salt, and pepper; cover and cook 1 minute or until vegetables are crisp-tender. Yield: 4 servings (53 calories per serving).

PROTEIN 1.5 / FAT 3.2 / CARBOHYDRATE 5.9 / CHOLESTEROL 0 / IRON 1.0 / SODIUM 186 / CALCIUM 25

BASIL-SCENTED PASTA

6 cups water
4 ounces vermicelli
1½ teaspoons corn oil
2 fresh basil leaves, chopped

Bring water to a boil in a small Dutch oven. Add vermicelli, and allow water to return to a boil. Cook, uncovered, until al dente; drain.

Combine cooked vermicelli, oil, and basil in a large bowl, tossing lightly to coat well. Serve hot. Yield: 4 servings (122 calories per serving).

PROTEIN 3.7 / FAT 2.1 / CARBOHYDRATE 21.8 / CHOLESTEROL 0 / IRON 1.2 / SODIUM 1 / CALCIUM 26

MAPLE MERINGUE ORANGE CUPS

2 medium-size navel oranges
2 tablespoons reduced-calorie maple syrup, divided
2 egg whites
⅛ teaspoon cream of tartar
⅛ teaspoon ground nutmeg
Orange rind strips

Cut oranges in half crosswise. Clip membranes, and remove pulp, being careful not to puncture bottom. Coarsely chop pulp; mix with 1 tablespoon maple syrup. Spoon pulp mixture into orange cups. Place in a microwave-safe 8-inch cake dish. Microwave, uncovered, at HIGH for 2 to 2½ minutes.

Beat egg whites (at room temperature) and cream of tartar until foamy. Gradually add remaining syrup, beating until stiff peaks form. Spread meringue over top of each shell; seal edges. Microwave, uncovered, at HIGH for 1 to 1½ minutes or until meringue is set. Sprinkle with nutmeg. Garnish with orange rind strips. Yield: 4 servings (44 calories per serving).

PROTEIN 2.4 / FAT 0.1 / CARBOHYDRATE 9.4 / CHOLESTEROL 0 / IRON 0.1 / SODIUM 34 / CALCIUM 30

Much of the preparation for this colorful Summer Salad Buffet can be done ahead of time: Beer-Zucchini-Leek Salad, Broccoli-Sweet Red Pepper Salad, Japanese Crab Salad, and Moroccan Carrot Salad (menu begins on page 85).

Vegetable-Noodle Soup borrows chic from julienned vegetables and vermicelli noodles.

Sophisticated Comfort Food

**Vegetable-Noodle Soup
Meat Loaf with Shiitake
Mushrooms
English Peas with Lettuce
Potato-Turnip Puree
Angel Food Cake with
Berries**

Serves 6
Total calories per serving: 621

Sometimes during our active (and sometimes hectic) lives, we long for those wonderful, comforting foods usually associated with our childhood—foods like chicken-noodle soup, meat loaf, mashed potatoes, peas, and light-as-a-feather angel food cake. But this is the '80s—a decade of "nouvelle cuisine," wholesome foods, exotic fare, and gourmet takeouts. How can we satisfy culinary longings and still meet the new sophisticated standards of taste and nutrition?

The answer to that question can be found in this nostalgic menu, teeming with sophistication. Vegetable-Noodle Soup, made with garden fresh vegetables, rich chicken broth, and delicate vermicelli noodles, will send its seductive aroma to greet your guests at the door.

Serve meat loaf, but add earthy shiitake mushrooms and spicy green peppercorns; serve English peas, but add sophistication with complementary sherry and shredded lettuce. Mashed potatoes are rendered more nutritious with a puree of turnips—in the French manner.

Angel food cake has always been low in calories. It's the fresh berries on top that make it right for the '80s. (Refrigerate the extra berry mixture, and store leftover cake for a quick dessert later in the week.) Who says you can't go home again?

VEGETABLE-NOODLE SOUP

3 (10½-ounce) cans no-salt-added chicken broth, undiluted
2 cups water
2 large carrots, scraped and cut into 1-inch julienne strips
1 large sweet red pepper, seeded and cut into 1-inch julienne strips
1 medium leek, cut into 1-inch julienne strips
2 ounces vermicelli, broken in half
½ teaspoon salt
¼ teaspoon white pepper
1 tablespoon chopped fresh parsley

Combine undiluted chicken broth and 2 cups water in a large Dutch oven. Bring mixture to a boil. Add carrots, sweet red pepper, and leek; cook over medium-high heat 4 minutes. Add vermicelli, salt, and white pepper; cook 6 minutes or until vermicelli is al dente and vegetables are tender. Ladle soup into individual serving bowls. Sprinkle with chopped fresh parsley, and serve hot. Yield: 6 cups (100 calories per 1-cup serving).

PROTEIN 3.9 / FAT 1.5 / CARBOHYDRATE 18.4 / CHOLESTEROL 0 / IRON 1.7 / SODIUM 249 / CALCIUM 37

MEAT LOAF WITH SHIITAKE MUSHROOMS

½ cup dried shiitake mushrooms
2 teaspoons green peppercorns
⅔ cup hot water
¾ pound ground chuck
1 small onion, chopped
¼ pound fresh mushrooms, chopped
½ cup fine, dry breadcrumbs
¼ cup quick-cooking oats, uncooked
1 egg, lightly beaten
3 tablespoons chopped fresh parsley
2 cloves garlic, minced
1 tablespoon Worcestershire sauce
½ teaspoon salt
⅛ teaspoon pepper
Vegetable cooking spray

Soak shiitake mushrooms and peppercorns in hot water 15 minutes; drain, reserving liquid. Coarsely chop mushrooms and peppercorns; set aside. Place reserved liquid in a small saucepan; cook until reduced by half. Set aside.

Combine ground chuck and remaining ingredients, except cooking spray, in a large bowl; stir well. Add reserved mushrooms, peppercorns, and liquid; stir well. Shape mixture into a 7½- x 4½- inch loaf. Place on a broiler pan coated with cooking spray. Bake, uncovered, at 375° for 45 minutes or until meat is no longer pink. Yield: 6 servings (211 calories per serving).

PROTEIN 15.5 / FAT 8.9 / CARBOHYDRATE 17.2 / CHOLESTEROL 81 / IRON 2.5 / SODIUM 316 / CALCIUM 35

ENGLISH PEAS WITH LETTUCE

1 (10-ounce) package frozen English peas
Vegetable cooking spray
½ cup sliced fresh mushrooms
¼ cup chopped onion
1 tablespoon dry sherry
¼ teaspoon salt
¼ teaspoon ground nutmeg
Dash of white pepper
1½ cups shredded iceberg lettuce

Cook peas according to package directions, omitting salt. Drain and set aside.

Coat a large skillet with cooking spray; place over medium heat until hot. Add mushrooms and onion; sauté until vegetables are tender. Add reserved cooked peas, sherry, salt, nutmeg, and white pepper; cook 1 minute or until vegetable mixture is thoroughly heated. Add shredded lettuce; remove from heat. Toss gently and serve immediately. Yield: 6 servings (46 calories per serving).

PROTEIN 2.8 / FAT 0.3 / CARBOHYDRATE 7.7 / CHOLESTEROL 0 / IRON 0.9 / SODIUM 152 / CALCIUM 16

POTATO-TURNIP PUREE

1½ pounds turnips, peeled and quartered
1½ pounds baking potatoes, peeled and sliced
1½ cups water
1½ teaspoons beef-flavored bouillon granules
1 tablespoon margarine
¼ teaspoon salt
⅛ teaspoon white pepper
2 tablespoons chopped fresh parsley

Place turnips in a large saucepan; cover with water, and bring to a boil. Cover; reduce heat, and simmer 20 minutes or until turnips are tender. Drain. Place turnips in container of an electric blender or food processor; process until smooth. Set aside.

Place potatoes in a large saucepan. Add 1½ cups water and bouillon granules; bring to a boil. Cover; reduce heat, and simmer 10 to 15 minutes or until tender. Drain and mash potatoes. Stir in reserved turnips, margarine, salt, pepper, and parsley. Yield: 6 servings (139 calories per serving).

PROTEIN 3.3 / FAT 2.3 / CARBOHYDRATE 27.6 / CHOLESTEROL 0 / IRON 1.3 / SODIUM 318 / CALCIUM 45

ANGEL FOOD CAKE WITH BERRIES

1 cup sifted cake flour
1 cup sugar, divided
½ teaspoon salt
10 egg whites
1 tablespoon water
1 tablespoon lemon juice
1 teaspoon cream of tartar
1 teaspoon vanilla extract
1½ cups fresh blackberries
1½ cups fresh raspberries
Fresh mint sprigs (optional)

Sift together cake flour, ¼ cup sugar, and salt 3 times.

Beat egg whites (at room temperature) until foamy. Add water, lemon juice, and cream of tartar; beat until soft peaks form. Gradually add remaining ¾ cup sugar, 2 tablespoons at a time, beating until stiff peaks form. Sift flour mixture over egg white mixture ¼ cup at a time, folding in carefully after each addition. Gently fold in vanilla.

Pour batter into an ungreased 10-inch tube pan; spread evenly with a spatula. Bake at 350° for 45 minutes or until cake springs back when lightly touched. Remove cake from oven. Invert pan on funnel or bottle; cool cake 1 hour, and remove from pan. Cut cake into 12 slices.

Combine berries; toss gently. To serve, spoon ¼ cup berries onto individual cake slices. Garnish with mint sprigs, if desired. Yield: 12 servings (125 calories per serving).

PROTEIN 3.7 / FAT 0.2 / CARBOHYDRATE 27.6 / CHOLESTEROL 0 / IRON 0.2 / SODIUM 157 / CALCIUM 14

SOUND NUTRITION GUIDELINES FOR THE GOLDEN YEARS

Why does one person live to age 70 and another to 94? Many reasons, but proper diet is at the top of the list. As people grow older, the basic guidelines for a nutritious diet remain about the same as for any healthy adult, regardless of age. The U. S. Recommended Dietary Allowance (RDA) now includes everyone 51 and older in the same category, although this could change as research on the vitamin, mineral, and protein requirements of older people continues.

Because of changes in activity level and perhaps metabolism, most older people gain weight more easily than in their younger years, so it becomes increasingly important to derive more benefits from every calorie. The most nutrient-dense foods from the Basic Four Food Groups (page 13) are the optimum choices. Foods from the Fifth Food Group (sweets, alcohol, and fats) should be consumed more sparingly because they provide plenty of calories, but few nutrients. Older people should build their diets around meals with the same variety of foods found in the Sophisticated Comfort Food menu (page 72). Included are fresh fruit, vegetables, protein sources, and high-fiber, high-calcium foods.

California Dreamin'

California Gazpacho
Grilled Herbed Chicken
Spaghetti Vegetables
Baked Sonoma
Goat Cheese Salad
Commercial Breadsticks
Sparkling Wine-Orange
Sorbet
White Wine

Serves 6
Total calories per serving: 658

A glistening dessert rich in vitamin C: Sparkling Wine-Orange Sorbet.

Much of the "revolution" in today's kitchen has its roots in California. There is a new sense of adventure about food that makes the most of fresh ingredients and simple preparations.

California Dreamin' is a tasty celebration of the West Coast's influence. The calorie count includes four breadsticks and 3½ ounces of California white wine per person.

CALIFORNIA GAZPACHO

3 medium tomatoes, peeled, seeded,
  and diced
3 cups no-salt-added tomato juice
¼ cup diced onion
¼ cup diced celery
1 medium-size green pepper, seeded
  and diced
¼ cup sliced green onions
1 medium cucumber, chopped
3 cloves garlic, minced
2 tablespoons chopped fresh parsley
1 teaspoon chopped fresh cilantro
3 tablespoons red wine vinegar
Dash of hot sauce
½ teaspoon salt
⅛ teaspoon freshly ground pepper

Combine all ingredients in a large bowl, stirring well. Cover and chill 8 hours or overnight. Ladle into soup bowls. Yield: 6 cups (53 calories per 1-cup serving).

PROTEIN 2.5 / FAT 0.3 / CARBOHYDRATE 12.1 / CHOLESTEROL 0 / IRON 0.8 / SODIUM 218 / CALCIUM 26

GRILLED HERBED CHICKEN

½ teaspoon dried whole basil
½ teaspoon dried whole thyme
½ teaspoon dried whole oregano
6 boneless chicken breast halves (1½ pounds),
  skinned
1 tablespoon olive oil
Juice of 1 lemon
Vegetable cooking spray

Combine basil, thyme, and oregano in a small bowl; set aside.

Trim excess fat from chicken. Rinse chicken with cold water, and pat dry. Place between 2 sheets of waxed paper; flatten to ¼-inch thickness, using a meat mallet or rolling pin. Brush surface of chicken with olive oil; sprinkle with lemon juice and reserved herbs.

Coat grill with cooking spray. Grill chicken 6 inches over medium coals 10 minutes or until chicken is tender, turning once. Yield: 6 servings (159 calories per serving).

PROTEIN 25.7 / FAT 5.2 / CARBOHYDRATE 0.8 / CHOLESTEROL 70 / IRON 1.1 / SODIUM 61 / CALCIUM 18

SPAGHETTI VEGETABLES

1 pound carrots, scraped and cut into 2- x 2½-inch
  pieces
1 pound zucchini, cut into 2- x 2½-inch pieces
Vegetable cooking spray
1 tablespoon margarine
⅛ teaspoon salt
⅛ teaspoon pepper

Position thin slicing blade in food processor
bowl. Arrange carrots horizontally in food chute;
slice, applying firm pressure with food pusher.
Stack carrot slices, keeping ends even. Place carrot slices in bottom of food chute with cut sides
parallel to chute sides; slice, applying firm
pressure with food pusher. Repeat procedure
with zucchini.

Cook carrots and zucchini in boiling water to
cover 2 minutes or until crisp-tender; drain.

Coat a large skillet with cooking spray; add
margarine. Place over medium-high heat until
margarine melts. Add carrots, zucchini, salt, and
pepper. Cook 3 minutes or until vegetables are
thoroughly heated. Yield: 6 servings (60 calories
per serving).

PROTEIN 1.6 / FAT 2.2 / CARBOHYDRATE 9.9 / CHOLESTEROL 0 /
IRON 0.7 / SODIUM 100 / CALCIUM 33

BAKED SONOMA GOAT CHEESE SALAD

½ cup soft breadcrumbs
½ teaspoon dried whole thyme
1 (5½-ounce) log fresh goat cheese, cut into 6
  equal rounds
2 cups torn romaine lettuce
2 cups torn Bibb lettuce
2 cups torn radicchio
Vinaigrette (recipe follows)

Combine breadcrumbs and thyme; toss gently.
Coat cheese rounds with breadcrumb mixture;
place on ungreased baking sheet. Bake at 400°
for 10 minutes or until lightly browned. Remove
from oven, and set aside.

Combine lettuces and vinaigrette; toss lightly.
Arrange lettuce mixture on 6 individual salad
plates. Place 1 reserved round of cheese on top
of lettuce. Serve immediately. Yield: 6 servings
(122 calories per serving).

Vinaigrette:

3 tablespoons red wine vinegar
2 tablespoons water
1 teaspoon Dijon mustard
1 clove garlic, crushed
1 tablespoon olive oil

Combine vinegar, water, mustard, and
crushed garlic in a small bowl; stir with a wire
whisk until well blended. Stir in oil. Yield: ¼ cup
plus 2 tablespoons.

PROTEIN 5.2 / FAT 8.2 / CARBOHYDRATE 6.8 / CHOLESTEROL 23 /
IRON 0.8 / SODIUM 361 / CALCIUM 144

SPARKLING WINE-ORANGE SORBET

1½ cups water
¾ cup sugar
¾ cup unsweetened orange juice
¾ cup sparkling white Zinfandel wine or champagne
Fresh mint sprigs (optional)

Combine water and sugar in a small saucepan; bring to a boil. Reduce heat, and simmer 2
minutes or until sugar dissolves, stirring frequently. Remove from heat, and stir in orange
juice and wine. Cool.

Pour mixture into freezer can of a hand-
turned or electric freezer. Freeze according to
manufacturer's instructions. Scoop mixture into
dessert bowls, and serve immediately. Garnish
with mint sprigs, if desired. Yield: 3 cups (130
calories per ½-cup serving).

PROTEIN 0.2 / FAT 0.0 / CARBOHYDRATE 28.4 / CHOLESTEROL 0 /
IRON 0.2 / SODIUM 2 / CALCIUM 5

 ## MARKING MILES IN THE MALL

Many people, especially older adults, are
taking advantage of the twelve-month,
climate-controlled atmosphere of malls. Friends meet
there to walk themselves to better health.

In a mall, you can always chart a level course.
When you're ready to increase the challenge, use
the stairs or quicken your pace. Check with the public
relations office of your local mall. Some doors open
as early as 7 A.M.; some even offer walkers special
health-related discounts.

Southwestern Patio Buffet

After the big game or an afternoon of snow skiing, what can you serve twelve hungry people who are chilled to the bone? Chili and all the fixin's, of course! All the Southwestern favorites are here in this light, nutritious menu. For starters, let everyone dip plain tortilla chips into fresh tomato salsa spiced with a jalapeño pepper and fresh cilantro. Then offer the hungry amigos a piping hot bowl of Turkey Chili,

Rio Grande Salsa with
Tortilla Chips
Turkey Chili
Fresh Corn Sticks
Chocolate Shortcake with
Mango Topping

Serves 12
Total calories per serving: 547

brimming with ground turkey, pinto beans, and vegetables.

Plenty of green onions and old-fashioned Fresh Corn Sticks (one per person), made with fresh yellow corn and low-fat buttermilk, are perfect chili-meal accompaniments. To streamline preparation, try enlisting your food processor for all the necessary chopping. The Southwestern flavor is complete with the combination of cocoa and cinnamon in the Chocolate Shortcake with Mango Topping.

RIO GRANDE SALSA WITH TORTILLA CHIPS

3 small tomatoes, peeled, seeded, and chopped
1 small green pepper, seeded and chopped
1 small purple onion, chopped
1 medium jalapeño pepper, seeded and chopped
1 clove garlic, minced
1 tablespoon chopped fresh cilantro
1½ teaspoons red wine vinegar
⅛ teaspoon salt
48 plain tortilla chips

Combine tomatoes, green pepper, onion, jalapeño pepper, garlic, chopped cilantro, red wine vinegar, and salt in a medium bowl, stirring until well blended. Cover and chill thoroughly. Serve salsa with tortilla chips. Yield: 3 cups. Serving size: ¼ cup salsa plus 4 tortilla chips (65 calories per serving).

PROTEIN 1.3 / FAT 3.0 / CARBOHYDRATE 8.8 / CHOLESTEROL 0 / IRON 0.6 / SODIUM 35 / CALCIUM 8

TURKEY CHILI

Vegetable cooking spray
2 (1-pound) packages raw ground turkey, thawed
2 medium-size green peppers, seeded and chopped
1 medium onion, chopped
1 medium jalapeño pepper, seeded and chopped
2 tablespoons minced garlic
1 tablespoon beef-flavored bouillon granules
3 cups water
2½ cups cooked pinto beans
2 (28-ounce) cans crushed tomatoes, undrained
1 (6-ounce) can tomato paste
3 tablespoons chili powder
2 teaspoons ground cumin
2 bay leaves
⅛ teaspoon salt
⅛ teaspoon pepper
½ cup chopped green onions

Coat a large Dutch oven with cooking spray; place over medium heat until hot. Add turkey; cook 5 minutes or until browned, stirring to crumble. Drain turkey in a colander. Wipe Dutch oven dry with a paper towel.

Recoat Dutch oven with cooking spray; place over medium heat until hot. Add green peppers, onion, jalapeño pepper, and garlic; sauté until tender. Add turkey to Dutch oven. Dissolve bouillon in water; add to Dutch oven with beans and next 7 ingredients. Cover and bring to a boil; reduce heat, and simmer 1 hour, stirring occasionally. Remove and discard bay leaves.

Ladle hot chili into a large serving bowl; top with chopped green onions. Yield: 12 cups (207 calories per serving).

PROTEIN 22.6 / FAT 4.1 / CARBOHYDRATE 21.3 / CHOLESTEROL 43 / IRON 4.2 / SODIUM 382 / CALCIUM 93

FRESH CORN STICKS

1 cup low-fat buttermilk
1 egg, separated
2 tablespoons margarine, melted
½ cup unbleached flour
½ cup yellow cornmeal
2 tablespoons sugar
1¼ teaspoons baking powder
½ teaspoon salt
Vegetable cooking spray
½ cup fresh yellow corn, cut from cob

Combine buttermilk, egg yolk, and margarine in a medium bowl, stirring well. Combine flour, cornmeal, sugar, baking powder, and salt in a small bowl. Gradually add flour mixture to buttermilk mixture, stirring just until dry ingredients are moistened.

Place 2 cast-iron corn stick pans coated with cooking spray in a 425° oven for 3 minutes or until hot.

Beat egg white (at room temperature) in a small bowl until stiff peaks form. Gently fold egg white and corn into flour mixture.

Remove pans from oven; spoon batter into pans, filling two-thirds full. Bake at 425° for 20 minutes or until lightly browned. Serve warm. Yield: 12 corn sticks (83 calories each).

PROTEIN 2.4 / FAT 2.9 / CARBOHYDRATE 12.0 / CHOLESTEROL 23 / IRON 0.5 / SODIUM 169 / CALCIUM 49

CHOCOLATE SHORTCAKE WITH MANGO TOPPING

2 cups all-purpose flour
¼ cup plus 2 tablespoons unsweetened cocoa
1 teaspoon ground cinnamon
¼ cup plus 1 tablespoon sugar
2 teaspoons baking powder
½ teaspoon baking soda
⅛ teaspoon salt
¼ cup margarine
1 (8-ounce) carton coffee low-fat yogurt
1 egg, beaten
Vegetable cooking spray
Mango Topping

Combine first 7 ingredients in a large bowl; stir well. Cut in margarine with a pastry blender

Spicy Rio Grande Salsa, Turkey Chili, Fresh Corn Sticks, and Chocolate Shortcake with Mango Topping.

until mixture resembles coarse meal. Add yogurt and egg to flour mixture; stir just until dry ingredients are moistened.

Turn dough out onto a lightly floured surface, and knead 1 minute. Press into bottom of a 9-inch square baking pan coated with cooking spray. Bake at 450° for 10 minutes; cool in pan on a wire rack. Cut into squares. Top each square with 2 tablespoons Mango Topping. Yield: 12 servings (192 calories per serving).

Mango Topping:

2 fresh ripe mangos, peeled, seeded, cubed, and divided
2 tablespoons lime juice, divided

Place 1 cubed mango and 1 tablespoon lime juice in container of an electric blender or food processor; process until smooth. Combine pureed mango, remaining cubed mango, and remaining 1 tablespoon lime juice in a small bowl; stir gently. Yield: 1½ cups.

PROTEIN 4.9 / FAT 5.2 / CARBOHYDRATE 31.9 / CHOLESTEROL 24 / IRON 1.4 / SODIUM 173 / CALCIUM 89

Mediterranean Vegetarian Dinner

Just as summer begins to turn to fall and thoughts begin to turn to heartier meals, look to this menu to satisfy the hearty appetites of vegetarians and nonvegetarians alike. Low-calorie, but hearty; intensely flavored, yet subtle, this menu's inspiration comes from southern Italy.

Start with an appetizer course of Antipasto: Marinated Artichoke Hearts, White Bean Salad, and Mushroom-Celery Salad—three carbohydrate rich marinated dishes that are sure to whet ap-

Antipasto:
Marinated Artichoke Hearts
White Bean Salad
Mushroom-Celery Salad
Eggplant Lasagna
Grissini
Fresh Figs
Espresso

Serves 8
Total calories per serving: 778

petites for the meal to come. The "lightened" Eggplant

Lasagna entrée features a low-fat white sauce that tastes every bit as good as its cholesterol-laden béchamel cousin. Add Grissini, your own homemade Italian breadsticks, for an impressive accompaniment. (The Grissini recipe will make 24 breadsticks; the calorie count includes one per person. Extras can be frozen.)

For dessert, offer sweet and simple ripe figs garnished with fresh sprigs of mint—and a steaming cup of freshly brewed Espresso. Buon appetito!

MARINATED ARTICHOKE HEARTS

4 (9-ounce) packages frozen artichoke hearts
½ teaspoon chicken-flavored bouillon granules
½ cup hot water
2 tablespoons balsamic vinegar
2 tablespoons vinegar
2 tablespoons olive oil
1 clove garlic, minced
1 teaspoon whole mustard seeds
1 tablespoon chopped fresh thyme or
  1 teaspoon dried whole thyme
1 tablespoon chopped fresh oregano or
  1 teaspoon dried whole oregano
1 teaspoon summer savory
½ teaspoon salt
⅛ teaspoon pepper

Cook artichoke hearts according to package directions, omitting salt. Drain, and transfer to a large serving bowl.

Dissolve bouillon granules in water in a medium bowl. Add vinegars and remaining ingredients, stirring well. Pour vinegar mixture over artichokes; toss gently. Cover and chill 30 minutes. Serve with a slotted spoon. Yield: 8 servings (83 calories per serving).

PROTEIN 3.5 / FAT 4.1 / CARBOHYDRATE 10.6 / CHOLESTEROL 0 / IRON 0.8 / SODIUM 231 / CALCIUM 34

WHITE BEAN SALAD

10 ounces dried Great Northern beans
½ cup diced purple onion
¼ cup chopped fresh parsley
1 (2-ounce) jar diced pimiento, drained
3 tablespoons water
2 tablespoons white wine vinegar
1 tablespoon lemon juice
1 tablespoon olive oil
½ teaspoon salt
¼ teaspoon freshly ground pepper

Sort and wash beans; place in a large Dutch oven. Cover with water 3 inches above beans. Bring to a boil; boil 5 minutes. Remove from heat. Cover, and let stand 1 hour. Drain beans; return to Dutch oven. Cover with water 3 inches above beans. Bring to a boil. Reduce heat, and simmer 1 hour or until beans are tender. Drain; rinse with cold water. Drain again.

Combine beans, onion, parsley, and pimiento in a large serving bowl. Combine water and remaining ingredients; stir well. Pour over bean mixture. Toss gently. Cover and marinate in refrigerator 8 hours or overnight, stirring occasionally. Yield: 8 servings (142 calories per serving).

PROTEIN 8.0 / FAT 2.1 / CARBOHYDRATE 23.5 / CHOLESTEROL 0 / IRON 2.2 / SODIUM 154 / CALCIUM 69

An assortment of hors d'oeuvres with lots of fiber: Mushroom-Celery Salad, White Bean Salad, and Marinated Artichoke Hearts. Fresh figs provide a simple, sweet ending to the Mediterranean Vegetarian Dinner.

MUSHROOM-CELERY SALAD

2 tablespoons lemon juice
1 tablespoon olive oil
¼ teaspoon chicken-flavored bouillon granules
3 tablespoons hot water
¼ teaspoon coarse salt
⅛ teaspoon coarsely ground pepper
1 pound fresh mushrooms, quartered
1 cup thinly sliced celery
¼ cup grated Parmesan cheese
1 tablespoon chopped fresh parsley
½ cup chopped pecans, toasted

Combine lemon juice and oil in a small bowl; stir with a wire whisk. Dissolve bouillon granules in water. Add to lemon juice mixture. Stir in salt and pepper.

Combine mushrooms, celery, cheese, and parsley in a large serving bowl. Pour lemon juice mixture over mushroom mixture. Add pecans; toss gently. Yield: 8 servings (94 calories per serving).

PROTEIN 2.9 / FAT 7.7 / CARBOHYDRATE 5.0 / CHOLESTEROL 2 / IRON 1.0 / SODIUM 147 / CALCIUM 47

EGGPLANT LASAGNA

2 medium eggplant (2 pounds)
Vegetable cooking spray
½ cup seasoned, dry breadcrumbs
½ cup freshly grated Parmesan cheese
1 (8-ounce) package lasagna noodles
1 medium onion, chopped
2 cloves garlic, minced
1 (28-ounce) can no-salt-added tomatoes, undrained and chopped
1 teaspoon dried whole oregano
⅜ teaspoon freshly ground pepper, divided
3 cups skim milk
¼ cup plus 2 tablespoons all-purpose flour
1 clove garlic, crushed
⅛ teaspoon ground nutmeg
1 cup (4 ounces) shredded part-skim mozzarella cheese

Slice eggplant into ¼-inch slices. Place slices on baking sheets coated with cooking spray. Broil 3 to 4 inches from heating element 4 minutes or until lightly browned, turning slices after 2 minutes. Set aside.

Combine breadcrumbs and Parmesan cheese in a small bowl; toss gently, and set aside.

Cook lasagna noodles according to package directions, omitting salt. Drain, and set aside.

Coat a large skillet with cooking spray. Place over medium heat until hot. Add onion and minced garlic; sauté until onion is tender. Add tomatoes, oregano, and ⅛ teaspoon pepper. Cook over medium-low heat 10 minutes or until slightly thickened, stirring occasionally. Remove from heat, and set aside.

Pour milk into a large saucepan. Sift flour over milk, stirring constantly until well blended. Bring to a boil, stirring constantly. Stir in crushed garlic, remaining ¼ teaspoon pepper, and nutmeg. Reduce heat to medium, and simmer 5 minutes, stirring constantly. (Mixture will be thick.) Remove from heat, and set aside.

Spread ⅓ cup tomato sauce mixture in bottom of a 13- x 9- x 2-inch baking dish coated with cooking spray. Top with 4 noodles and one-half eggplant slices. Sprinkle with ⅓ cup breadcrumb mixture. Top with 1½ cups tomato sauce mixture, ¾ cup white sauce mixture, ½ cup mozzarella cheese, and 4 noodles.

Repeat layers once, beginning and ending with noodles. Top with remaining white sauce and breadcrumb mixtures. Cover and bake at 400° for 30 minutes. Uncover; bake an additional 10 minutes or until thoroughly heated. Let stand 10 minutes before serving. Yield: 8 servings (306 calories per serving).

PROTEIN 16.4 / FAT 5.1 / CARBOHYDRATE 49.4 / CHOLESTEROL 15 / IRON 2.6 / SODIUM 292 / CALCIUM 388

GRISSINI

1 package dry yeast
1 tablespoon honey
1 tablespoon olive oil
1 cup warm water (105° to 115°)
3½ cups unbleached all-purpose flour
1 teaspoon salt
Vegetable cooking spray
1 egg white, lightly beaten
¼ cup sesame seeds

Combine yeast, honey, olive oil, and warm water in a small bowl; let stand 5 minutes.

Combine flour and salt in a large bowl. Add yeast mixture, stirring until well blended.

Turn dough out onto a lightly floured surface; knead 8 to 10 minutes or until dough is smooth and elastic. Place in a large bowl coated with cooking spray, turning to grease top. Cover and let rise in a warm place (85°), free from drafts, 1 hour or until doubled in bulk.

Punch dough down. Shape into a 12- x 24-inch rectangle. Cut dough crosswise into 24 (1-inch) strips. Stretch dough strips gently and place 2 inches apart on baking sheets coated with cooking spray. Gently brush with egg white; sprinkle with sesame seeds. Bake at 400° for 12 minutes or until lightly browned. Remove from oven and serve warm. Yield: 2 dozen breadsticks (77 calories each).

PROTEIN 2.3 / FAT 1.5 / CARBOHYDRATE 13.8 / CHOLESTEROL 0 / IRON 0.9 / SODIUM 101 / CALCIUM 16

Savory new flavor combinations are yours to explore with this menu from Eastern India.

Indian Tandoori Feast

When the first heat wave of summer hits, this Indian-inspired menu is the perfect repast. The aromatic spices and cool yogurt in Indian cookery will tantalize the palate as few other cuisines can. In fact, the wonderful, exotic tastes of this menu disguise its "light" nature.

Keeping the lazy, hot days of summer in mind, much of the preparation can be done in advance with minimal stove-top

Tandoori Cornish Hens
Vegetables with
Saffron Rice
Cucumber-Yogurt Salad
Indian Flat Bread
Sweetly Spiced Oranges

Serves 8
Total calories per serving: 634

cooking. Yogurt-marinated Tandoori Cornish Hens and spicy

Vegetables with Saffron Rice are perfect partners. Cucumber-Yogurt Salad provides the cool, crunchy contrast. Rounds of Indian Flat Bread and Sweetly Spiced Oranges complete the balance of textures and flavors.

Arrange the food on pretty platters, and garnish with lots of fresh cilantro or mint and lemon twists. Your quests will be delighted with the profusion of colors, aromas, and tastes.

TANDOORI CORNISH HENS

4 (1-pound, 6-ounce) Cornish hens
½ cup plain non-fat yogurt
½ cup lemon juice
3 cloves garlic
1 tablespoon paprika
1 teaspoon ground cardamom
½ teaspoon ground ginger
½ teaspoon red pepper
Vegetable cooking spray
Fresh cilantro sprigs (optional)

Remove giblets from hens; reserve for other uses. Rinse hens with cold water, and pat dry. Split each hen lengthwise, using an electric knife. Remove and discard skin. Place hens, cavity side up, in a shallow dish.

Combine yogurt and next 6 ingredients in container of an electric blender or food processor; process until smooth. Pour mixture over hens; cover and marinate in refrigerator 8 hours or overnight, turning occasionally.

Arrange hens, cavity side down, on broiler pans coated with cooking spray; brush with yogurt mixture. Broil 6 inches from heating element 7 minutes; turn and broil 5 minutes or until tender. Transfer to a platter, and garnish with cilantro, if desired. Serve immediately. Yield: 8 servings (228 calories per serving).

PROTEIN 33.2 / FAT 8.4 / CARBOHYDRATE 3.6 / CHOLESTEROL 99 / IRON 1.6 / SODIUM 107 / CALCIUM 51

VEGETABLES WITH SAFFRON RICE

1 tablespoon vegetable oil
½ cup chopped onion
¼ teaspoon ground cinnamon
⅛ teaspoon ground cloves
⅛ teaspoon ground turmeric
⅛ teaspoon cumin seeds
1 bay leaf
1½ cups water
½ pound carrots, scraped and sliced
    diagonally
¾ cup uncooked regular rice
¼ teaspoon salt
⅛ teaspoon powdered saffron
1 cup frozen English peas

Heat vegetable oil in a medium skillet over medium heat until hot. Add chopped onion and next 5 ingredients; sauté until onion is tender. Set aside.

Bring water to a boil in a large Dutch oven. Stir in sliced carrots, rice, reserved onion mixture, salt, and saffron. Reduce heat to medium; cover and simmer 10 minutes. Stir in English peas; cover and simmer an additional 10 minutes or until rice is tender. Remove and discard bay leaf. Transfer rice mixture to a serving bowl, and serve immediately. Yield: 8 servings (102 calories per serving).

PROTEIN 2.4 / FAT 1.9 / CARBOHYDRATE 18.7 / CHOLESTEROL 0 / IRON 1.0 / SODIUM 99 / CALCIUM 17

CUCUMBER-YOGURT SALAD

2 large English cucumbers, thinly sliced
1 tablespoon coarse salt
2 (8-ounce) cartons plain low-fat yogurt
½ cup low-fat sour cream
¼ cup chopped fresh cilantro
1 teaspoon ground cumin
½ teaspoon salt
2 medium tomatoes, seeded and chopped
Curly leaf lettuce leaves

Sprinkle cucumbers with coarse salt. Cover and let stand 30 minutes. Rinse cucumbers several times in cold water. Drain well, squeezing out excess moisture with paper towels. Set cucumbers aside.

Combine yogurt, sour cream, cilantro, cumin, and ½ teaspoon salt, stirring well. Cover and chill thoroughly.

Just before serving, combine reserved cucumbers, yogurt mixture, and tomatoes in a large bowl; toss gently to mix well. Spoon mixture into a lettuce-lined salad bowl. Yield: 8 servings (84 calories per serving).

PROTEIN 4.7 / FAT 2.9 / CARBOHYDRATE 10.9 / CHOLESTEROL 9 / IRON 0.9 / SODIUM 205 / CALCIUM 152

INDIAN FLAT BREAD

2 cups all-purpose flour
1½ teaspoons baking powder
1 teaspoon sugar
¼ teaspoon salt
⅛ teaspoon baking soda
¼ cup plain low-fat yogurt
1 egg, slightly beaten
¼ cup skim milk
Vegetable cooking spray

Combine flour, baking powder, sugar, salt, and soda, stirring well. Add yogurt, egg, and milk, stirring just until dry ingredients are moistened and a soft dough forms. Turn mixture out onto a lightly floured surface; knead 5 minutes or until smooth and elastic. Place in a medium bowl coated with cooking spray, turning to grease top. Cover and let rise in a warm place (85°), free from drafts, 3 hours. (Dough will not double in bulk.)

Punch dough down, and divide into eight equal portions. Turn dough out onto a lightly floured surface. Roll each portion into a 5- x 3-inch leaf shape, about ¼-inch thick.

Place 2 baking sheets in a 450° oven for 5 minutes or until hot. Transfer dough to baking sheets, and bake at 450° for 6 minutes or until lightly browned. Remove from baking sheets, and let cool on wire racks. Yield: 8 flat breads (144 calories each).

PROTEIN 5.0 / FAT 1.2 / CARBOHYDRATE 27.6 / CHOLESTEROL 35 / IRON 1.1 / SODIUM 161 / CALCIUM 70

SWEETLY SPICED ORANGES

8 large navel oranges
1 tablespoon orange flower water
¼ cup powdered sugar
¼ teaspoon ground cinnamon

Finely grate rind of 2 oranges; set rind aside. Remove and discard peel and pith of all oranges. Slice oranges crosswise into ¼-inch-thick slices, and arrange on a serving platter. Sprinkle with orange flower water; sift powdered sugar over top, and sprinkle with reserved rind. Cover and refrigerate at least 2 hours. Sprinkle with cinnamon just before serving. Yield: 8 servings (76 calories per serving).

PROTEIN 1.3 / FAT 0.2 / CARBOHYDRATE 19.6 / CHOLESTEROL 0 / IRON 0.2 / SODIUM 0 / CALCIUM 56

SELENIUM SUPPLEMENTS

Preliminary studies show that the mineral selenium may act in much the same way as beta-carotene, vitamin A, and vitamin E in decreasing the risk of developing certain types of cancer. But the U.S. Food and Nutrition Board has determined that only small amounts of this trace mineral are required and have set adequate daily requirements at between 50 and 200 micrograms. Meeting this requirement is not difficult if the diet consists of a variety of foods grown in the soil. Selenium supplements can be toxic and even fatal. The margin between too much and too little is narrow.

Summer Salad Buffet

Broccoli-Sweet Red Pepper
Salad
Beet-Zucchini-Leek Salad
Moroccan Carrot Salad
Japanese Crab Salad
Smoked Turkey and
Wild Rice Salad

Serves 16
Total calories per serving: 291

If asked to name a favorite warm-weather food, most people would probably say "salad!" Crunchy or creamy, tart or sweet, the salads in this buffet comprise the perfect do-ahead menu.

Arrange all the salads on attractive platters, and let your guests help themselves to this appealing and nutritious summertime buffet!

Smoked Turkey and Wild Rice Salad—a summer-salad sensation.

BROCCOLI-SWEET RED PEPPER SALAD

3 pounds fresh broccoli
4 medium-size sweet red peppers, seeded and coarsely chopped
Cottage Cheese Dressing

Wash broccoli. Trim off large leaves and tough lower ends of stalks. Peel stalks, and cut into ¼-inch-thick slices. Cut remaining broccoli into flowerets. Combine broccoli and water to cover in a large Dutch oven. Cover and bring to a boil. Boil 2 minutes or until crisp-tender. Drain and rinse with cold water.

Arrange broccoli and peppers in a large, shallow serving bowl or on a platter. Drizzle Cottage Cheese Dressing over top of vegetables. Yield: 16 servings (47 calories per serving).

Cottage Cheese Dressing:

1 cup low-fat cottage cheese
½ cup chopped fresh parsley
¼ cup reduced-calorie mayonnaise
3 tablespoons minced green onions
3 tablespoons lemon juice
2 tablespoons skim milk
1 tablespoon tarragon vinegar
2 teaspoons Dijon mustard
¼ teaspoon salt
⅛ teaspoon pepper

Place all ingredients in container of an electric blender or food processor; process 30 seconds or until smooth, scraping sides of container as necessary. Cover and chill until serving time. Yield: 1¼ cups.

PROTEIN 4.0 / FAT 1.6 / CARBOHYDRATE 5.5 / CHOLESTEROL 2 / IRON 1.0 / SODIUM 158 / CALCIUM 44

BEET-ZUCCHINI-LEEK SALAD

5 medium zucchini
1½ teaspoons coarse salt
2 pounds beets
2 medium leeks
¼ cup chopped fresh parsley
Dijon Vinaigrette

Thinly slice zucchini. Combine zucchini slices and salt in a large bowl, tossing well. Let stand 30 minutes, and rinse. Press with paper towels to remove excess moisture. Set aside.

Leave root and 1 inch of stem on beets; scrub with a vegetable brush. Place beets in a large Dutch oven; cover with water, and bring to a boil. Cover; reduce heat, and simmer 35 minutes or until beets are tender. Drain. Rinse beets with cold water, and drain again. Trim off roots and stems, and rub off skins. Cut beets into julienne strips. Combine beets and half of Dijon Vinaigrette in a medium bowl. Cover and chill thoroughly.

Cut leeks in half lengthwise, then cut crosswise into ⅛-inch slices. Rinse well under cold running water, and drain well. Combine reserved zucchini slices, leek slices, and chopped fresh parsley in a large serving bowl; add remaining half of Dijon Vinaigrette, and toss lightly. Cover and chill thoroughly.

Add beet mixture to zucchini mixture just before serving; toss gently. Yield: 16 servings (59 calories per serving).

Dijon Vinaigrette:

¼ cup red wine vinegar
2 tablespoons Dijon mustard
2 teaspoons dried whole dillweed
1 teaspoon salt
½ cup low-sodium chicken broth
¼ cup water
2 tablespoons olive oil
⅛ teaspoon pepper

Combine vinegar, mustard, dillweed, and salt in a small bowl; beat well with a wire whisk. Combine chicken broth, water, and olive oil, beating well with whisk. Gradually add chicken broth mixture to vinegar mixture in a slow, steady stream, beating with wire whisk until mixture is well blended and thickened. Stir in pepper. Yield: 1½ cups.

PROTEIN 1.6 / FAT 2.1 / CARBOHYDRATE 9.2 / CHOLESTEROL 0 / IRON 1.1 / SODIUM 250 / CALCIUM 28

GUIDELINES FOR TRAINING WITH HAND AND ANKLE WEIGHTS

Hand and ankle weights are popular training devices. Walkers hold small 1- to 5-pound weights with a handle or wrap weighted bands around the wrists. Runners wrap weights around ankles or lace weights to training shoes. For what gain? To enhance aerobic conditioning and improve strength. As more weight is added, however, the risk of having an injury increases. Moderation and proper use of weights can reduce that risk. Here are some guidelines:
• Walking with hand weights is the safest way to work out with weights. But first establish a regular walking program—without weights.
• Select 1½- to 2-pound weights; anything heavier causes too much stress.
• Weighted wrist bands should fit snugly.
• Begin a walking workout with weights by bending the elbows slightly and swinging arms rhythmically back and forth in a controlled manner. Overzealous arm movements can strain the shoulder joints and tendons.
• Don't grip hand weights too tightly. Tensing muscles to squeeze weights can strain the forearm tendons and biceps.
• For runners, it's safer to run a little harder or run a little longer to add a challenge to your workout routine rather than to add hand weights. Weights may interrupt your body's rhythm, balance, and normal running stride.
• Ankle weights are not recommended while running. A 2-pound weight around the ankle exerts a 6-pound force on the foot and increases the tendency for feet to roll inward to handle the stress. But ankle weights are good for calesthenics (leg lifts, etc.). They're especially suitable for those who have reached higher levels of fitness.

MOROCCAN CARROT SALAD

3 pounds carrots, scraped and
    diagonally sliced
2¼ cups water
½ cup lemon juice
3 tablespoons red wine vinegar
8 cloves garlic, crushed
1 teaspoon salt
½ teaspoon red pepper
Fresh dill sprigs (optional)

Combine carrots and water to cover in a large
Dutch oven. Cover and bring to a boil. Boil 6
minutes or until crisp-tender. Drain carrots, and
place in a large shallow dish.

Combine 2¼ cups water, lemon juice, red
wine vinegar, garlic, salt, and red pepper; pour
over carrots. Cover and refrigerate 8 hours or
overnight. Drain off marinade. Place carrots in a
large serving bowl, and garnish with fresh dill
sprigs, if desired. Yield: 16 servings (41 calories
per serving).

PROTEIN 1.0 / FAT 0.2 / CARBOHYDRATE 9.8 / CHOLESTEROL 0 /
IRON 0.5 / SODIUM 177 / CALCIUM 27

JAPANESE CRAB SALAD

Sunomono Dressing
1 pound fresh spinach, washed, trimmed
    and torn
1 large English cucumber
1 pound fresh lump crabmeat, drained
    and flaked
3 green onions, sliced
1 tablespoon sesame seeds, toasted

Toss ½ cup Sunomono Dressing with torn spinach. Arrange spinach mixture on a large serving
platter. Slice cucumber in half lengthwise; scoop
out pulp from each half. Cut cucumber into ¼-
inch slices. Arrange cucumber slices on top of
spinach mixture.

Combine crabmeat and sliced green onions in
a medium bowl; toss with remaining ½ cup Sunomono Dressing. Arrange crabmeat mixture on
top of cucumber slices. Sprinkle with toasted sesame seeds. Yield: 16 servings (53 calories per
serving).

Sunomono Dressing:

½ cup rice vinegar
¼ cup dry sherry
¼ cup reduced-sodium soy sauce
1 tablespoon sesame seeds, toasted
    and crushed

Combine all ingredients in a small bowl. Stir
with a wire whisk until mixture is well blended.
Yield: 1 cup.

PROTEIN 6.4 / FAT 1.2 / CARBOHYDRATE 3.5 / CHOLESTEROL 28 /
IRON 1.5 / SODIUM 233 / CALCIUM 61

SMOKED TURKEY AND WILD RICE
SALAD

1½ cups uncooked wild rice, rinsed
½ pound smoked turkey, cut into ¼-inch cubes
½ pound snow peas, blanched
1 medium-size sweet red pepper,
    seeded and chopped
¼ cup chopped fresh parsley
Orange Vinaigrette

Cook rice according to package directions,
omitting salt and fat. Drain well, and cool to
room temperature. Combine rice and next 4 ingredients in a large serving bowl; add vinaigrette, and toss well. Yield: 16 servings (91
calories per serving).

Orange Vinaigrette:

2 tablespoons red wine vinegar
1 tablespoon Dijon mustard
1½ teaspoons grated orange rind
½ teaspoon salt
¼ teaspoon chicken-flavored bouillon granules
¼ cup plus 2 tablespoons water
1 tablespoon walnut oil
¼ teaspoon pepper

Combine vinegar, mustard, orange rind, and
salt in a small bowl; beat well with a wire
whisk. Combine bouillon granules, water, oil,
and pepper; beat well with wire whisk. Gradually add bouillon mixture to vinegar mixture in a
slow, steady stream, beating with wire whisk
until well blended and thickened. Yield: ¾ cup.

PROTEIN 6.1 / FAT 1.9 / CARBOHYDRATE 12.8 / CHOLESTEROL 8 /
IRON 1.4 / SODIUM 207 / CALCIUM 13

Light Recipes

In this chapter you will discover a full range of recipes that capture the best flavors of fresh wholesome foods. Because they all meet certain standards, you can use them to create nutritionally balanced meals for family and guests. *Light* is the key word. *Cooking Light* recipes must be relatively light in calories, light in fat, light in sodium and processed sugar. They include the kinds of foods nutrition professionals urge us to eat: chicken and fish, fresh fruits and vegetables, and whole grains.

But it is important to remember that wholesome recipes alone do not make balanced meals. Daily guidelines detailed in the "Food and Fitness" chapter are the key to achieving balance. Use the nutrient breakdown following *Cooking Light* recipes to determine each serving's contribution of fat, carbohydrates, and protein. Also note which recipes boost calcium and iron.

When planning meals, never abandon freshness and variety. They work together to make nutrient-dense, low-calorie meals that are colorful and flavorful. And fresh foods, as a rule, can be prepared quickly. It's easy, for example, to start breakfast with fresh fruit, feature a fresh salad in a meal each day, serve more fruit desserts, offer vegetables and fruits as snacks. A slice of meat is not a requisite for a balanced meal. Featuring more salad entrées or meatless main courses can make meals more lively and, at the same time, contribute essential vitamins, minerals, and fiber. There is no substitute for vegetables in a healthy diet, and the leafy greens that make up so many tasty salads are particularly rich in food value.

Italian Linguine Ring (page 146) and Praline-Banana Tart (page 242) make a dramatic presentation just brimming with wholesome goodness and appeal.

Don't forget to work in at least five servings of fiber-rich foods in your meals, ideally more than one kind. Breakfast is the obvious meal for a cereal fiber source. If fruit is served, that's another type of fiber. Berries and fresh figs, both hot items with culinary trend setters, make an outstanding fiber source. After breakfast, you'll need three or four additional servings of fiber during the day. Traditional main courses, such as meat, fish, cheese, and eggs, are fiber free, so you might consider choosing such foods for only one meal a day or serve a fiber-rich accompaniment made with legumes (dried peas and beans and peanuts). That will add yet another type of fiber (water-soluble) to the daily total. You'll find recipes for such accompaniments in Salads and Salad Dressings, Soups and Stews, and Side Dishes. For an alternative entrée to meats, look to the Meatless Main chapter for recipes with ample protein and fiber. Of course, appetizers, snacks, and soups made with vegetables, fruits, or whole grains can tally up an adequate amount of fiber before the main course is ever served. And don't forget desserts! So many of the *Cooking Light* desserts include the nutritional blessings of fruits and grains.

Attention to presentation and flavor will invite success as you plan light meals. Appearances count, especially when introducing new and different foods to family and guests. The key to visual appeal is color and texture. Fruits and vegetables provide bright, natural food colors that complement meats or meatless main dishes. Look for the unusual and the beautiful in the produce section. The contrast between hot and cold courses adds interest to meals. A cold, fruity soup is the perfect introduction to a piping hot entrée. Or, the reverse—hot soup with a cold sandwich. When the natural texture and color of food is intact, meals are more appetizing. The shortest possible cooking time will help you avoid such culinary disasters as tough, dry fish; limp vegetables; hard pastry; stale bread; and soggy pasta. A healthy meal will benefit no one if it is not eaten because it doesn't taste good or look good.

Whether it's an intimate duo, backyard gathering, formal dinner, or holiday celebration, there's something in the following recipe sections to help you create exciting meals that meet today's standards for the best in nutrition. And you'll be pleased to discover that many of the dishes are as economical and time-efficient as they are appealing and wholesome.

Whether for family or friends, these nutritious appetizers are sure to whet appetites: Cranberry-Grapefruit Fizz (page 99), Pita Wedges with Artichoke Relish (page 93), Fruit and Brie Kabobs (page 92), and Spiced Almonds (page 92).

Appetizers & Beverages

SPICED ALMONDS

1 egg white
1 tablespoon water
2 cups whole blanched almonds
2 teaspoons chili powder
½ teaspoon ground cumin
½ teaspoon red pepper
¼ teaspoon salt
Vegetable cooking spray

Beat egg white (at room temperature) and water in a medium bowl until foamy. Add almonds, tossing gently to coat.

Combine chili powder, cumin, red pepper, and salt; stir well. Add to almonds, tossing well to coat. Spread almonds in a single layer on a baking sheet coated with cooking spray. Bake at 275° for 45 minutes. Transfer almonds to wax paper to cool. Break almonds apart, and store in an airtight container. Yield: 22 appetizer servings. Serving size: 10 almonds (79 calories per serving).

PROTEIN 2.9 / FAT 7.0 / CARBOHYDRATE 2.6 / CHOLESTEROL 0 / IRON 0.5 / SODIUM 33 / CALCIUM 34

TARRAGON BRUSSELS SPROUTS AND MUSHROOMS

1 pound small fresh mushrooms
¾ pound small fresh brussels sprouts
½ cup water
¼ cup tarragon vinegar
¼ cup Chablis or other dry white wine
2 medium cloves garlic, minced
1 teaspoon sugar
¼ teaspoon salt
¼ teaspoon pepper
¼ teaspoon dried whole tarragon
¼ cup chopped green onions
1 (2-ounce) jar sliced pimiento, drained
Leaf lettuce

Wipe mushrooms clean, using damp paper towels; set aside.

Wash brussels sprouts thoroughly; remove discolored leaves. Trim stem ends, and slash bottom of each sprout with a shallow X. Place in a vegetable steamer over boiling water. Cover and steam 8 minutes or until brussels sprouts are crisp-tender. Cool completely. Combine brussels sprouts and reserved mushrooms in a 10- x 6- x 2-inch baking dish or shallow container.

Combine water and next 7 ingredients in a small saucepan; bring to a boil. Remove from heat; stir in onions and pimiento. Pour over vegetables, tossing lightly to coat. Cover and chill 8 hours or overnight. Drain, and serve with wooden picks on a lettuce-lined platter. Yield: 12 appetizer servings. Serving size: ½ cup vegetables (24 calories per serving).

PROTEIN 1.7 / FAT 0.2 / CARBOHYDRATE 4.2 / CHOLESTEROL 0 / IRON 0.8 / SODIUM 58 / CALCIUM 20

FRUIT AND BRIE KABOBS

1 (3-pound) fresh pineapple
1 (8-ounce) round Brie cheese, cut into ¾-inch cubes
4 cups fresh strawberries
Leaf lettuce
2 tablespoons honey
1 tablespoon lemon juice
1 tablespoon plus 1½ teaspoons chopped almonds, toasted

Peel and trim eyes from pineapple; remove core. Cut pineapple into 1-inch pieces. Thread cheese cubes, pineapple, and strawberries onto 40 (6-inch) bamboo skewers.

To serve, line a serving platter with leaf lettuce. Arrange kabobs over lettuce. Combine honey and lemon juice; drizzle over fruit kabobs. Sprinkle with almonds. Yield: 40 appetizers. Serving size: 1 kabob (37 calories each).

PROTEIN 1.4 / FAT 1.8 / CARBOHYDRATE 4.1 / CHOLESTEROL 6 / IRON 0.2 / SODIUM 36 / CALCIUM 15

APPLE-CHEESE SPREAD

½ cup low-fat cottage cheese
½ (8-ounce) package Neufchâtel cheese, softened
½ cup (2 ounces) finely shredded Cheddar cheese
1 tablespoon brandy
½ cup shredded apple
1 tablespoon finely chopped almonds, toasted

Place cottage cheese in container of an electric blender; process until smooth. Spoon into a small bowl. Add remaining ingredients to cottage cheese, and stir well. Top with chopped almonds. Cover and chill thoroughly. Serve with apple wedges or melba toast rounds. Yield: 1⅓ cups. Serving size: 1 tablespoon (35 calories per serving).

PROTEIN 2.0 / FAT 2.5 / CARBOHYDRATE 0.9 / CHOLESTEROL 7 / IRON 0.1 / SODIUM 60 / CALCIUM 28

PITA WEDGES WITH ARTICHOKE RELISH

4 (8-inch) whole wheat pita bread rounds
1 (14-ounce) can artichoke hearts, drained and chopped
1 (2-ounce) jar diced pimiento, drained
2 green onions, thinly sliced
3 tablespoons freshly grated Parmesan cheese
1 clove garlic, minced
2 tablespoons lemon juice
1 tablespoon olive oil
½ teaspoon dried whole oregano
⅛ teaspoon pepper
1 tablespoon chopped fresh parsley

Split each pita round in half crosswise; quarter each half, making 8 wedges. Place on baking sheets, smooth side down, and bake at 350° for 8 minutes or until lightly browned. Set aside in an airtight container.

Combine artichokes and next 8 ingredients in a medium bowl; stir well. Cover and chill 8 hours or overnight.

Sprinkle artichoke relish with parsley before serving. Serve with reserved pita wedges. Yield: 16 appetizer servings. Serving size: 2 pita wedges plus 2 tablespoons relish (69 calories per serving).

PROTEIN 1.8 / FAT 1.6 / CARBOHYDRATE 11.3 / CHOLESTEROL 1 / IRON 0.8 / SODIUM 31 / CALCIUM 39

HONEY-CITRUS DIP

¾ cup low-fat cottage cheese
½ cup plain low-fat yogurt
1 teaspoon grated orange rind
½ teaspoon grated lemon rind
½ teaspoon grated lime rind
2 tablespoons honey
1 tablespoon unsweetened orange juice

Place cottage cheese in container of an electric blender; process until smooth. Spoon into a

bowl. Add remaining ingredients to cottage cheese; stir well. Cover and chill thoroughly. Serve with fresh fruit. Yield: 1½ cups. Serving size: 1 tablespoon (15 calories per serving).

PROTEIN 1.2 / FAT 0.2 / CARBOHYDRATE 2.1 / CHOLESTEROL 1 / IRON 0.0 / SODIUM 32 / CALCIUM 14

SNOW PEAS WITH ORIENTAL DIP

¼ pound fresh snow peas
½ cup plain low-fat yogurt
¼ cup reduced-calorie mayonnaise
1½ teaspoons reduced-sodium soy sauce
1 teaspoon grated fresh gingerroot
Dash of garlic powder
2 tablespoons chopped water chestnuts
1 tablespoon chopped fresh parsley

Trim ends from snow peas. Place snow peas in a vegetable steamer over boiling water; cover and steam 1 minute. Remove snow peas and rinse in cold water. Chill 2 hours.

Combine remaining ingredients in a small bowl; mix well. Chill 2 hours.

Place snow peas on a serving platter. Serve with dip. Yield: 12 appetizer servings (25 calories per serving).

PROTEIN 0.9 / FAT 1.5 / CARBOHYDRATE 2.1 / CHOLESTEROL 2 / IRON 0.2 / SODIUM 69 / CALCIUM 22

HERBED VEGETABLE DIP

1 cup low-fat cottage cheese
½ (8-ounce) package Neufchâtel cheese, softened
2 small cloves garlic, minced
2 tablespoons minced fresh chives
½ teaspoon dried whole thyme
¼ cup shredded carrots
¼ cup minced sweet red pepper

Place cottage cheese in container of an electric blender; process until smooth. Add Neufchâtel, and process until smooth. Add remaining ingredients, and process until well blended. Spoon into a small bowl; cover and chill thoroughly. Serve with raw vegetables or unsalted crackers. Yield: 1½ cups. Serving size: 1 tablespoon (22 calories per serving).

PROTEIN 1.8 / FAT 1.3 / CARBOHYDRATE 0.8 / CHOLESTEROL 4 / IRON 0.1 / SODIUM 58 / CALCIUM 12

ZUCCHINI-SHRIMP CANAPÉS

½ (8-ounce) package Neufchâtel cheese,
  softened
½ cup reduced-calorie mayonnaise
¼ cup minced onion
½ teaspoon dried whole dillweed
1 large zucchini (9 ounces), cut into 48
  (⅛-inch-thick) slices
1 (4½-ounce) can tiny shrimp, rinsed and
  drained
Fresh dill sprigs (optional)

Combine first 4 ingredients in a small bowl;
mix well. Cover and chill thoroughly. Arrange
zucchini slices on a serving platter. Top each
slice with 1 teaspoon of chilled mixture. Top
each canapé with 1 shrimp. Garnish with dill
sprigs, if desired. Yield: 4 dozen appetizers. Serving size: 1 canapé (17 calories each).

PROTEIN 0.9 / FAT 1.3 / CARBOHYDRATE 0.5 / CHOLESTEROL 6 /
IRON 0.1 / SODIUM 32 / CALCIUM 6

PARMESAN CHICKEN STRIPS

2 pounds boneless chicken breast halves,
  skinned
1 egg, lightly beaten
¼ cup skim milk
½ cup fine, dry breadcrumbs
½ cup grated Parmesan cheese
1 teaspoon dried whole basil
½ teaspoon dried whole thyme
⅛ teaspoon onion powder
⅛ teaspoon freshly ground pepper
Vegetable cooking spray

Trim excess fat from chicken. Cut chicken into
4- x 1-inch strips.
Combine egg and milk, stirring well. Combine
breadcrumbs and next 5 ingredients; stir well.
Dip chicken strips in egg mixture; dredge in
breadcrumb mixture.
Place strips on baking sheets coated with
cooking spray. Bake at 400° for 18 minutes or
until lightly browned. Yield: 2½ dozen appetizers. Serving size: 1 chicken strip (53 calories
per serving).

PROTEIN 7.9 / FAT 1.4 / CARBOHYDRATE 1.4 / CHOLESTEROL 29 /
IRON 0.4 / SODIUM 57 / CALCIUM 28

MINI-CHICKEN TOSTADAS

1 cup finely chopped, cooked chicken breast,
  (skinned before cooking and cooked without salt)
½ cup chopped, peeled jicama
1 (4-ounce) can chopped green chiles, drained
½ cup (2 ounces) shredded Cheddar cheese
3 tablespoons reduced-calorie mayonnaise
12 (6-inch) corn tortillas

Combine chicken and next 4 ingredients in a
small bowl; stir well. Set aside.
Cut each tortilla into 3 circles using a 2-inch
biscuit cutter. Place tortilla chips on an ungreased baking sheet. Bake at 350° for 5 minutes. Spread 1 tablespoon of reserved chicken
mixture on each tortilla chip. Broil 4 to 5 inches
from heating element 3 minutes or until hot
and bubbly. Yield: 3 dozen appetizers. Serving
size: 1 tostada (40 calories per serving).

PROTEIN 2.3 / FAT 1.4 / CARBOHYDRATE 4.6 / CHOLESTEROL 5 /
IRON 0.5 / SODIUM 42 / CALCIUM 26

 KIDS' SNACKS—LIGHT IS RIGHT

Children older than two years old need
heart-healthy diets, too, and snack-time favorites such as chips, candy, and sodas can sabatoge
other efforts to give children a balanced diet. Offering nutritious snacks that are appealing and satisfying
helps children develop positive attitudes toward
healthy eating—before they learn firsthand the
meaning of words like obesity and atherosclerosis.
Determine a special time each day for snacks, and
make it fun. Include variety and create surprises.
Corn tortillas cut into favorite cookie-cutter shapes
and baked, as in Mini-Chicken Tostadas, evoke more
excitement than potato chips. Crisp jicama slices can
be turned into great cookie-cutter snacks, too! (See
page 59.) Celery sticks stuffed with a mixture of
peanut butter, chopped carrots, honey, and raisins
upstage even a candy
bar. And frozen fruit or
yogurt bars refresh and
satisfy more than a
soda. "Can't wait until
snacktime tomorrow!"
will convince the most
skeptical mother that
healthful snacks can be
good-tasting snacks.

GRILLED QUESADILLAS WITH YOGURT SALSA

½ cup (2 ounces) shredded Monterey Jack cheese
½ cup (2 ounces) shredded Colby cheese
4 (8-inch) flour tortillas
1 tablespoon plus 1 teaspoon chopped green chiles
Vegetable cooking spray
Yogurt Salsa

Sprinkle 2 tablespoons each Monterey Jack and Colby cheese just off center of each tortilla. Top each with 1 teaspoon chiles. Arrange tortillas on a grill coated with cooking spray. Grill 6 inches over hot coals 1 minute or until undersides of tortillas are golden brown. Fold in half; grill 30 seconds or until cheese melts. Cut each tortilla into 4 wedges. Top each wedge with Yogurt Salsa, and serve immediately. Yield: 16 appetizers. Serving size: 1 quesadilla plus 1½ teaspoons salsa (64 calories each).

Yogurt Salsa:

¼ cup plain low-fat yogurt
2 tablespoons chopped tomato
1 tablespoon chopped onion
2 teaspoons minced fresh cilantro
½ teaspoon lemon juice
¼ teaspoon salt

Combine yogurt, tomato, onion, cilantro, lemon juice, and salt in a small bowl; stir well. Cover and chill 2 hours. Yield: ½ cup.

PROTEIN 2.7 / FAT 3.0 / CARBOHYDRATE 7.4 / CHOLESTEROL 6 / IRON 0.3 / SODIUM 97 / CALCIUM 67

SPINACH PIES

1 (10-ounce) package frozen chopped spinach, thawed and drained
⅔ cup reduced-calorie mayonnaise
½ cup (2 ounces) shredded Cheddar cheese
½ cup (2 ounces) shredded Swiss cheese
½ teaspoon garlic powder
2 egg whites
6 whole wheat English muffins, split and toasted

Place spinach on paper towels; squeeze until barely moist. Combine spinach and next 4 ingredients, stirring well. Beat egg whites (at room temperature) until stiff, but not dry; gently fold into spinach mixture. Spread mixture evenly over 12 muffin halves, mounding slightly. Place on a baking sheet and bake at 350° for 10 minutes. Cut each muffin half into 4 wedges. Serve immediately. Yield: 4 dozen appetizers. Serving size: 1 wedge (42 calories per serving).

PROTEIN 1.6 / FAT 1.8 / CARBOHYDRATE 4.9 / CHOLESTEROL 3 / IRON 0.4 / SODIUM 83 / CALCIUM 40

EGGPLANT-STUFFED MUSHROOMS

1 small eggplant, chopped
½ teaspoon salt
24 large fresh mushrooms (about 20 ounces)
Vegetable cooking spray
½ cup finely chopped onion
⅓ cup finely chopped sweet red pepper
1 medium clove garlic, minced
1 tablespoon chopped fresh parsley
1 tablespoon red wine vinegar
⅛ teaspoon salt
⅛ teaspoon ground coriander
⅛ teaspoon dried whole basil
Dash of pepper
2 tablespoons grated Parmesan cheese
2 tablespoons fine, dry breadcrumbs

Place eggplant in a colander; sprinkle with ½ teaspoon salt; let stand 30 minutes. Rinse thoroughly, and pat dry with paper towels.

Clean mushrooms with damp paper towels. Remove mushroom stems; finely chop ⅓ cup stems, reserving remaining stems for other uses. Set aside mushroom caps and chopped stems.

Coat a large skillet with cooking spray; place over medium heat until hot. Add eggplant; sauté 2 minutes or until tender. Drain well on paper towels. Add onion, red pepper, garlic, and reserved chopped stems to skillet; sauté 2 minutes or until tender. Drain well on paper towels.

Combine eggplant, onion mixture, parsley, vinegar, ⅛ teaspoon salt, coriander, basil, pepper, cheese, and breadcrumbs; stir well. Spoon 1 tablespoon mixture into each reserved mushroom cap. Place in a shallow baking pan coated with cooking spray, and bake at 350° for 10 minutes. Yield: 2 dozen appetizers. Serving size: 1 mushroom (14 calories per serving).

PROTEIN 0.9 / FAT 0.3 / CARBOHYDRATE 2.4 / CHOLESTEROL 0 / IRON 0.4 / SODIUM 38 / CALCIUM 12

ITALIAN-STUFFED CLAMS

10 littleneck clams (1¾ pounds)
Vegetable cooking spray
¼ cup finely chopped onion
2 tablespoons finely chopped sweet red pepper
1 clove garlic, crushed
½ cup soft whole wheat breadcrumbs
2 teaspoons lemon juice
½ teaspoon dried whole oregano
½ teaspoon dried whole basil
⅛ teaspoon pepper
1 tablespoon plus 1½ teaspoons freshly grated
   Parmesan cheese
1 tablespoon finely chopped fresh parsley

Wash clams thoroughly. Place clams in a vegetable steamer over simmering water. Cover and steam 10 minutes; drain. Pry open shells, reserving 3 tablespoons clam juice. Discard top shells. Loosen meat from the bottom shell and remove. Drain bottom shells on paper towels. Mince clams, and set aside.

Coat a small skillet with cooking spray; place over medium heat until hot. Add onion, sweet red pepper, and crushed garlic; sauté until tender. Set aside.

Strain reserved clam juice. Combine reserved clams, clam juice, and reserved sautéed vegetable mixture. Stir in breadcrumbs, lemon juice, oregano, basil, and pepper.

Spoon 1½ teaspoons clam mixture into each shell half; arrange shells in shallow baking pans. Combine cheese and parsley in a small bowl. Sprinkle evenly over tops of stuffed clams.

Bake at 400° for 8 minutes or until thoroughly heated. Yield: 10 appetizers. Serving size: 1 clam (25 calories each).

PROTEIN 1.8 / FAT 0.5 / CARBOHYDRATE 3.5 / CHOLESTEROL 4 / IRON 0.8 / SODIUM 58 / CALCIUM 26

Italian-Stuffed Clams make an elegant appetizer for a special occasion.

CRABMEAT-ARTICHOKE QUICHES

3 eggs
¼ cup all-purpose flour
½ teaspoon baking powder
¼ teaspoon salt
1 (14-ounce) can artichoke hearts, drained and finely chopped
½ pound fresh crabmeat, drained and flaked
¾ cup low-fat cottage cheese
½ cup (2 ounces) shredded Monterey Jack cheese
¼ cup (1 ounce) shredded Cheddar cheese
⅓ cup minced green onions
½ teaspoon hot sauce
½ cup seasoned, dry breadcrumbs
Vegetable cooking spray

Beat eggs at high speed of an electric mixer 3 minutes or until thick. Combine flour, baking powder, and salt; add to egg mixture. Beat at low speed of an electric mixer until thoroughly blended.

Stir in artichoke hearts and next 6 ingredients. Coat miniature muffin pans with cooking spray; sprinkle with breadcrumbs to coat. Pour artichoke mixture into prepared muffin pans, filling to the rim. Bake at 350° for 30 to 35 minutes or until set. Cool in pans 10 minutes. Yield: 3 dozen appetizers. Serving size: 1 quiche (38 calories each).

PROTEIN 3.3 / FAT 1.5 / CARBOHYDRATE 2.8 / CHOLESTEROL 32 / IRON 0.3 / SODIUM 87 / CALCIUM 33

SPICY CHAFING DISH OYSTERS

Vegetable cooking spray
½ cup minced green pepper
¼ cup minced onion
2 cloves garlic, minced
1 (6-ounce) can no-salt-added tomato paste
½ cup tomato sauce
2 tablespoons lemon juice
1 tablespoon firmly packed brown sugar
⅛ to ¼ teaspoon red pepper
⅛ to ¼ teaspoon hot sauce
3 (12-ounce) containers Standard oysters, rinsed and drained
2 tablespoons minced fresh parsley

Coat a large saucepan with cooking spray. Add green pepper, onion, and garlic; sauté until tender. Add tomato paste and next 5 ingredients; stir well. Bring to a boil. Cover; reduce heat, and simmer 5 minutes. Stir in oysters. Cook over medium heat 5 minutes or until edges of oysters curl. Transfer mixture to a chafing dish. Sprinkle with parsley. Serve oysters with melba toast rounds. Yield: 3 dozen appetizers. Serving size: 1 oyster (22 calories per serving).

PROTEIN 2.1 / FAT 0.4 / CARBOHYDRATE 2.6 / CHOLESTEROL 11 / IRON 1.4 / SODIUM 38 / CALCIUM 24

CURRIED TUNA BITES

2 (6½-ounce) cans water-packed white tuna
½ (8-ounce) package Neufchâtel cheese, softened
½ cup soft whole wheat breadcrumbs
1 egg, beaten
1 tablespoon minced onion
1 teaspoon curry powder
½ cup crushed corn flakes
Vegetable cooking spray
Mustard Sauce

Place tuna in a colander, and rinse under cold tap water 1 minute; set colander aside to let tuna drain 1 minute.

Beat cheese at medium speed of an electric mixer until light and fluffy. Add tuna, breadcrumbs, egg, onion, and curry powder; stir gently until well blended. Shape into 54 balls, using 1 teaspoon mixture for each ball. Roll in crushed corn flakes. Place on baking sheets coated with cooking spray. Bake at 350° for 18 minutes or until lightly browned. Serve with Mustard Sauce. Yield: 4½ dozen appetizer servings. Serving size: 1 tuna bite plus ½ teaspoon sauce (23 calories each).

Mustard Sauce:

¼ cup reduced-calorie mayonnaise
¼ cup Dijon mustard
1 tablespoon honey
½ teaspoon curry powder

Combine all ingredients in a small bowl; stir well. Cover and chill. Yield: about ½ cup.

PROTEIN 1.8 / FAT 1.0 / CARBOHYDRATE 1.5 / CHOLESTEROL 10 / IRON 0.2 / SODIUM 70 / CALCIUM 4

Quenching beverages to please all (clockwise from front): Hot Tomato Cocktail (page 100), Spiced Apple Spritzer, Minted White Grape Cooler, and Four Fruit Shake.

SPICED APPLE SPRITZER

2 (6-ounce) cans frozen apple juice concentrate, thawed and undiluted
1 orange, sliced
1 lemon, sliced
1 (3-inch) stick cinnamon
4 whole cloves
2½ cups club soda, chilled

Combine apple juice concentrate, orange slices, lemon slices, cinnamon, and cloves in a saucepan; bring to a boil. Cover; reduce heat, and simmer 15 minutes. Strain mixture, discarding spices and fruit. Cover and chill thoroughly.

Just before serving, combine chilled mixture and club soda. Pour into glasses and serve immediately. Yield: 4 cups (141 calories per 1-cup serving).

PROTEIN 0.4 / FAT 0.3 / CARBOHYDRATE 34.9 / CHOLESTEROL 0 / IRON 0.8 / SODIUM 21 / CALCIUM 17

The low-nutrient calories in alcohol don't mix with dieting. A drink made with cola and 1½ ounces of liquor contains about 250 calories; a 6-ounce glass of wine, about 200 calories; and a 12-ounce can of beer, over 100 calories. Caloric enough by themselves, alcoholic drinks encourage snacking on salty, fat-laden foods. A recent University of Washington study showed that men who drank alcoholic beverages also consumed more snack foods. Not surprisingly, they weighed more than non-drinkers.

By American Heart Association standards, a diet restricted to 1,200 calories a day should allow for no more than 180 calories from alcohol or 15 percent of total calories. This suggests that one glass of wine or one beer is enough.

If you want to drink and conserve calories, dilute alcohol by adding water, seltzer, club soda, or diet beverages. Three ounces of wine mixed with club soda makes a refreshing low-calorie alternative to a full glass of wine.

CRANBERRY-GRAPEFRUIT FIZZ

2 cups cranberry juice cocktail, chilled
2 cups club soda, chilled
1 cup pink grapefruit juice cocktail, chilled

Combine all ingredients in a large pitcher; mix well. Pour over ice in serving glasses, and serve immediately. Yield: 5 cups (76 calories per 1-cup serving).

PROTEIN 0.0 / FAT 0.0 / CARBOHYDRATE 19.4 / CHOLESTEROL 0 /
IRON 0.1 / SODIUM 8 / CALCIUM 3

MINTED WHITE GRAPE COOLER

2 cups unsweetened white grape juice
2 cups loosely packed fresh mint sprigs
½ cup water
Fresh mint sprigs

Combine all ingredients in container of an electric blender; process until smooth. Cover and chill overnight; strain before serving. Pour over crushed ice in serving glasses, and garnish with fresh mint sprigs. Yield: 2 cups (96 calories per ½-cup serving).

PROTEIN 1.2 / FAT 0.1 / CARBOHYDRATE 23.3 / CHOLESTEROL 0 /
IRON 2.1 / SODIUM 16 / CALCIUM 52

HONEYDEW COOLER

1 medium honeydew melon, peeled, seeded, and cut into chunks
2 medium limes
1 cup unsweetened pineapple juice
½ cup tightly packed fresh mint leaves
1 (10-ounce) bottle club soda, chilled

Freeze honeydew chunks 3 hours or until partially frozen.

Carefully remove rind in strips from 1 lime, using a small paring knife and being careful to avoid white pith. Remove juice from limes to equal 2 tablespoons.

Combine lime rind, lime juice, pineapple juice, and mint in a small non-aluminum saucepan. Bring to a boil, stirring constantly. Reduce heat; cover and simmer 3 minutes. Remove from heat, and let stand 1 hour. Strain mixture, discarding mint leaves and rind. Reserve pineapple juice mixture.

Combine half each frozen honeydew and reserved pineapple juice mixture in container of an electric blender; process until smooth. Transfer to a serving pitcher. Repeat procedure; stir in club soda, and serve immediately. Yield: 8 cups (61 calories per 1-cup serving).

PROTEIN 1.2 / FAT 0.4 / CARBOHYDRATE 14.9 / CHOLESTEROL 0 /
IRON 0.9 / SODIUM 16 / CALCIUM 31

FOUR FRUIT SHAKE

1 cup unsweetened orange juice
1 cup skim milk
1½ cups fresh strawberries, washed and hulled
1 (8-ounce) can unsweetened crushed pineapple, undrained
1 medium-size ripe banana
¼ teaspoon coconut extract
1 cup ice cubes
Fresh strawberry slices (optional)

Combine first 6 ingredients in container of an electric blender; process until smooth. Add ice cubes, and process until smooth. Pour into glasses and garnish with strawberry slices, if desired. Serve immediately. Yield: 6 cups (87 calories per 1-cup serving).

PROTEIN 2.2 / FAT 0.4 / CARBOHYDRATE 19.8 / CHOLESTEROL 1 /
IRON 0.6 / SODIUM 23 / CALCIUM 69

RASPBERRY REFRESHER

1 (10-ounce) package frozen raspberries in light syrup, thawed and undrained
2 medium-size ripe peaches, peeled and sliced
½ cup unsweetened orange juice, chilled
1 cup skim milk
1 tablespoon sugar
12 ice cubes

Place raspberries in container of an electric blender; process until smooth. Press puree through a sieve to remove seeds. Return puree to container of electric blender and add next 4 ingredients; process until smooth. Gradually add ice cubes; process until smooth. Pour into glasses, and serve immediately. Yield: 5 cups (113 calories per 1-cup serving).

PROTEIN 2.5 / FAT 0.3 / CARBOHYDRATE 26.2 / CHOLESTEROL 1 / IRON 0.6 / SODIUM 27 / CALCIUM 74

SPICED CRANBERRY-WINE PUNCH

1 (32-ounce) bottle cranberry juice cocktail
1 cup unsweetened orange juice
½ teaspoon ground cardamom
6 whole allspice
6 whole cloves
1 (3-inch) stick cinnamon
2 cups Burgundy or other dry red wine

Combine first 3 ingredients in a large Dutch oven. Tie remaining spices in a cheesecloth bag. Add to Dutch oven. Bring mixture to a boil. Cover; reduce heat, and simmer 5 minutes. Add wine, and simmer 1 minute. (Do not boil.) Discard spices. Serve hot. Yield: 7 cups (140 calories per 1-cup serving).

PROTEIN 0.4 / FAT 0.1 / CARBOHYDRATE 24.1 / CHOLESTEROL 0 / IRON 0.8 / SODIUM 13 / CALCIUM 12

SPIRITED PEPPERMINT COCOA

¼ cup plus 1 teaspoon sugar
¼ cup unsweetened cocoa
1 cup water
4 cups skim milk
¼ cup plus 1 tablespoon peppermint schnapps
½ teaspoon vanilla extract

Combine sugar and cocoa in a medium saucepan, stirring well. Stir in water, and bring to a boil. Add milk, and reduce heat to medium. Cook, stirring constantly, until thoroughly heated.

Remove from heat, and stir in schnapps and vanilla. Beat at medium speed of an electric mixer until frothy. Serve immediately. Yield: 6 cups (149 calories per 1-cup serving).

PROTEIN 6.6 / FAT 0.8 / CARBOHYDRATE 22.4 / CHOLESTEROL 3 / IRON 0.7 / SODIUM 85 / CALCIUM 206

HOT TOMATO COCKTAIL

1 (46-ounce) can no-salt-added tomato juice
1 cup water
2 tablespoons lemon juice
2 tablespoons sherry
2 teaspoons Worcestershire sauce
1 teaspoon beef-flavored bouillon granules
¼ teaspoon pepper
¼ teaspoon hot sauce
Thin lemon slices

Combine first 8 ingredients in a large saucepan. Bring mixture to a boil. Cover; reduce heat, and simmer 10 minutes. Serve hot; garnish with lemon slices. Yield: 7 cups (48 calories per 1-cup serving).

PROTEIN 2.0 / FAT 0.1 / CARBOHYDRATE 10.7 / CHOLESTEROL 0 / IRON 0.0 / SODIUM 103 / CALCIUM 2

AN OLD SPIRIT HAS NEW PROOF

Drinks made with schnapps are becoming popular with people who want to limit their alcohol intake. New varieties range from 48 to 60 proof, rather than the traditional 100 proof.

Try making your own "schnappy" concoction with the refreshing flavor of peppermint schnapps in Spirited Peppermint Cocoa.

Nutty Whole-Grain Crackers (page 102), Hot Cross Rolls (page 110), and Blueberry-Banana Bread (page 103) include healthy measures of high-fiber ingredients such as wheat germ, oats, and whole wheat flour.

Breads, Grains & Pastas

HERBED PITA TOAST

2 (6-inch) pita bread rounds
3 tablespoons margarine, softened
1 tablespoon plus 1 teaspoon minced
   fresh parsley
½ teaspoon dried whole dillweed
½ teaspoon fines herbes

Split each pita round in half crosswise. Quarter each half, making 8 wedges; set wedges aside. Combine margarine, parsley, dillweed, and fines herbes in a small bowl, stirring well. Spread each reserved pita wedge with ¼ teaspoon herb mixture. Place wedges, smooth side down, on a baking sheet, and bake at 350° for 5 minutes or until crisp. Yield: 8 servings (76 calories per serving).

PROTEIN 0.8 / FAT 4.6 / CARBOHYDRATE 7.2 / CHOLESTEROL 0 / IRON 0.5 / SODIUM 51 / CALCIUM 16

 ## CORNMEAL: YELLOW, WHITE, AND NOW BLUE

Blue cornmeal from New Mexico is gaining in popularity in the marketplace as a unique departure from the standard yellow and white cornmeal varieties. Besides adding a blue cast to foods, blue cornmeal lends its more refined texture and distinctive but subtle flavor. Adding blue cornmeal to cornbread muffins and pancakes will add up-to-date interest to traditional cornmeal recipes.

Mix up a batch of Blue Cornmeal Crackers, and keep them around in an air-tight container for tasty high-carbohydrate, low-fat, low-sodium snacks. Slip a few of the crisp crackers into brown bags to provide some lunchtime crunch for the children.

BLUE CORNMEAL CRACKERS

¾ cup plus 2 teaspoons blue cornmeal,
   divided
½ cup all-purpose flour
¼ teaspoon salt
⅓ cup margarine, softened
¼ cup skim milk

Combine ¾ cup blue cornmeal, flour, and salt in a medium bowl. Cut in softened margarine with a pastry blender until mixture resembles coarse meal. Sprinkle skim milk over cornmeal mixture, stirring just until dry ingredients are moistened.

Turn dough out onto a lightly floured surface; knead 5 to 6 times. Roll dough to ⅛-inch thickness on a lightly floured surface; cut into rounds with a 2-inch biscuit cutter. Place on ungreased baking sheets. Sprinkle evenly with remaining 2 teaspoons cornmeal. Bake at 375° for 8 to 10 minutes or until lightly browned. Remove from baking sheets, and cool on wire racks. Store in an airtight container. Yield: 5 dozen crackers (20 calories each).

PROTEIN 0.3 / FAT 1.1 / CARBOHYDRATE 2.2 / CHOLESTEROL 0 / IRON 0.1 / SODIUM 22 / CALCIUM 2

NUTTY WHOLE-GRAIN CRACKERS

1½ cups quick-cooking oats,
   uncooked
½ cup all-purpose flour
½ cup whole wheat flour
¼ cup wheat germ
¼ cup ground walnuts
1 tablespoon sugar
⅔ cup water
¼ cup vegetable oil
2 teaspoons water, divided
¼ teaspoon salt, divided

Combine first 6 ingredients in a large bowl; stir well. Add ⅔ cup water and oil, stirring just until dry ingredients are moistened.

Divide dough in half. Roll half of dough to a 12- x 12-inch square on an ungreased baking sheet. Cut into 2-inch squares. Brush dough with 1 teaspoon water; sprinkle evenly with ⅛ teaspoon salt. Repeat procedure with remaining half of dough. Bake at 350° for 25 minutes or until crisp and lightly browned.

Separate crackers; remove from baking sheets, and cool on wire racks. Store in an airtight container. Yield: 6 dozen crackers (32 calories each).

PROTEIN 1.0 / FAT 1.3 / CARBOHYDRATE 4.2 / CHOLESTEROL 0 / IRON 0.3 / SODIUM 8 / CALCIUM 3

TOMATO-MOZZARELLA BREAD

1 (16-ounce) loaf unsliced Italian bread
2 tablespoons margarine, melted
1 tablespoon olive oil
2 medium tomatoes, thinly sliced
½ teaspoon dried whole basil
⅔ cup (2⅔ ounces) shredded part-skim mozzarella cheese

Slice bread in half crosswise; reserve one-half for other uses. Slice remaining bread in half lengthwise. Place bread slices on a baking sheet, and broil 6 inches from heating element until lightly browned.

Combine margarine and olive oil. Brush over bread slices. Arrange tomato slices evenly over bread. Sprinkle with basil. Top with shredded cheese. Broil 6 inches from heating element until cheese melts. Yield: 8 servings (149 calories per serving).

PROTEIN 5.2 / FAT 6.3 / CARBOHYDRATE 17.8 / CHOLESTEROL 6 / IRON 0.8 / SODIUM 246 / CALCIUM 70

APPLE YOGURT BREAD

1 cup whole wheat flour
¾ cup all-purpose flour
1½ teaspoons baking powder
1 teaspoon baking soda
½ teaspoon ground cinnamon
¼ teaspoon salt
1 (8-ounce) carton Dutch apple low-fat yogurt with fruit on the bottom
2 eggs, beaten
2 tablespoons skim milk
¼ cup plus 2 tablespoons firmly packed brown sugar
¼ cup vegetable oil
Vegetable cooking spray

Combine first 6 ingredients in a large bowl, and set aside.

Combine yogurt, eggs, milk, sugar, and oil; mix well. Add to dry ingredients, stirring just until dry ingredients are moistened.

Spoon batter into an 8½- x 4½- x 3-inch loaf-pan coated with cooking spray. Bake at 350° for 40 minutes or until a wooden pick inserted in center comes out clean. Cool in pan 10 minutes. Remove to wire rack; cool completely. Yield: 1 loaf or 16 (½-inch) slices (123 calories per slice).

PROTEIN 3.1 / FAT 4.5 / CARBOHYDRATE 18.2 / CHOLESTEROL 35 / IRON 0.8 / SODIUM 135 / CALCIUM 64

BLUEBERRY-BANANA BREAD

1 cup fresh blueberries
1¾ cups all-purpose flour, divided
2 teaspoons baking powder
¼ teaspoon baking soda
¼ teaspoon salt
¼ teaspoon ground nutmeg
¼ cup unsalted margarine, softened
¼ cup plus 2 tablespoons sugar
2 eggs
1 cup mashed ripe banana
Vegetable cooking spray

Toss blueberries with 2 tablespoons flour, and set aside.

Combine remaining flour, baking powder, soda, salt, and nutmeg in a small bowl. Cream margarine in a large bowl; gradually add sugar, beating at medium speed of electric mixer. Add eggs, one at a time, beating well after each addition. Add flour mixture alternately with mashed banana, beginning and ending with flour mixture. Mix just until dry ingredients are moistened. Gently fold in reserved blueberries.

Spoon batter into an 8½- x 4½- x 3-inch loaf-pan coated with cooking spray. Bake at 350° for 45 minutes or until a wooden pick inserted in center comes out clean. Let cool in pan 10 minutes; remove to wire rack, and cool completely. Yield: 1 loaf or 16 (½-inch) slices (127 calories per slice).

PROTEIN 2.6 / FAT 3.8 / CARBOHYDRATE 21.0 / CHOLESTEROL 34 / IRON 0.6 / SODIUM 97 / CALCIUM 35

MAPLE OAT BRAN COFFEE CAKE

1 cup unprocessed oat bran
½ cup all-purpose flour
2 tablespoons firmly packed brown sugar, divided
1 tablespoon baking powder
1 teaspoon ground cinnamon
½ teaspoon ground nutmeg
⅓ cup margarine, softened
1 egg plus 1 egg white, beaten
½ cup skim milk
¼ cup reduced-calorie maple syrup
2 teaspoons vanilla extract
Vegetable cooking spray
2 tablespoons wheat germ

Combine oat bran, flour, 1 tablespoon brown sugar, baking powder, cinnamon, and nutmeg; stir well. Cut in margarine with a pastry blender until mixture resembles coarse meal.

Combine egg and egg white, milk, syrup, and vanilla; add to oat bran mixture, stirring just until dry ingredients are moistened.

Spoon mixture into an 8-inch round cakepan heavily coated with cooking spray. Combine wheat germ and remaining brown sugar; sprinkle over top. Bake at 375° for 30 minutes or until a wooden pick inserted in center comes out clean. Cool in pan on a wire rack. Serve warm or at room temperature. Yield: 10 servings (152 calories per serving).

PROTEIN 4.4 / FAT 7.9 / CARBOHYDRATE 15.9 / CHOLESTEROL 28 / IRON 1.0 / SODIUM 183 / CALCIUM 91

ORANGE PINWHEEL BISCUITS

2⅓ cups all-purpose flour
1 tablespoon baking powder
½ teaspoon salt
¼ cup plus 1 tablespoon margarine, softened
½ cup skim milk
3 tablespoons unsweetened orange juice
1 egg, lightly beaten
1 tablespoon margarine, melted
3 tablespoons plus 1 teaspoon sugar, divided
2 teaspoons grated orange rind
½ teaspoon ground allspice
Vegetable cooking spray
⅔ cup unsweetened orange juice
1½ teaspoons cornstarch

Combine flour, baking powder, and salt in a large bowl; stir well. Cut in margarine with a pastry blender until mixture resembles coarse meal. Make a well in center of mixture. Combine milk, 3 tablespoons orange juice, and egg. Add to dry ingredients, stirring just until dry ingredients are moistened.

Turn dough out onto a heavily floured surface; knead 10 to 12 times. Chill dough 15 minutes. Roll dough to a 12- x 8-inch rectangle on a lightly floured surface. Brush with melted margarine. Combine 3 tablespoons sugar, orange rind, and allspice; stir well. Sprinkle evenly over dough. Roll up jellyroll fashion, beginning at long side. Pinch edges to seal. Chill roll 30 minutes. Cut roll into sixteen ¾-inch slices; place slices, cut side down, in muffin pans coated with cooking spray. Bake at 400° for 14 minutes.

Combine ⅔ cup orange juice, cornstarch, and remaining sugar in a small saucepan. Cook over medium heat, stirring constantly, until thickened. Drizzle 2 teaspoons glaze over each biscuit. Yield: 16 biscuits (136 calories each).

PROTEIN 2.9 / FAT 4.9 / CARBOHYDRATE 20.1 / CHOLESTEROL 17 / IRON 0.7 / SODIUM 189 / CALCIUM 54

RYE BISCUITS

1½ cups all-purpose flour
½ cup medium rye flour
1 tablespoon baking powder
¼ teaspoon salt
1 teaspoon caraway seeds, crushed
3 tablespoons margarine, softened
¾ cup low-fat buttermilk
Vegetable cooking spray

Sift together first 4 ingredients; stir in caraway seeds. Cut in margarine with a pastry blender until mixture resembles coarse meal. Add buttermilk, stirring just until dry ingredients are moistened.

Turn dough out onto a lightly floured surface; knead 3 to 4 times. Roll to ¾-inch thickness; cut into rounds with a 2-inch biscuit cutter. Place on a baking sheet coated with cooking spray. Bake at 450° for 12 minutes or until golden brown. Yield: 12 biscuits (110 calories each).

PROTEIN 2.8 / FAT 3.3 / CARBOHYDRATE 16.9 / CHOLESTEROL 0 / IRON 0.6 / SODIUM 166 / CALCIUM 72

Whole Wheat Madeleines keep the traditional madeleine shape, but with new, whole wheat goodness.

CAFÉ AU LAIT MUFFINS

1 tablespoon instant coffee granules
½ cup plus 2 tablespoons skim milk
¼ cup water
1 cup wheat bran flakes cereal
½ cup regular oats, uncooked
¼ cup firmly packed brown sugar
¼ cup vegetable oil
1 egg
1¼ cups all-purpose flour
1 tablespoon baking powder
⅛ teaspoon salt
Vegetable cooking spray

Combine coffee, milk, and water in a medium saucepan; place over low heat and cook, stirring frequently, until mixture is thoroughly heated and coffee granules dissolve. Remove from heat. Stir in cereal and oats, and let stand 10 minutes.

Combine sugar, oil, and egg in a medium bowl; beat well. Combine flour, baking powder, and salt; add to egg mixture along with cereal mixture, stirring just until dry ingredients are moistened.

Spoon batter into muffin pans coated with cooking spray, filling two-thirds full. Bake at 400° for 12 minutes or until golden. Yield: 1 dozen muffins (145 calories each).

PROTEIN 3.4 / FAT 5.5 / CARBOHYDRATE 21.0 / CHOLESTEROL 23 / IRON 1.8 / SODIUM 144 / CALCIUM 76

WHOLE WHEAT MADELEINES

1½ cups whole wheat flour
½ cup all-purpose flour
1 tablespoon sugar
1 teaspoon baking powder
¼ teaspoon salt
1¼ cups plus 2 tablespoons skim milk
¼ cup vegetable oil
Vegetable cooking spray

Combine first 5 ingredients in a large bowl; make a well in center of mixture. Combine milk and oil, stirring well. Add to flour mixture, stirring just until dry ingredients are moistened. Spoon batter into 3-inch madeleine pans coated with cooking spray, filling two-thirds full. Bake at 425° for 15 minutes or until lightly browned. Yield: 2½ dozen (50 calories each).

PROTEIN 1.4 / FAT 2.0 / CARBOHYDRATE 7.0 / CHOLESTEROL 0 / IRON 0.3 / SODIUM 36 / CALCIUM 23

DIJON-DILL MUFFINS

1½ cups whole wheat flour
½ cup all-purpose flour
¾ teaspoon dried whole dillweed or 1 tablespoon chopped fresh dillweed
2 teaspoons baking powder
¼ teaspoon salt
1 cup skim milk
¼ cup vegetable oil
3 tablespoons Dijon mustard
1 egg, beaten
Vegetable cooking spray

Combine first 5 ingredients in a large bowl; stir until well blended. Make a well in center of mixture. Combine milk, oil, mustard, and egg; stir with a wire whisk. Add to dry ingredients, stirring just until dry ingredients are moistened.

Spoon batter into muffin pans coated with cooking spray, filling two-thirds full. Bake at 400° for 20 minutes or until lightly browned. Yield: 12 muffins (130 calories each).

PROTEIN 3.8 / FAT 5.7 / CARBOHYDRATE 16.4 / CHOLESTEROL 23 / IRON 0.8 / SODIUM 227 / CALCIUM 68

MINIATURE JALAPEÑO MUFFINS

¾ cup yellow cornmeal
¼ cup all-purpose flour
1 tablespoon plus 1 teaspoon finely chopped sweet red pepper
1 tablespoon minced jalapeño pepper
1½ teaspoons baking powder
¼ teaspoon garlic salt
⅓ cup skim milk
1 egg, beaten
1 tablespoon vegetable oil
Vegetable cooking spray

Combine first 6 ingredients in a medium bowl, stirring well. Combine milk, egg, and oil; stir well. Add to dry ingredients, stirring just until dry ingredients are moistened. Spoon batter into miniature muffin pans coated with cooking spray, filling two-thirds full. Bake at 425° for 10 to 15 minutes or until lightly browned. Yield: 18 muffins (39 calories each).

PROTEIN 1.2 / FAT 1.2 / CARBOHYDRATE 5.9 / CHOLESTEROL 15 / IRON 0.3 / SODIUM 60 / CALCIUM 24

PEACH-ALMOND MUFFINS

3 cups peeled, sliced fresh peaches
½ cup sugar
½ cup vegetable oil
2 eggs
1 teaspoon almond extract
2 cups all-purpose flour
1 teaspoon baking powder
1 teaspoon baking soda
1 teaspoon ground cinnamon
½ teaspoon ground nutmeg
¼ teaspoon salt
Vegetable cooking spray

Place peaches in container of an electric blender or food processor; process until smooth, and set aside.

Combine sugar, oil, eggs, and almond extract in a large mixing bowl; beat well. Combine remaining dry ingredients, and add to egg mixture along with reserved peach puree, stirring just until dry ingredients are moistened.

Spoon batter into muffin pans coated with cooking spray, filling two-thirds full. Bake at 400° for 15 minutes or until golden. Yield: 20 muffins (136 calories each).

PROTEIN 2.2 / FAT 6.2 / CARBOHYDRATE 18.1 / CHOLESTEROL 27 / IRON 0.7 / SODIUM 93 / CALCIUM 27

CARROT-WHOLE WHEAT POPOVERS

2 eggs
¾ cup whole wheat flour
¼ cup all-purpose flour
1 cup skim milk
⅛ teaspoon salt
⅓ cup shredded carrots
Vegetable cooking spray

Combine first 6 ingredients in container of an electric blender; process until smooth.

Coat six (6-ounce) custard cups with cooking spray. Place cups in oven at 475° for 3 minutes. Remove from oven; fill two-thirds full with batter. Bake at 475° for 20 minutes; reduce heat to 350°, and bake 25 minutes. Serve hot. Yield: 6 popovers (112 calories each).

PROTEIN 6.1 / FAT 2.3 / CARBOHYDRATE 17.4 / CHOLESTEROL 92 / IRON 1.0 / SODIUM 94 / CALCIUM 68

LEMON-WHEAT GERM PANCAKES

1 cup all-purpose flour
2 tablespoons wheat germ
1 tablespoon sugar
1 tablespoon grated lemon rind
1½ teaspoons baking powder
½ teaspoon baking soda
¼ teaspoon salt
1 cup skim milk
1 egg, beaten
2 tablespoons lemon juice
1 tablespoon plus 1½ teaspoons
  margarine, melted
Vegetable cooking spray

Combine first 7 ingredients in a medium bowl, stirring well. Combine milk, egg, lemon juice, and margarine; add to dry ingredients, stirring just until blended.

For each pancake, pour 2 tablespoons batter onto hot griddle or skillet coated with cooking spray. Cook over medium heat, turning pancakes when tops are bubbly and edges are browned. Repeat procedure until all pancake batter is used. Yield: 14 (4-inch) pancakes (66 calories each).

PROTEIN 2.4 / FAT 1.9 / CARBOHYDRATE 10.0 / CHOLESTEROL 20 / IRON 0.4 / SODIUM 132 / CALCIUM 54

GINGERBREAD WAFFLES

¼ cup margarine, softened
¼ cup molasses
2 eggs
1¼ cups all-purpose flour
1 cup whole wheat flour
2 teaspoons ground ginger
1 teaspoon ground cinnamon
¼ teaspoon salt
¼ teaspoon ground cloves
2 cups boiling water
Vegetable cooking spray

Cream margarine in a medium bowl; add molasses and eggs, beating well. Combine flours, ginger, cinnamon, salt, and cloves in a small bowl; stir well. Add flour mixture to creamed mixture alternately with water, beginning and ending with flour mixture. Mix well after each addition.

Coat an 8-inch square waffle iron with cooking spray; allow to preheat. Pour 1¼ cups batter into hot waffle iron. Bake about 8 minutes or until steaming stops. Repeat procedure until all batter is used. Yield: 12 (4-inch) waffles (150 calories each).

PROTEIN 3.9 / FAT 5.1 / CARBOHYDRATE 22.6 / CHOLESTEROL 46 / IRON 1.4 / SODIUM 108 / CALCIUM 36

 ## THE GOODNESS OF FIBER IS ON THE LABEL—SOMEWHERE

Most breads contain some form of wheat flour, either refined or whole grain. Refining removes about two-thirds of wheat's fiber content; it also removes nutrients, though vitamins and minerals are added during the enrichment process.

If you want the fiber benefits of whole wheat, look beyond the name and color of the bread. Don't assume that "wheat" or "natural whole-grain goodness" on a label means whole wheat. Breads made from refined white flour can be made to look brown by adding caramel or malt coloring. These darkened white breads may still be labeled "wheat bread";

the missing word "whole" provides the clue that refined flour has been used.

Breads made of whole grain wheat flour are labeled "whole wheat" or list whole wheat flour as the first ingredient. The following information on bread labels guarantees a high fiber content: 10 percent whole wheat flour, cracked wheat, stone-ground wheat, sprouted wheat, wheat berries, wheat germ, wheat bran, rye flour, or oat-bran flour.

Whole Wheat Madeleines (page 105) with a 3:1 ratio of whole wheat flour to all-purpose flour have the *real* color and rich, nutty flavor of whole wheat.

BROWN RICE BREAD

1 cup plus 2 tablespoons skim milk
2 tablespoons margarine
2 tablespoons honey
1 teaspoon salt
1 package dry yeast
1 teaspoon sugar
¼ cup warm water (105° to 115°)
1 cup cooked brown rice (cooked without salt or fat)
1¾ cups all-purpose flour, divided
1½ cups whole wheat flour
Vegetable cooking spray

Scald milk in a small saucepan; add margarine, honey, and salt, stirring until margarine melts. Let mixture cool to 105° to 115°.

Dissolve yeast and sugar in warm water in a large bowl; let stand 5 minutes or until foamy. Add cooled milk mixture, rice, 1 cup all-purpose flour, and whole wheat flour; stir well. Stir in remaining all-purpose flour to make a soft dough. (Dough will be sticky.)

Turn dough out onto a floured surface; knead until smooth and elastic (8 to 10 minutes). Place dough in a bowl coated with cooking spray, turning to grease top. Cover and let rise in a warm place (85°), free from drafts, 40 minutes or until doubled in bulk.

Punch dough down; cover and let stand 10 minutes. Turn dough out onto floured surface, and knead 4 or 5 times. Shape into a loaf, and place in a 9- x 5- x 3-inch loafpan coated with cooking spray. Cover and let rise in a warm place (85°), free from drafts, 20 minutes or until doubled in bulk.

Bake at 375° for 40 minutes or until loaf sounds hollow when tapped. Cool in pan 10 minutes; remove to a wire rack to cool completely. Yield: 1 loaf or 16 (½-inch) slices (134 calories per slice).

PROTEIN 4.1 / FAT 1.9 / CARBOHYDRATE 25.6 / CHOLESTEROL 0 / IRON 0.9 / SODIUM 173 / CALCIUM 31

WHOLE WHEAT BATTER BREAD

1 package dry yeast
1¼ cups warm water (105° to 115°)
2 tablespoons honey, divided
2 cups whole wheat flour, divided
1 cup all-purpose flour, divided
¼ teaspoon salt
2 tablespoons reduced-calorie margarine, softened
Vegetable cooking spray

Dissolve yeast in water and 1 tablespoon honey in a large bowl; stir well. Let stand 5 minutes or until foamy. Combine yeast mixture, 1 cup whole wheat flour, ½ cup all-purpose flour, salt, and margarine in a large bowl. Beat at medium speed of an electric mixer 2 minutes, scraping sides of bowl frequently.

Combine remaining flours, stirring well. Scrape sides of bowl. Cover and let rise in a warm place (85°), free from drafts, until doubled in bulk.

Stir dough down; beat 25 strokes by hand. Spread batter into an 8½- x 4½- x 3-inch loafpan coated with cooking spray. Smooth top with floured hands and pat into shape. Cover and let rise until doubled in bulk. Bake at 375° for 40 to 50 minutes or until loaf sounds hollow when tapped. Yield: 1 loaf or 16 (½-inch) slices (98 calories per slice).

PROTEIN 3.1 / FAT 1.3 / CARBOHYDRATE 19.5 / CHOLESTEROL 0 / IRON 0.8 / SODIUM 51 / CALCIUM 8

DECIDING TO DINE OUT DEFENSIVELY BUT DIVINELY

Eating right while eating out is becoming less of a challenge than in years past. Fast-food restaurants serve salads, low-fat milk, whole-grain buns, and baked potatoes. Some chains even offer baked, broiled, or steamed entrées served with vegetables and use vegetable oil for frying foods.

Regardless of the standard fare, you're in control. Don't hesitate to ask for less butter in sautéed items.

Many seafood restaurants will broil fish without butter or margarine on request. If you don't want meat, request vegetable side orders in main-dish portions. At steak houses, choose lean cuts like sirloin and tenderloin. Limit portions of cooked meat to 3 ounces—a cut about the size of the palm of a woman's hand. Share any extra portions with someone else, or take leftovers home.

SESAME SEED BAGELS

1 package dry yeast
2 tablespoons sugar, divided
1½ cups warm water (105° to 115°)
4 cups all-purpose flour
1 teaspoon salt
Vegetable cooking spray
1 gallon water
1 egg white
3 tablespoons sesame seeds

Dissolve yeast and 1 tablespoon sugar in warm water in a large bowl; let stand 5 minutes or until foamy. Add flour and salt, stirring well. (Dough will be sticky.) Turn dough out onto a heavily floured surface, and knead 8 to 10 minutes or until smooth and elastic. Place in a bowl coated with cooking spray, turning to grease top. Cover and let rise in a warm place (85°), free from drafts, 15 minutes.

Punch dough down; turn out onto a floured surface, and knead 4 or 5 times. Divide dough into 18 pieces, and shape each into a smooth ball. Punch a hole in the center of each ball with a floured finger. Gently pull dough away from center to make a 1- to 1½-inch hole. Return bagels to floured surface; cover and let rise 20 minutes.

Bring 1 gallon water and remaining 1 tablespoon sugar to a boil in a large Dutch oven; reduce heat to medium, and drop bagels, 6 at a time, into water. Simmer, uncovered, 2½ minutes on each side. Drain bagels well on paper towels.

Place bagels on ungreased baking sheets. Bake at 375° for 10 minutes; remove bagels from oven, and brush with egg white. Sprinkle bagels with sesame seeds, and bake an additional 20 minutes or until golden brown. Cool bagels on wire racks. Yield: 1½ dozen bagels (127 calories each).

PROTEIN 3.8 / FAT 1.1 / CARBOHYDRATE 25.1 / CHOLESTEROL 0 / IRON 1.2 / SODIUM 134 / CALCIUM 21

HERBED DINNER ROLLS

1 cup skim milk
2 tablespoons margarine
1 tablespoon sugar
1 teaspoon dried Italian seasoning
½ teaspoon salt
¼ teaspoon garlic powder
2 packages dry yeast
½ cup warm water (105° to 115°)
1 egg
2 cups whole wheat flour
¼ cup grated Parmesan cheese
1½ cups all-purpose flour
Vegetable cooking spray

Combine first 6 ingredients in a small saucepan; cook over medium heat, stirring constantly, until margarine melts. Cool mixture to lukewarm (105° to 115°).

Dissolve yeast in warm water in a large mixing bowl, stirring well; let stand 5 minutes. Add milk mixture, egg, and whole wheat flour; beat at low speed of electric mixer just until blended. Beat at high speed for an additional 3 minutes; gradually stir in Parmesan cheese and all-purpose flour to make a stiff dough.

Turn dough out onto a lightly floured surface, and knead 5 to 7 minutes or until dough is smooth and elastic. Place dough in a large mixing bowl coated with cooking spray, turning to grease top. Cover and let rise in a warm place (85°), free from drafts, 45 minutes or until doubled in bulk.

Punch dough down. Turn out onto a lightly floured surface; cover and let rest 10 minutes. Shape dough into thirty 1½-inch balls. Place 15 balls in each of two 9-inch round baking pans that have been coated with cooking spray. Cover and repeat rising procedure 35 minutes or until doubled in bulk. Bake at 375° for 25 minutes or until rolls are golden brown. Remove from pans and serve warm. Yield: 2½ dozen rolls (70 calories each).

PROTEIN 2.7 / FAT 1.4 / CARBOHYDRATE 12.0 / CHOLESTEROL 10 / IRON 0.6 / SODIUM 68 / CALCIUM 27

HOT CROSS ROLLS

1 package dry yeast
2 tablespoons sugar
¼ cup warm water
  (105° to 115°)
4¾ cups all-purpose flour, divided
1 teaspoon ground cinnamon
¼ teaspoon salt
¼ teaspoon ground nutmeg
1 cup warm skim milk
  (105° to 115°)
2 eggs, beaten
¼ cup vegetable oil
⅓ cup currants
Vegetable cooking spray
½ cup sifted powdered sugar
2 teaspoons skim milk

Dissolve yeast and 2 tablespoons sugar in warm water in a large bowl; let stand 5 minutes or until foamy.

Combine 2 cups flour, cinnamon, salt, and nutmeg in a medium bowl; stir well. Add flour mixture to yeast mixture with warm milk; beat at medium speed of electric mixer until smooth.

Stir in eggs, oil, and currants. Gradually add enough flour to make a soft dough, stirring well after each addition.

Turn dough out onto a floured surface, and knead 8 to 10 minutes or until smooth and elastic. Place in a bowl coated with cooking spray, turning to grease top. Cover and let rise in a warm place (85°), free from drafts, 1 hour or until doubled in bulk.

Punch dough down, and divide into 24 pieces; shape each piece into a ball. Place balls in muffin pans coated with cooking spray. Cover and let rise in a warm place (85°), free from drafts, 45 minutes or until doubled in bulk. Bake at 375° for 15 minutes. Cool rolls in pans 10 minutes; remove from pans and transfer to cooling racks.

Combine powdered sugar and milk, stirring well. Drizzle 1 teaspoon sugar glaze in an X pattern over top of each roll. Yield: 2 dozen rolls (150 calories each).

PROTEIN 3.9 / FAT 3.1 / CARBOHYDRATE 26.3 / CHOLESTEROL 23 / IRON 1.0 / SODIUM 37 / CALCIUM 23

MEXICAN JALAPEÑO ROLLS

1 package dry yeast
¼ cup warm water (105° to 115°)
1 teaspoon sugar
2½ cups bread flour
½ cup masa harina
½ teaspoon salt
1 egg, beaten
¼ cup unsalted margarine, melted
½ cup skim milk
1 (8-ounce) can whole kernel corn, drained
2 jalapeño peppers, seeded and minced
Vegetable cooking spray

Dissolve yeast in ¼ cup warm water and 1 teaspoon sugar. Set aside, and let stand 5 minutes or until foamy.

Combine flour, masa harina, and salt in a large bowl; set mixture aside. Combine beaten egg, margarine, milk, corn, jalapeño peppers, and yeast mixture; pour into flour mixture, stirring well.

Turn dough out onto a lightly floured surface, and knead 5 minutes or until dough is smooth and elastic. Place dough in a large bowl that has been coated with cooking spray, turning to grease top. Cover and let rise in a warm place (85°), free from drafts, 1 hour or until dough is doubled in bulk.

Punch dough down, and divide into 16 equal portions. Shape each portion into a smooth ball; place balls in two 8-inch round pans coated with cooking spray. Cover and let rise in a warm place (85°), free from drafts, 45 minutes or until doubled in bulk. Bake at 325° for 35 minutes or until rolls are golden brown. Yield: 16 rolls (125 calories each).

PROTEIN 3.6 / FAT 3.7 / CARBOHYDRATE 19.4 / CHOLESTEROL 17 / IRON 1.0 / SODIUM 84 / CALCIUM 23

VEGETABLE COUSCOUS

Vegetable cooking spray
2 medium-size yellow squash, diced
1 medium zucchini, diced
8 small fresh mushrooms, sliced
1 small sweet red pepper, seeded and diced
¼ cup plus 1 tablespoon reduced-calorie Italian
  salad dressing, divided
¼ cup water
¼ teaspoon salt
½ cup couscous, uncooked

Coat a large skillet with cooking spray, and place over medium heat until hot. Add yellow squash, zucchini, mushrooms, and sweet red pepper; sauté until crisp-tender. Combine squash mixture and 3 tablespoons salad dressing in a large serving bowl; toss well. Set aside, and keep warm.

Combine water, remaining 2 tablespoons salad dressing, and salt in a small saucepan; bring to a boil. Remove from heat, and stir in couscous. Continue to stir until all liquid is absorbed (about 3 minutes). Add to reserved vegetable mixture, and stir well. Yield: 8 servings (30 calories per serving).

PROTEIN 1.3 / FAT 0.2 / CARBOHYDRATE 6.3 / CHOLESTEROL 0 / IRON 0.5 / SODIUM 160 / CALCIUM 11

COUSCOUS—AN ETHNIC WINNER

A Middle Eastern grain preparation called couscous is yet another ethnic dish to please the eclectic American palate. Made from precooked semolina, couscous is usually served with spicy meat and vegetable mixtures that complement its delicate and unobtrusive flavor.

Look for this tiny golden grain in the supermarket or specialty food store, and then create a dining adventure with Vegetable Couscous. When flavored with reduced-calorie salad dressing, each serving is remarkably low in fat and high in carbohydrates.

Sweet red pepper, yellow squash, and zucchini add bright color appeal to Vegetable Couscous.

CHEESY APPLE GRITS

2 cups water
1 tablespoon firmly packed brown sugar
¼ teaspoon salt
½ cup quick-cooking grits, uncooked
½ cup (2 ounces) shredded sharp Cheddar
  cheese
¼ cup skim milk
1 egg, beaten
Vegetable cooking spray
1 medium apple, cored and cut into
  wedges
¼ teaspoon ground cinnamon

Combine water, sugar, and salt in a medium saucepan; bring to a boil. Stir in grits. Cover; reduce heat, and simmer 6 minutes or until thickened, stirring occasionally. Remove from heat; add cheese, milk, and egg. Stir well. Pour mixture into a 9-inch pieplate coated with cooking spray. Arrange apple wedges on top; sprinkle with cinnamon. Cover and bake at 450° for 40 minutes or until set. Let stand 5 to 10 minutes. Yield: 8 servings (91 calories per serving).

PROTEIN 3.6 / FAT 3.2 / CARBOHYDRATE 12.2 / CHOLESTEROL 42 / IRON 0.6 / SODIUM 131 / CALCIUM 68

WALDORF RICE

Vegetable cooking spray
¾ cup uncooked regular rice
1½ cups unsweetened apple juice
½ cup chopped celery
1 cup chopped baking apple
1 tablespoon lemon juice
¼ cup chopped pecans, toasted
Celery leaves (optional)

Coat a large skillet with cooking spray, and place over medium heat until hot. Add rice and cook, stirring frequently, until rice is lightly browned. Remove from heat, and slowly stir apple juice into rice.

Bring mixture to a boil. Cover; reduce heat to medium low, and cook 15 minutes. Stir in chopped celery; cover and cook an additional 5 minutes or until liquid is absorbed and rice is tender.

Toss apple with lemon juice, and add to rice mixture. Stir in pecans. Transfer to a serving bowl, and garnish with celery leaves, if desired. Serve immediately. Yield: 8 servings (118 calories per serving).

PROTEIN 1.5 / FAT 2.7 / CARBOHYDRATE 22.3 / CHOLESTEROL 0 / IRON 0.8 / SODIUM 9 / CALCIUM 13

WILD RICE WITH ARTICHOKES

¼ cup uncooked wild rice
Vegetable cooking spray
½ cup uncooked parboiled rice
1¼ cups water
1½ teaspoons chicken-flavored bouillon
  granules
¾ cup Chablis or other dry white wine
1 (9-ounce) package frozen artichoke hearts,
  thawed and chopped
4 ounces fresh mushrooms, sliced
1 small onion, chopped
1 clove garlic, minced
1 teaspoon fines herbes

Wash wild rice in a strainer under cold running water; drain.

Coat a large skillet with cooking spray; place over medium heat until hot. Add rice and cook, stirring frequently, until rice is lightly browned. Stir in remaining ingredients, and remove mixture from heat.

Place rice mixture in a 1½-quart baking dish; cover and bake at 350° for 1 hour or until all liquid is absorbed. Yield: 6 servings (110 calories per serving).

PROTEIN 3.8 / FAT 0.5 / CARBOHYDRATE 24.0 / CHOLESTEROL 0 / IRON 1.4 / SODIUM 120 / CALCIUM 31

Bow-Tie Pasta with Vegetables makes a carbohydrate- and vitamin-rich meal accompaniment.

BOW-TIE PASTA WITH VEGETABLES

½ cup (3 ounces) crumbled feta cheese
6 ounces bow-tie pasta
2 medium zucchini, cut into ½-inch cubes
2 medium tomatoes, seeded and chopped
½ cup chopped sweet yellow pepper
½ cup sliced green onions
⅓ cup white wine vinegar
2 tablespoons olive oil
1 clove garlic, crushed
½ teaspoon dried whole basil
⅛ teaspoon salt
¼ teaspoon pepper

Place feta cheese in a colander, and rinse under cold tap water 1 minute; set colander aside to let cheese drain 1 minute.

Cook bow-tie pasta according to package directions, omitting salt. Drain, and set aside.

Place zucchini in a vegetable steamer. Place rack over boiling water; cover and steam 3 to 5 minutes or until zucchini is crisp-tender.

Combine reserved cheese, pasta, zucchini, and vegetables in a large bowl. Combine vinegar, oil, garlic, basil, salt, and pepper; stir well. Pour vinegar mixture over pasta mixture; toss gently. Serve warm or chilled. Yield: 6 servings (206 calories per serving).

PROTEIN 6.8 / FAT 8.1 / CARBOHYDRATE 26.7 / CHOLESTEROL 13 / IRON 1.6 / SODIUM 215 / CALCIUM 95

TURKEY CANNELLONI

1 (8-ounce) package cannelloni shells
1 (10-ounce) package frozen chopped spinach, thawed
4 cups no-salt-added tomato juice
1 (6-ounce) can no-salt-added tomato paste
1½ teaspoons dried whole chervil
1 teaspoon dried whole basil
¼ teaspoon garlic powder
Vegetable cooking spray
½ (1-pound) package raw ground turkey, thawed
¾ cup chopped fresh mushrooms
½ cup chopped onion
1 clove garlic, crushed
⅛ teaspoon pepper
1 (8-ounce) package Neufchâtel cheese, softened
2 eggs
1 cup (4 ounces) shredded part-skim mozzarella cheese, divided

Cook cannelloni shells according to package directions, omitting salt. Drain, and set aside. Drain thawed spinach; squeeze out excess moisture between paper towels, and set aside.

Combine tomato juice and next 4 ingredients, stirring well. Spread 2 cups tomato mixture in a 13- x 9- x 2-inch baking dish coated with cooking spray. Set aside remaining tomato mixture.

Combine turkey, mushrooms, onion, garlic, and pepper in a large skillet. Cook over medium heat until turkey is browned, stirring to crumble. Drain in a colander; pat with a paper towel to remove excess grease. Set aside.

Beat Neufchâtel cheese and eggs until smooth. Stir in spinach, turkey mixture, and ½ cup mozzarella cheese. Stuff cannelloni shells, and place in baking dish. Top with remaining tomato mixture. Cover and bake at 350° for 30 to 40 minutes. Uncover; sprinkle with remaining ½ cup mozzarella cheese. Let stand, covered, 10 minutes. Serve immediately. Yield: 8 servings (338 calories per serving).

PROTEIN 23.0 / FAT 12.2 / CARBOHYDRATE 35.4 / CHOLESTEROL 120 / IRON 2.9 / SODIUM 266 / CALCIUM 187

CALIENTE NOODLES

4 ounces medium egg noodles
Vegetable cooking spray
1 teaspoon vegetable oil
1 small onion, chopped
1 (14½-ounce) can no-salt-added stewed
  tomatoes, undrained and chopped
2 jalapeño peppers, seeded and
  chopped
¼ cup (1 ounce) shredded sharp
  Cheddar cheese

Cook noodles according to package directions, omitting salt. Drain, and set aside.

Coat a skillet with cooking spray; add oil, and place over medium heat until hot. Add onion, and sauté until tender. Remove from heat. Combine onion, reserved noodles, and remaining ingredients except cheese in a medium bowl, stirring well. Spoon mixture into a 1½-quart casserole coated with cooking spray; sprinkle with cheese. Cover and bake at 350° for 25 to 30 minutes or until thoroughly heated. Yield: 4 servings (180 calories per serving).

PROTEIN 6.5 / FAT 4.8 / CARBOHYDRATE 28.3 / CHOLESTEROL 32 /
IRON 1.5 / SODIUM 65 / CALCIUM 97

BLUE CHEESE PASTA SHELLS

4 ounces shell macaroni
½ cup chopped green onions
5 radishes, thinly sliced
¼ cup crumbled blue cheese
1 tablespoon chopped fresh parsley
¼ cup reduced-calorie mayonnaise
1 tablespoon lemon juice
⅛ teaspoon pepper

Cook macaroni according to package directions, omitting salt; drain well.

Combine macaroni, onions, radishes, blue cheese, and parsley in a medium mixing bowl; toss gently. Combine mayonnaise, lemon juice, and pepper in a 1-cup glass measure, mixing well; add to macaroni mixture. Toss gently and chill thoroughly. Yield: 4 servings (151 calories per serving).

PROTEIN 4.6 / FAT 6.4 / CARBOHYDRATE 18.9 / CHOLESTEROL 10 /
IRON 0.9 / SODIUM 215 / CALCIUM 53

EGGPLANT VERMICELLI

4 ounces vermicelli
Vegetable cooking spray
1 teaspoon olive oil
1 cup peeled and cubed eggplant
1 cup finely chopped onion
2 cloves garlic, minced
1½ teaspoons dried whole basil
1½ teaspoons dried whole oregano
¼ teaspoon crushed red pepper
1 small zucchini, thinly sliced
¼ pound fresh mushrooms, sliced
2 large tomatoes, chopped
1 tablespoon plus 2 teaspoons grated Parmesan
  cheese

Cook vermicelli according to package directions, omitting salt. Drain, and set aside.

Coat a large skillet with cooking spray; add olive oil, and place over medium-high heat until hot. Add eggplant and next 5 ingredients. Sauté until vegetables are tender. Add zucchini, mushrooms, and tomatoes; sauté 2 minutes or until mixture is thoroughly heated. Combine reserved vermicelli and vegetable mixture on a large serving platter; toss gently. Sprinkle with Parmesan cheese. Yield: 6 servings (124 calories per serving).

PROTEIN 5.0 / FAT 1.8 / CARBOHYDRATE 23.4 / CHOLESTEROL 1 /
IRON 1.7 / SODIUM 37 / CALCIUM 58

A breezy combination fit for a night in the tropics: slices of kiwifruit, a trio of sweet peppers, and chunks of fresh pineapple meet in Pompano with Fruit and Pepper Relish (page 121).

Fish & Shellfish

LEMONY BASS WITH AVOCADO SAUCE

4 bass fillets (1 pound)
2 tablespoons lemon juice
1 tablespoon reduced-sodium soy sauce
1 teaspoon grated lemon rind
1 teaspoon Dijon mustard
⅓ cup fine, dry breadcrumbs
Vegetable cooking spray
Avocado Topping

Rinse fillets with cold water, and pat dry. Combine lemon juice and next 3 ingredients in a shallow dish; dredge fillets in lemon juice mixture and then in breadcrumbs. Place on a baking sheet coated with cooking spray. Bake at 450° for 7 minutes on each side or until fish flakes easily when tested with a fork.

Transfer fillets to a serving platter, and top with Avocado Sauce. Yield: 4 servings (193 calories per serving).

Avocado Sauce:

1 small ripe avocado, coarsely chopped
¼ cup skim milk
1 tablespoon lime juice
1 clove garlic, minced
Dash of hot sauce

Combine all ingredients in container of an electric blender, and process until mixture is smooth. Yield: ⅔ cup.

PROTEIN 23.6 / FAT 6.0 / CARBOHYDRATE 10.0 / CHOLESTEROL 63 / IRON 1.6 / SODIUM 332 / CALCIUM 57

BAKED CATFISH DELUXE

4 catfish fillets (1 pound)
¼ cup lemon juice
¼ teaspoon Italian seasoning
Vegetable cooking spray
½ cup chopped green onions
1 medium-size sweet red pepper, seeded and chopped
1 clove garlic, minced
1 small tomato, diced
¼ teaspoon salt
⅛ teaspoon pepper
1 cup (4 ounces) shredded part-skim mozzarella cheese

Rinse fillets with cold water, and pat dry. Place in a shallow dish. Pour lemon juice over fillets; sprinkle with Italian seasoning. Cover and refrigerate 1 hour.

Coat a large skillet with cooking spray and place over medium heat until hot. Add onions, sweet red pepper, and garlic; sauté until vegetables are tender. Add tomato, and sauté until thoroughly heated. Remove mixture from heat, and drain.

Remove fillets from lemon juice; place in a 12- x 8- x 2-inch baking dish. Sprinkle with salt and pepper. Bake, uncovered, at 350° for 30 minutes. Spoon vegetable mixture evenly over fillets; sprinkle with cheese. Bake at 350° for an additional 10 minutes or until fish flakes easily when tested with a fork. Yield: 4 servings (207 calories per serving).

PROTEIN 27.6 / FAT 8.1 / CARBOHYDRATE 5.4 / CHOLESTEROL 79 / IRON 1.3 / SODIUM 350 / CALCIUM 226

CATFISH WITH JALAPEÑO SAUCE

6 catfish fillets (1½ pounds)
Vegetable cooking spray
2 tablespoons lime juice
⅛ teaspoon garlic salt
Jalapeño Sauce

Rinse fillets with cold water, and pat dry. Place in a 13- x 9- x 2-inch baking dish coated with cooking spray.

Combine lime juice and garlic salt; brush fillets with mixture. Broil 5 inches from heating element 15 to 18 minutes or until fish flakes easily when tested with a fork. Transfer fillets to a serving platter. Spoon Jalapeño Sauce over fillets and serve. Yield: 6 servings (153 calories per serving).

Jalapeño Sauce:

1 tablespoon margarine
1 tablespoon all-purpose flour
½ cup skim milk
2 tablespoons chopped fresh parsley
1 teaspoon chopped jalapeño pepper
1 green onion, chopped
1 tablespoon lime juice
⅛ teaspoon salt

Melt margarine in a small saucepan over low heat; add flour, stirring until smooth. Cook 1 minute, stirring constantly. Gradually add milk. Cook over medium heat, stirring constantly, until mixture begins to thicken. Remove from heat.

Position knife blade in food processor bowl; add parsley, pepper, onion, lime juice, and salt. Process until smooth. Add to milk mixture; blend well. Yield: ½ cup.

PROTEIN 21.0 / FAT 5.4 / CARBOHYDRATE 3.9 / CHOLESTEROL 63 / IRON 0.7 / SODIUM 195 / CALCIUM 57

CATFISH ORIENTAL

½ pound fresh snow pea pods
4 catfish fillets (1 pound)
Vegetable cooking spray
1 tablespoon vegetable oil, divided
1 cup sliced fresh mushrooms
¾ cup sliced green onions
¾ cup shredded carrots
½ cup sliced water chestnuts
1 medium-size sweet red pepper, seeded and cut into strips
2 tablespoons reduced-sodium soy sauce
2 tablespoons lemon juice
2 teaspoons firmly packed brown sugar
½ teaspoon ground ginger
2 tablespoons sesame seeds

Wash snow peas; trim ends, and remove tough strings. Set aside.

Rinse fillets with cold water, and pat dry. Cut into 2- x ¾-inch strips. Set aside.

Coat a nonstick wok or large skillet with cooking spray. Add 1 teaspoon oil. Heat at medium-high (325°) for 2 minutes. Add snow peas and next 5 ingredients; stir-fry 3 minutes. Remove vegetables from wok.

Add remaining 2 teaspoons oil to wok; heat at medium-high (325°) for 2 minutes. Add fish; stir-fry 2 minutes or until fish flakes easily when tested with a fork. Reduce heat to 225°. Add vegetables to wok. Combine soy sauce, lemon juice, sugar, and ginger. Pour over fish and vegetables; cook at low heat (225°) for 2 minutes. Sprinkle with sesame seeds. Yield: 4 servings (248 calories per serving).

PROTEIN 24.1 / FAT 9.5 / CARBOHYDRATE 16.6 / CHOLESTEROL 62 / IRON 3.3 / SODIUM 375 / CALCIUM 112

CATFISH: A "HEART HEALTHY" CATCH

The catfish has a new image. The classic fried "mud cat" served with hush puppies and coleslaw is making way for new catfish cuisine.

Why all the hoopla over a fish almost as old as the river? Apparently, a farm-fed catfish is a milder, more tender catfish than its river counterpart and is available year round at a reasonable price.

Best of all—catfish are nutritionally attractive. Three ounces of the fish have less fat and cholesterol and fewer calories than the same amount of skinned chicken breast. Find pleasure in dining on Baked Catfish Deluxe or Catfish with Jalapeño Sauce. Catfish Oriental will convince even the most skeptical of cooks that a catfish is at home anywhere—even in a Chinese stir-fry.

FLOUNDER ROLLS WITH LEMON-CARROT FILLING

Vegetable cooking spray
⅔ cup shredded carrots
¼ cup sliced green onions
½ cup part-skim ricotta cheese
2 tablespoons chopped fresh parsley
1 tablespoon grated lemon rind
¾ teaspoon dried whole thyme
¼ teaspoon salt
⅛ teaspoon pepper
6 flounder fillets (1½ pounds)
Lemon slices
Fresh parsley sprigs

Coat a skillet with cooking spray; place over medium heat until hot. Add carrots and green onions; sauté until crisp-tender. Remove from heat. Add cheese and next 5 ingredients; stir well. Set aside.

Rinse fillets with cold water, and pat dry. Spoon 2 tablespoons of mixture in center of each fillet; roll up jellyroll fashion, beginning at narrow end. Place rolls, seam side down, in a 12- x 8- x 2-inch baking dish coated with cooking spray. Bake, uncovered, at 350° for 20 minutes. Transfer rolls to a serving platter, and garnish with lemon slices and fresh parsley. Yield: 6 servings (122 calories per serving).

PROTEIN 21.3 / FAT 2.4 / CARBOHYDRATE 2.5 / CHOLESTEROL 63 / IRON 1.4 / SODIUM 214 / CALCIUM 76

ORANGE FLOUNDER IN PAPILLOTE

½ cup unsweetened orange juice
1 teaspoon honey
1 teaspoon grated fresh gingerroot
¾ teaspoon cornstarch
¼ teaspoon salt
1 large orange, peeled, sectioned, and seeded
   (about ½ cup)
4 flounder fillets (1 pound)
2 cups fresh broccoli flowerets

Combine first 5 ingredients in a non-aluminum saucepan. Cook over medium heat, stirring constantly, until mixture is thickened and bubbly. Remove mixture from heat; stir in orange sections, and set aside.

Cut four 15- x 14-inch pieces of parchment paper; fold in half lengthwise, creasing firmly. Trim each into a large heart shape. Place parchment hearts on baking sheets.

Rinse fillets with cold water, and pat dry. Place a fillet on one half of each parchment heart near the crease. Spoon ¼ cup reserved orange juice mixture over each fillet. Top each fillet with ½ cup broccoli flowerets. Starting with rounded edge of each heart, pleat and crimp edges together to make a seal. Twist end tightly to seal.

Bake at 400° for 12 minutes or until bags are puffed and lightly browned and fish flakes easily when tested with a fork. Yield: 4 servings (134 calories per serving).

PROTEIN 20.7 / FAT 1.1 / CARBOHYDRATE 10.3 / CHOLESTEROL 57 / IRON 1.4 / SODIUM 247 / CALCIUM 48

Orange Flounder in Papillote—a complicated name given to the simple technique of cooking in parchment paper and allowing food to steam in its own juices. The presentation is dramatic, the food delicious!

GROUPER PARMESAN

1 tablespoon plus 1 teaspoon lemon juice
1 tablespoon plus 1 teaspoon dry sherry
⅓ cup seasoned, dry breadcrumbs
2 tablespoons grated Parmesan cheese
1 teaspoon grated lemon rind
⅛ teaspoon garlic powder
2 grouper fillets (1 pound)
Vegetable cooking spray

Combine lemon juice and sherry. Combine breadcrumbs, cheese, lemon rind, and garlic powder. Rinse fillets with cold water, and pat dry. Dip fillets in lemon juice mixture; roll in breadcrumb mixture. Place fillets in a 10- x 6- x 2-inch baking dish coated with cooking spray. Sprinkle with remaining breadcrumb mixture. Bake, uncovered, at 400° for 20 to 25 minutes or until fish flakes easily when tested with a fork. Yield: 4 servings (150 calories per serving).

PROTEIN 23.9 / FAT 1.7 / CARBOHYDRATE 6.9 / CHOLESTEROL 65 / IRON 1.0 / SODIUM 178 / CALCIUM 72

GROUPER WITH CORIANDER VINAIGRETTE

3 grouper fillets (1½ pounds)
2 tablespoons white wine vinegar
2 teaspoons olive oil
½ teaspoon ground coriander
¼ teaspoon paprika
1 clove garlic, minced
Vegetable cooking spray
1 cup shredded carrots
¼ cup finely chopped green pepper

Rinse fillets with cold water, and pat dry. Place fillets in a 12- x 8- x 2-inch baking dish. Combine vinegar, olive oil, coriander, paprika, and garlic, stirring well. Brush vinaigrette mixture over fillets. Bake, uncovered, at 350° for 30 minutes or until fish flakes easily when tested with a fork; turn and baste often with vinegar mixture. Transfer to a platter, and keep warm.

Coat a small skillet with cooking spray, and place over medium heat until hot. Add carrots and green pepper, and sauté until tender. Spoon sautéed vegetables over warm fillets, and serve immediately. Yield: 6 servings (122 calories per serving).

PROTEIN 22.0 / FAT 2.1 / CARBOHYDRATE 2.3 / CHOLESTEROL 62 / IRON 0.9 / SODIUM 76 / CALCIUM 33

CURRIED GROUPER WITH WINE SAUCE

3 grouper fillets (1½ pounds), cut into 1-inch cubes
Vegetable cooking spray
¼ cup lemon juice
2 teaspoons curry powder
Wine Sauce
3 tablespoons sliced almonds, toasted

Rinse fillets with cold water, and pat dry. Coat rack of a broiler pan with cooking spray; place fillets on rack. Combine lemon juice and curry powder, stirring well. Brush curry mixture over fillets. Bake, uncovered, at 400° for 15 minutes or until fish flakes easily when tested with a fork.

Transfer to a serving platter; pour Wine Sauce over fillets. Sprinkle with sliced almonds. Yield: 4 servings (235 calories per serving).

Wine Sauce:

1 tablespoon margarine
2 tablespoons all-purpose flour
½ cup skim milk
2 tablespoons Chablis or other dry white wine
⅛ teaspoon salt
Dash of freshly ground pepper

Melt margarine in a small saucepan over low heat; add flour, stirring until smooth. Gradually add milk. Cook 1 minute, stirring constantly, until thickened and bubbly. Add wine, salt, and pepper, stirring well. Yield: ⅔ cup.

PROTEIN 35.3 / FAT 6.3 / CARBOHYDRATE 7.9 / CHOLESTEROL 94 / IRON 1.7 / SODIUM 228 / CALCIUM 98

HADDOCK À L'ORANGE

2 pounds haddock fillets
Vegetable cooking spray
¼ cup unsweetened orange juice
1 tablespoon margarine, melted
1 tablespoon grated orange rind
¼ teaspoon salt
⅛ teaspoon white pepper
1 tablespoon chopped fresh parsley
Orange slices

Rinse fillets with cold water, and pat dry. Arrange in a 13- x 9- x 2-inch baking dish coated with cooking spray.

Combine orange juice and next 4 ingredients; pour over fillets. Bake, uncovered, at 350° for 25 minutes or until fish flakes easily when tested with a fork. Transfer to a serving platter; sprinkle with parsley. Garnish with orange slices. Yield: 8 servings (106 calories per serving).

PROTEIN 20.7 / FAT 2.2 / CARBOHYDRATE 1.1 / CHOLESTEROL 68 / IRON 0.7 / SODIUM 159 / CALCIUM 30

ORANGE ROUGHY WITH SPINACH SAUCE

Vegetable cooking spray
¾ cup diced sweet red pepper
¼ cup shredded yellow squash
¼ cup shredded zucchini
¼ cup shredded carrots
1 clove garlic, minced
1 tablespoon margarine
6 orange roughy fillets (1¼ pounds)
Spinach Sauce

Coat a medium skillet with cooking spray; place over medium heat until hot. Add next 5 ingredients; sauté until tender. Remove from heat; set aside, and keep warm.

Coat a large skillet with cooking spray; add margarine. Place over medium heat until margarine melts. Add fillets, and cook 7 minutes on each side or until fish flakes easily when tested with a fork.

Spoon equal amounts of Spinach Sauce onto 6 individual serving plates. Transfer fillets to serving plates. Top with reserved vegetable mixture. Yield: 6 servings (207 calories per serving).

Spinach Sauce:

Vegetable cooking spray
¼ cup chopped onion
1 clove garlic, minced
6 ounces fresh spinach leaves, trimmed and washed
⅓ cup evaporated skim milk
⅓ cup fresh basil leaves
1 egg yolk
½ teaspoon chicken-flavored bouillon granules
⅛ teaspoon white pepper

Coat a large saucepan with cooking spray. Place over medium heat until hot. Add onion and garlic; sauté until onion is tender. Add spinach leaves; cover, and cook over high heat 3 minutes or until spinach wilts.

Transfer mixture to container of an electric blender. Add remaining ingredients; process until smooth. Return mixture to saucepan. Cook over low heat, stirring constantly, until thickened and bubbly. Yield: about 1 cup.

PROTEIN 20.8 / FAT 10.8 / CARBOHYDRATE 6.2 / CHOLESTEROL 98 / IRON 2.3 / SODIUM 147 / CALCIUM 140

ZESTY BROILED PERCH

1 (1-pound) package frozen perch fillets, thawed
Vegetable cooking spray
3 tablespoons lemon juice
1 tablespoon margarine, melted
1 teaspoon Worcestershire sauce
1 teaspoon chili powder
1 clove garlic, crushed
⅛ teaspoon salt
⅛ teaspoon dry mustard
Dash of pepper
2 tablespoons minced fresh parsley

Rinse fillets with cold water, and pat dry. Place in a 12- x 8- x 2-inch baking dish coated with cooking spray. Combine lemon juice and next 7 ingredients; stir well, and pour over fillets.

Broil 6 inches from heat for 5 minutes or until fish flakes easily when tested with a fork. Transfer fillets to a serving platter; spoon cooking juices over top. Sprinkle with parsley, and serve. Yield: 4 servings (151 calories per serving).

PROTEIN 19.3 / FAT 7.0 / CARBOHYDRATE 2.0 / CHOLESTEROL 55 / IRON 1.0 / SODIUM 176 / CALCIUM 59

POMPANO WITH FRUIT AND PEPPER RELISH

½ small green pepper, seeded and
   chopped
½ small sweet red pepper, seeded and
   chopped
½ small sweet yellow pepper, seeded
   and chopped
½ cup chopped fresh pineapple
1 kiwifruit, peeled and thinly sliced
1 tablespoon white wine vinegar
1½ teaspoons water
1 teaspoon firmly packed brown sugar
1 teaspoon grated fresh gingerroot
⅛ teaspoon crushed red pepper
1 tablespoon lemon juice
2 teaspoons margarine, melted
¼ teaspoon curry powder
⅛ teaspoon salt
6 pompano fillets (1½ pounds)
Vegetable cooking spray
Sweet yellow pepper strips (optional)

Combine first 5 ingredients in a medium bowl; set aside. Combine vinegar, water, sugar, gingerroot, and crushed red pepper; stir well. Pour mixture over reserved pepper-fruit mixture. Toss gently to coat. Cover and refrigerate 2 hours, tossing gently after 1 hour.

Combine lemon juice, margarine, curry powder, and salt in a small bowl; stir well. Rinse fillets with cold water, and pat dry. Place on rack of a broiler pan that has been coated with cooking spray. Brush with lemon juice mixture. Broil 4 to 6 inches from heating element 8 minutes or until fish flakes easily when tested with a fork. Transfer fillets to a serving platter. Garnish with sweet yellow pepper strips, if desired, and serve with ¼ cup chilled fruit and pepper relish per serving. Yield: 6 servings (222 calories per serving).

PROTEIN 21.6 / FAT 12.3 / CARBOHYDRATE 5.1 / CHOLESTEROL 62 / IRON 1.6 / SODIUM 118 / CALCIUM 59

GINGERED POACHED SALMON

4 (½-inch-thick) salmon steaks (1 pound)
2 cups Chablis or other dry white wine
½ cup water
1 small lemon, sliced
8 green onions, cut into 1-inch pieces
¼ cup minced fresh gingerroot
¼ teaspoon salt

Rinse steaks with cold water, and pat dry. Set steaks aside.

Combine wine, water, lemon, onions, gingerroot, and salt in a 10-inch skillet, stirring well. Bring to a boil. Cover; reduce heat, and simmer 10 minutes. Add salmon steaks; cover and simmer 8 minutes or until fish flakes easily when tested with a fork. Yield: 4 servings (176 calories per serving).

PROTEIN 23.7 / FAT 4.4 / CARBOHYDRATE 11.6 / CHOLESTEROL 40 / IRON 1.9 / SODIUM 228 / CALCIUM 190

POACHING FISH ENHANCES FLAVOR AND NUTRITION

Poaching fish is a quick-cook method of preparing fish without using oil or fat. If you don't have a poacher, fill a wide skillet with enough liquid to cover the fish. The liquid can be water that has been seasoned with herbs and spices, vegetable juices, or wine. Bring the liquid to a boil and add the fish; reduce the heat and simmer until done. It's as easy as poaching an egg, and the tender flesh of the fish remains moist and intact. Keep in mind that the microwave oven is ideal for poaching both fish and chicken. A dry white wine, lemon slices, green onions, and the flavor of fresh gingerroot come together in Gingered Poached Salmon to create elegant simplicity.

RATATOUILLE-TOPPED SALMON STEAKS

6 (½-inch-thick) salmon steaks (1½ pounds)
Vegetable cooking spray
2 teaspoons olive oil
2 cloves garlic, minced
1 small eggplant, cubed
1 red onion, sliced
1 medium-size green pepper, seeded
  and cut into strips
2 medium tomatoes, seeded and
  chopped
1 medium zucchini, sliced
½ teaspoon dried whole basil
½ teaspoon dried whole oregano
½ teaspoon dried whole thyme
⅛ teaspoon salt
Dash of pepper
3 tablespoons grated Parmesan cheese

Rinse steaks with cold water, and pat dry. Place in a 13- x 9- x 2-inch baking dish coated with cooking spray. Set aside.

Coat a large skillet with cooking spray; add oil. Place over medium-high heat until hot. Add garlic, eggplant, and onion; sauté until tender. Add remaining ingredients, except cheese; stir well, and remove from heat. Spoon vegetable mixture over steaks. Cover and bake at 400° for 20 minutes. Remove from heat, and sprinkle with cheese; bake, uncovered, 5 minutes. Yield: 6 servings (197 calories per serving).

PROTEIN 25.3 / FAT 6.8 / CARBOHYDRATE 8.5 / CHOLESTEROL 42 / IRON 2.0 / SODIUM 175 / CALCIUM 213

SCAMP WITH LEMON-ZUCCHINI SAUCE

4 scamp fillets (1 pound)
¼ cup cornmeal
¼ teaspoon paprika
⅛ teaspoon salt
Vegetable cooking spray
Lemon-Zucchini Sauce

Rinse fillets with cold water, and pat dry. Combine cornmeal, paprika, and salt; stir well. Dredge fillets in cornmeal mixture to coat well.

Place on a baking sheet coated with cooking spray. Bake at 450° for 12 minutes or until fish flakes easily when tested with a fork, turning

carefully after 6 minutes. Transfer fillets to individual plates; spoon equal amounts of Lemon-Zucchini Sauce over each serving. Serve immediately. Yield: 4 servings (251 calories per serving).

Lemon-Zucchini Sauce:

Vegetable cooking spray
½ cup chopped zucchini
2 tablespoons minced onion
¼ cup reduced-calorie mayonnaise
2 tablespoons lemon juice
½ teaspoon dried whole oregano

Coat a small skillet with cooking spray; place over medium heat until hot. Add zucchini and onion. Sauté 2 minutes. Drain, and transfer to container of an electric blender. Process until pureed. Transfer pureed mixture to a medium saucepan. Add remaining ingredients. Cook over low heat, stirring constantly, until thoroughly heated. (Do not boil.) Yield: ½ cup.

PROTEIN 22.4 / FAT 13.4 / CARBOHYDRATE 8.6 / CHOLESTEROL 67 / IRON 0.9 / SODIUM 244 / CALCIUM 38

HERBED SHARK STEAKS

2 (¾-inch-thick) shark steaks (about 2 pounds)
¾ cup Chablis or other dry white wine
1 tablespoon plus 1½ teaspoons olive oil
2 teaspoons dried whole basil
1 teaspoon dried whole oregano
¾ teaspoon dried whole thyme
¼ teaspoon salt
¼ teaspoon garlic powder
⅛ teaspoon white pepper
Vegetable cooking spray

Rinse steaks with cold water, and pat dry. Place in a shallow dish. Combine remaining ingredients, except cooking spray, stirring well; pour over steaks. Cover and refrigerate 8 hours or overnight, turning steaks occasionally.

Remove steaks from marinade, reserving marinade. Coat grill with cooking spray. Grill steaks over medium coals 6 minutes on each side, or until fish flakes easily when tested with a fork. Baste frequently with reserved marinade. Yield: 8 servings (216 calories per serving).

PROTEIN 20.1 / FAT 12.8 / CARBOHYDRATE 0.5 / CHOLESTEROL 62 / IRON 1.0 / SODIUM 136 / CALCIUM 34

Grecian Snapper with Feta Cheese is a big catch in flavor but a small-fry in calories.

GRECIAN SNAPPER WITH FETA CHEESE

2 ounces feta cheese, crumbled
Vegetable cooking spray
1 tablespoon olive oil
1 cup chopped onion
1 clove garlic, minced
3 medium tomatoes, peeled, seeded, and
  chopped
¼ cup Chablis or other dry white wine
1 teaspoon dried whole oregano
¼ teaspoon salt
⅛ teaspoon pepper
6 (¼-pound) red snapper fillets
2 tablespoons chopped fresh parsley
1 tablespoon chopped ripe olives
Lemon twist (optional)
Fresh parsley sprig (optional)

Place feta cheese in a colander, and rinse under cold tap water 1 minute; set colander aside to let cheese drain 1 minute.

Coat a large skillet with cooking spray; add olive oil, and place over medium heat until hot. Add onion and garlic; sauté until tender. Stir in tomatoes, wine, oregano, salt, and pepper. Bring to a boil; reduce heat, and simmer, uncovered, 20 minutes.

Rinse fillets with cold water, and pat dry. Place in a 13- x 9- x 2-inch baking dish coated with cooking spray; spoon sauce over fillets. Bake, uncovered, at 350° for 15 minutes or until fish flakes easily when tested with a fork. Sprinkle reserved cheese, parsley, and olives over fillets, and serve immediately. Garnish with lemon twist and parsley, if desired. Yield: 6 servings (178 calories per serving).

PROTEIN 24.8 / FAT 5.7 / CARBOHYDRATE 5.8 / CHOLESTEROL 71 / IRON 1.6 / SODIUM 235 / CALCIUM 313

SNAPPER WITH TARRAGON-LIME MAYONNAISE

4 (½-inch-thick) red snapper fillets (1 pound)
Vegetable cooking spray
⅓ cup reduced-calorie mayonnaise
2 tablespoons plain low-fat yogurt
½ teaspoon grated lime rind
1 tablespoon lime juice
1 teaspoon dried whole tarragon
Dash of white pepper
Chopped fresh parsley
Lime slices

Rinse fillets with cold water, and pat dry. Arrange in a 12- x 8- x 2-inch baking dish coated with cooking spray.

Combine mayonnaise, yogurt, lime rind, juice, tarragon, and pepper; spoon evenly over fillets. Bake, uncovered, at 350° for 20 minutes or until fish flakes easily when tested with a fork. Transfer fillets to a serving platter, and garnish with parsley and lime slices. Yield: 4 servings (166 calories per serving).

PROTEIN 23.0 / FAT 6.4 / CARBOHYDRATE 2.4 / CHOLESTEROL 69 / IRON 1.0 / SODIUM 171 / CALCIUM 261

SOLE PROVOLONE

1 (9-ounce) package frozen artichoke hearts
Vegetable cooking spray
½ pound sliced fresh mushrooms
¼ cup Marsala wine
¼ cup water
1 tablespoon lemon juice
½ teaspoon chicken-flavored bouillon granules
Dash of white pepper
4 sole fillets (1 pound)
½ cup (2 ounces) shredded provolone cheese
2 tablespoons grated Parmesan cheese
2 tablespoons chopped fresh parsley

Cook artichokes according to package directions, omitting salt; drain, and set aside.

Coat a large skillet with cooking spray; place over medium heat until hot. Add mushrooms, and sauté 3 minutes. Stir in wine and next 4 ingredients; simmer 5 minutes. Add reserved artichokes. Remove from heat.

Rinse fillets with cold water, and pat dry.

Place in a 13- x 9- x 2-inch baking dish coated with cooking spray. Spoon reserved mushroom mixture over fillets. Combine provolone and Parmesan cheeses; sprinkle over mushroom mixture. Bake at 375° for 15 minutes or until fish flakes easily when tested with a fork. Sprinkle with chopped fresh parsley. Yield: 4 servings (196 calories per serving).

PROTEIN 26.6 / FAT 6.0 / CARBOHYDRATE 9.6 / CHOLESTEROL 68 / IRON 2.1 / SODIUM 340 / CALCIUM 174

HONEY-MUSTARD SWORDFISH

2 (1-inch-thick) swordfish steaks (1¼ pounds)
¼ cup Chablis or other dry white wine
2 tablespoons Dijon mustard
2 tablespoons reduced-sodium soy sauce
1 tablespoon honey
½ teaspoon curry powder
Vegetable cooking spray

Rinse steaks with cold water, and pat dry. Place in a 13- x 9- x 2-inch baking dish. Combine remaining ingredients, except cooking spray; stir with a wire whisk until well blended. Pour over steaks. Cover and marinate in refrigerator 1 hour.

Remove steaks from marinade, reserving marinade. Coat grill with cooking spray. Grill steaks 6 inches over hot coals 8 minutes on each side or until fish flakes easily when tested with a fork. Baste often with reserved marinade. Remove from grill, and transfer to a serving platter. Yield: 6 servings (140 calories per serving).

PROTEIN 18.6 / FAT 4.1 / CARBOHYDRATE 3.9 / CHOLESTEROL 52 / IRON 0.9 / SODIUM 394 / CALCIUM 20

SPICY GRILLED TROUT

6 trout fillets (1½ pounds)
¼ cup lemon juice
1 tablespoon vegetable oil
1½ teaspoons chili powder
¼ teaspoon ground cumin
¼ teaspoon paprika
1 clove garlic, minced
Dash of red pepper
Vegetable cooking spray
3 tablespoons sliced ripe olives

Rinse fillets with cold water, and pat dry. Combine lemon juice and next 6 ingredients; stir well. Place fillets in a zip top heavy-duty plastic bag. Pour marinade over fillets, and seal bag tightly. Place bag in a shallow pan, and refrigerate 1 hour, turning occasionally.

Remove fillets from marinade, reserving marinade. Coat a wire grilling basket with cooking spray. Place fillets in basket; grill 4 inches over medium coals 5 minutes on each side or until fish flakes easily when tested with a fork. Baste often with reserved marinade. Transfer to a serving platter, and garnish with olive slices. Yield: 6 servings (221 calories per serving).

PROTEIN 20.8 / FAT 14.2 / CARBOHYDRATE 1.6 / CHOLESTEROL 62 / IRON 1.1 / SODIUM 116 / CALCIUM 36

TUNA-SWISS BAKED PATTIES

2 (6-1/2-ounce) cans water-packed white tuna
1 tablespoon margarine
¼ cup minced onion
2 tablespoons all-purpose flour
¾ cup skim milk
1 tablespoon chopped fresh parsley
2 teaspoons Worcestershire sauce
1 teaspoon Dijon mustard
1 teaspoon lemon juice
¼ teaspoon pepper
1 egg yolk, beaten
½ cup (2 ounces) shredded Swiss cheese
½ cup soft whole wheat breadcrumbs
1 egg
1 tablespoon water
½ cup fine, dry breadcrumbs

Place tuna in a colander; rinse under cold tap water 1 minute. Set colander aside to let tuna drain 1 minute.

Melt margarine in a large skillet over low heat. Add onion and sauté until tender. Add flour, stirring until smooth. Cook 1 minute, stirring constantly. Gradually add milk, stirring constantly, until thickened and bubbly. Remove from heat. Stir in reserved tuna, parsley and next 7 ingredients. Cover and chill thoroughly.

Divide mixture into 6 equal portions; shape each portion into a patty. Combine egg and water; beat well. Dip patties in egg mixture; dredge in breadcrumbs to coat lightly. Place in a 12- x 8- x 2-inch baking dish. Bake at 350° for 20 minutes or until lightly browned. Yield: 6 servings (210 calories per serving).

PROTEIN 19.5 / FAT 7.5 / CARBOHYDRATE 15.2 / CHOLESTEROL 128 / IRON 1.7 / SODIUM 297 / CALCIUM 169

OYSTER-SPINACH CASSEROLE

Vegetable cooking spray
1 cup sliced fresh mushrooms
¼ cup minced green onions
1 clove garlic, minced
2 (10-ounce) packages frozen chopped spinach
1 tablespoon margarine
2 tablespoons all-purpose flour
1 cup skim milk
1 teaspoon lemon juice
¼ teaspoon ground nutmeg
Dash of white pepper
2 (12-ounce) containers Select oysters, drained and rinsed
¼ cup grated Parmesan cheese
2 tablespoons fine, dry breadcrumbs
Pimiento strips (optional)

Coat a medium skillet with cooking spray; place over medium heat until hot. Add mushrooms, green onions, and garlic; sauté until tender. Drain, and set aside.

Cook spinach according to package directions, omitting salt; drain spinach well, and set aside.

Melt margarine in a medium saucepan over low heat; add flour, stirring until smooth. Cook 1 minute, stirring constantly. Gradually add milk; cook over medium heat, stirring constantly with a wire whisk, until thickened and bubbly. Stir in lemon juice, nutmeg, and white pepper.

Remove sauce from heat, and add reserved sautéed vegetables and spinach, stirring well. Spoon mixture into a 10- x 6- x 2-inch baking dish coated with cooking spray. Arrange oysters over spinach mixture, and sprinkle with cheese and breadcrumbs.

Bake, uncovered, at 350° for 20 minutes or until oyster edges curl. Garnish with pimiento strips, if desired, and serve hot. Yield: 6 servings (169 calories per serving).

PROTEIN 15.9 / FAT 5.4 / CARBOHYDRATE 14.6 / CHOLESTEROL 60 / IRON 8.6 / SODIUM 275 / CALCIUM 315

LOBSTER IN ORANGE SAUCE

2 quarts water
4 (7- to 8-ounce) frozen lobster tails,
  thawed
Vegetable cooking spray
1 tablespoon plus 1½ teaspoons margarine
1 tablespoon grated fresh gingerroot
1 clove garlic, minced
1½ cups unsweetened orange juice
1 tablespoon plus 1½ teaspoons cornstarch
1 tablespoon plus 1½ teaspoons honey
1½ teaspoons grated orange rind
¼ teaspoon curry powder
4 cups hot cooked rice (cooked without
  salt or fat)
¼ cup chopped green onions

Bring water to a boil in a large Dutch oven. Add lobster tails; return to a boil, and cook 5 minutes. Remove tails from water with kitchen tongs; rinse under cold water, and drain.

Cut down outer edge of tail to remove shell, using a sharp knife. Remove meat; cut into chunks, and set aside. Discard shell.

Coat a large skillet with cooking spray; add margarine. Place over medium heat until margarine melts. Add gingerroot and garlic to skillet; sauté 1 minute. Combine orange juice, cornstarch, honey, orange rind, and curry powder; stir well. Add to skillet, stirring constantly, until thickened and bubbly. Stir in reserved lobster, and cook until lobster is thoroughly heated.

Serve over hot cooked rice, and sprinkle with chopped green onions. Yield: 8 servings (236 calories per serving).

PROTEIN 13.4 / FAT 3.5 / CARBOHYDRATE 36.4 / CHOLESTEROL 128 / IRON 1.3 / SODIUM 161 / CALCIUM 35

SHRIMP AND TORTELLINI IN ZESTY TOMATO SAUCE

1 (9-ounce) package fresh Parmesan-filled spinach
  tortellini
Vegetable cooking spray
½ cup chopped green pepper
½ cup chopped onion
2 cloves garlic, minced
2 tablespoons chopped fresh parsley
1 (14½-ounce) can whole tomatoes, undrained
1 (6-ounce) can tomato paste
2 tablespoons Burgundy or other dry red wine
1 teaspoon sugar
½ teaspoon dried whole oregano
½ teaspoon dried whole basil
⅛ teaspoon pepper
1 pound uncooked shrimp, peeled and deveined

Cook tortellini according to package directions, omitting salt. Drain and set aside.

Coat a small Dutch oven with cooking spray; place over medium heat until hot. Add green pepper, onion, garlic, and parsley. Sauté until tender, and set aside.

Place tomatoes in container of an electric blender; process until smooth. Add to reserved onion mixture, and stir in tomato paste, wine, sugar, oregano, basil, and pepper. Bring mixture to a boil; cover, reduce heat, and simmer 20 minutes.

Add shrimp to tomato sauce mixture; cook, uncovered, stirring constantly, 3 to 4 minutes or until shrimp turn pink. Stir in reserved tortellini; cook over low heat until thoroughly heated. Yield: 6 servings (230 calories per serving).

PROTEIN 19.3 / FAT 3.0 / CARBOHYDRATE 32.3 / CHOLESTEROL 102 / IRON 3.8 / SODIUM 211 / CALCIUM 173

NEW CHOLESTEROL COUNTS FOR SHELLFISH

Presently, all fish and shellfish can be included (in moderation) in low-cholesterol diets. But this was not always so. Shellfish were once categorized as a high-cholesterol food to be shunned by people watching their cholesterol levels.

Old tests that were designed to measure cholesterol really measured an entire group of chemicals called sterols. Cholesterol is just one of many substances that falls into this category. More modern tests, which single out cholesterol, show that shellfish contain far less cholesterol than was previously thought. In 1945, seven oysters were thought to have 325 milligrams of cholesterol; today we know they have only 55 milligrams. In fact, Oyster-Spinach Casserole (page 125) makes a delicious low-cholesterol entrée.

Salsa Shrimp and Zucchini boasts both zippy flavor and unique visual appeal.

SALSA SHRIMP AND ZUCCHINI

3 medium zucchini (about 1 pound)
Vegetable cooking spray
1 medium tomato, peeled, seeded, and chopped
½ cup chopped green pepper
½ cup chopped onion
2 cloves garlic, crushed
1 medium jalapeño pepper, seeded and minced
1 (8-ounce) can no-salt-added tomato sauce
1 tablespoon chopped fresh cilantro or 1 teaspoon
   dried whole cilantro
1 tablespoon lime juice
¼ teaspoon salt
1 pound uncooked medium shrimp, peeled and
   deveined

Cut zucchini in half crosswise, then lengthwise into ⅛-inch-thick strips. Coat a large skillet with cooking spray; place over medium heat until hot. Add zucchini, and sauté until crisp-tender. Transfer to a serving platter, and keep warm.

Add tomato, green pepper, onion, garlic, and jalapeño pepper to skillet. Sauté over medium heat until vegetables are tender. Stir in tomato sauce, cilantro, lime juice, and salt; bring mixture to a boil. Cover; reduce heat, and simmer 10 minutes.

Add shrimp to tomato sauce mixture; reduce heat to low and cook, stirring frequently, 4 minutes or until shrimp turn pink. Spoon shrimp mixture over zucchini, and serve immediately. Yield: 4 servings (132 calories per serving).

PROTEIN 17.8 / FAT 1.0 / CARBOHYDRATE 13.4 / CHOLESTEROL 128 / IRON 2.3 / SODIUM 284 / CALCIUM 82

HOT AND SPICY SEAFOOD KABOBS

¼ cup lemon juice
1 tablespoon vegetable oil
3 tablespoons minced onion
1 clove garlic, minced
1 teaspoon paprika
1 teaspoon dried whole thyme
½ teaspoon dried whole oregano
¼ teaspoon red pepper
¼ teaspoon freshly ground pepper
½ pound sea scallops
⅓ pound uncooked medium shrimp, peeled and
   deveined
1 medium-size green pepper, seeded and cut into
   1-inch pieces
1 medium-size sweet red pepper, seeded and cut
   into 1-inch pieces
12 pearl onions

Combine first 9 ingredients; stir well. Rinse scallops and shrimp with cold water, and pat dry. Place seafood in a zip top heavy-duty plastic bag. Pour marinade over seafood, and seal bag tightly. Place bag in a shallow pan, and refrigerate 2 hours, turning occasionally.

Cook green pepper, sweet red pepper, and onions in boiling water to cover 4 to 5 minutes or just until crisp-tender; drain.

Remove scallops and shrimp from marinade, reserving marinade. Alternate scallops, shrimp, green pepper, sweet red pepper, and onions on 4 skewers. Grill kabobs 4 inches over medium-hot coals 5 minutes on each side or until seafood is done, basting frequently with marinade. Yield: 4 servings (155 calories per serving).

PROTEIN 15.3 / FAT 4.5 / CARBOHYDRATE 15.1 / CHOLESTEROL 62 / IRON 3.0 / SODIUM 194 / CALCIUM 81

SCALLOP MEDLEY OREGANO

1 pound fresh bay scallops
Vegetable cooking spray
2 teaspoons olive oil
1 cup sliced fresh mushrooms
2 green onions with tops, sliced
1 tablespoon dried whole oregano or 3 tablespoons
   chopped fresh oregano
12 cherry tomatoes, cut in half
2 tablespoons grated Parmesan cheese

Rinse scallops with cold water, and pat dry. Coat a large skillet with cooking spray; add olive oil, and place over medium heat until hot. Add scallops, and sauté 3 minutes. Remove scallops from skillet; discard liquid.

Add mushrooms, green onions, and oregano to skillet. Sauté 2 to 3 minutes. Add reserved scallops and tomatoes. Sauté 1 minute or until thoroughly heated. Sprinkle with cheese, and serve immediately, using a slotted spoon. Yield: 4 servings (142 calories per serving).

PROTEIN 19.4 / FAT 4.2 / CARBOHYDRATE 7.7 / CHOLESTEROL 42 / IRON 2.9 / SODIUM 340 / CALCIUM 89

SURIMI—SEAFOOD INCOGNITO

Surimi may not be a word you're familiar with, but chances are you have eaten it—especially if you enjoy dining on shellfish. Made by an ancient Japanese process, surimi is evolving into a big-time American industry. White-fleshed fish (usually Pacific pollack) is made into a paste and then given various attributes of flavor, texture, and shape to enable it to appear in the form of at least 2,000 different food products. Surimi's most popular "shapes" at present imitate crab meat, shrimp, lobster, and scallops. These seafood analogues are a good source of low-fat, low-cholesterol protein. Unfortunately, they are not low in sodium. Three ounces of surimi scallops contain 900 milligrams of sodium compared to 146 milligrams in the same amount of real scallops.

FDA regulations require that surimi products be labeled appropriately to avoid confusion with the real thing, but the potential for misrepresentation increases when the package is removed altogether, as in restaurants and deli counters. A bit of healthy skepticism may keep you from paying lobster prices for white-fish fare.

The spinach-ricotta filling, fresh tomato sauce, and beautiful presentation make Spinach Lasagna Rolls (page 137) a meatless main dish that is pleasing to the palate and the eye.

For a fresh idea, try this Fruit Frittata with pockets of creamy Neufchâtel cheese.

FRUIT FRITTATA

6 eggs
4 egg whites
½ cup skim milk
1 teaspoon powdered sugar
1 cup fresh blueberries
1 (8-ounce) can unsweetened crushed pineapple, drained
½ cup (3 ounces) diced Neufchâtel cheese
Vegetable cooking spray
1 teaspoon unsalted margarine
2 tablespoons wheat germ
Additional fresh blueberries (optional)
Fresh mint sprig (optional)

Combine first 4 ingredients in a large bowl; beat well. Stir in 1 cup blueberries, pineapple, and Neufchâtel cheese.

Coat a 10-inch ovenproof skillet with cooking spray; add margarine, and place over medium-low heat until margarine melts. Pour egg mixture into skillet; cover and cook over medium-low heat 15 minutes or until eggs are set. Remove from heat, and sprinkle with 2 tablespoons wheat germ.

Broil 6 inches from heating element 1 minute or until lightly browned. Cut into wedges to serve. Garnish with additional blueberries and mint sprig, if desired. Yield: 6 servings (174 calories per serving).

PROTEIN 11.5 / FAT 10.0 / CARBOHYDRATE 10.1 / CHOLESTEROL 285 / IRON 1.4 / SODIUM 171 / CALCIUM 71

CRUSTLESS VEGETARIAN QUICHE

1 pound tofu
Vegetable cooking spray
2 medium zucchini, chopped
½ cup chopped onion
¼ pound fresh mushrooms, chopped
3 eggs
2 tablespoons grated Parmesan cheese
½ teaspoon dried whole chervil
½ teaspoon dried whole basil
¼ teaspoon salt
¼ teaspoon white pepper
½ cup (2 ounces) shredded part-skim mozzarella
  cheese
1 small tomato, cut into wedges (optional)
1 sprig fresh basil leaves (optional)

Wrap tofu with several layers of cheesecloth or paper towels; press lightly to remove excess liquid. Remove cheesecloth, and cut tofu into 1-inch cubes; set aside.

Coat a large skillet with cooking spray; place over medium heat until hot. Add zucchini, onion, and mushrooms, and sauté until tender. Drain well, and set aside.

Place reserved tofu, eggs, Parmesan cheese, chervil, basil, salt, and pepper in container of electric blender or food processor; process until smooth.

Combine reserved sautéed vegetables, tofu mixture, and mozzarella cheese; stir well. Pour into a 10-inch pieplate coated with cooking spray. Bake at 350° for 40 minutes or until set. Let quiche stand 10 minutes before serving. Garnish with tomato wedges and basil, if desired. Yield: 6 servings (141 calories per serving).

PROTEIN 13.0 / FAT 8.1 / CARBOHYDRATE 5.6 / CHOLESTEROL 144 / IRON 2.4 / SODIUM 215 / CALCIUM 208

NEW MEXICO OVEN OMELET

1 tablespoon cornstarch
¼ teaspoon salt
¼ teaspoon pepper
½ cup skim milk
4 eggs, separated
Vegetable cooking spray
¼ teaspoon cream of tartar
1 (8½-ounce) can whole kernel corn, drained
1 cup (4 ounces) shredded Colby cheese
1 (8-ounce) can no-salt-added tomato sauce
2 tablespoons drained chopped green chiles
4 drops hot sauce

Combine first 4 ingredients in a small saucepan; bring to a boil. Reduce heat, and cook, stirring frequently, until mixture thickens. Remove from heat, and set aside.

Beat egg yolks at high speed of an electric mixer 5 minutes or until thick and lemon colored. Add cornstarch mixture, beating well.

Place a 10-inch ovenproof skillet coated with cooking spray in a 350° oven for 4 minutes.

Beat egg whites (at room temperature) until foamy; add cream of tartar, and beat until stiff peaks form. Fold into yolk mixture, then gently fold in corn. Pour into heated skillet, and bake at 350° for 20 minutes or until puffed and browned. Sprinkle with cheese, and bake 1 minute or until cheese melts.

Combine tomato sauce, chiles, and hot sauce in a small saucepan. Cook over medium heat, stirring frequently, until thoroughly heated.

Cut omelet into 6 wedges and top with 2 tablespoons sauce; serve immediately. Yield: 6 servings (189 calories per serving).

PROTEIN 10.7 / FAT 10.2 / CARBOHYDRATE 14.6 / CHOLESTEROL 201 / IRON 1.1 / SODIUM 297 / CALCIUM 175

UPPER BODY AEROBICS—A TRUE JOGGING ALTERNATIVE?

"Jarming," jogging with the arms in a series of upper-body exercises, evolved as an alternative to jogging or cycling. Jarming enthusiasts claim less stress to the body and equal aerobic conditioning benefits. While jarming is an excellent aerobic activity for people with limited mobility, exercising the larger muscle mass of the leg burns more energy than exercising the smaller muscle mass of the arm. Ideally, a healthy workout would include *both* upper- and lower-body aerobics. However, certain people, namely those with heart problems, should be cautious about concentrated upper-body exercise; upper-body aerobics elevates blood pressure faster than lower-body exercise.

ORIENTAL SCRAMBLE

Vegetable cooking spray
1 teaspoon vegetable oil
1 medium carrot, scraped and
    diagonally sliced
½ cup chopped onion
½ cup fresh broccoli flowerets
⅓ cup diced sweet red pepper
¼ cup diced green pepper
1 teaspoon grated fresh gingerroot
6 eggs
5 egg whites
¼ cup skim milk
½ teaspoon reduced-sodium soy sauce
¼ teaspoon pepper
¼ cup frozen English peas,
    thawed and drained
¼ cup sliced water chestnuts

Coat a large nonstick skillet with cooking spray; add oil, and place over medium-high heat until hot. Add carrot and next 5 ingredients; sauté until vegetables are tender.

Combine eggs, egg whites, milk, soy sauce, and pepper. Stir well. Pour over vegetables. Add peas and water chestnuts. Cook over medium-low heat 5 minutes. As mixture begins to cook, gently lift edges with a spatula, and tilt pan to allow uncooked portions to flow underneath. Cover and cook 5 minutes or until egg mixture is set. Yield: 6 servings (130 calories per serving).

PROTEIN 10.3 / FAT 6.5 / CARBOHYDRATE 7.1 / CHOLESTEROL 274 / IRON 1.6 / SODIUM 147 / CALCIUM 57

BLACK BEAN-STUFFED TORTILLAS

1 (15-ounce) can black beans
Vegetable cooking spray
1 small onion, finely chopped
1 clove garlic, minced
1 teaspoon lime juice
¼ teaspoon dried whole oregano
¼ cup low-fat sour cream
2 teaspoons minced fresh cilantro
4 (6-inch) corn tortillas
1 (8-ounce) can no-salt-added tomato sauce
1 cup (4 ounces) shredded Monterey
    Jack cheese with jalapeño peppers

Place black beans in a colander, and rinse under cold tap water 1 minute; set colander aside to let beans drain 1 minute. Mash half of beans with a wooden spoon; set aside.

Coat a large skillet with cooking spray; place over medium heat until hot. Add onion and garlic; sauté until tender. Remove from heat, and stir in reserved beans, lime juice, and oregano; set aside. Combine sour cream and cilantro in a small bowl; stir well, and set aside.

Wrap tortillas in aluminum foil; bake at 325° for 10 minutes or until thoroughly heated. Spread 1 tablespoon reserved sour cream mixture on each tortilla. Spread reserved bean mixture evenly over tortillas, and fold in half.

Spread ⅓ cup tomato sauce in a 10- x 6- x 2-inch baking dish coated with cooking spray. Arrange folded tortillas over sauce. Top with remaining tomato sauce. Cover and bake at 350° for 15 minutes. Uncover, and sprinkle with shredded cheese. Bake an additional 5 minutes or until cheese melts. Yield: 4 servings (279 calories per serving).

PROTEIN 14.1 / FAT 11.8 / CARBOHYDRATE 30.4 / CHOLESTEROL 28 / IRON 3.0 / SODIUM 224 / CALCIUM 296

BEAN AND RICE-STUFFED PEPPERS

1 (16-ounce) can red kidney beans
6 medium-size green peppers
½ cup chopped onion
1 teaspoon chili powder
1 cup hot cooked parboiled rice (cooked
    without salt or fat)
1 (4-ounce) can chopped green chiles,
    drained
1 (14½-ounce) can no-salt-added stewed
    tomatoes, undrained
1½ cups (6 ounces) shredded extra sharp
    Cheddar cheese, divided

Place kidney beans in a colander, and rinse under cold tap water 1 minute; set colander aside to let beans drain 1 minute.

Cut off tops and remove seeds from peppers. Discard seeds and tops. Place peppers in boiling water; boil 5 minutes. Drain and set aside.

Combine reserved beans, onion, chili powder,

rice, chiles, tomatoes, and 1 cup cheese in a medium bowl; mix well. Stuff peppers with bean mixture; place in a 12- x 8- x 2-inch baking dish. Pour ½-inch hot water into dish. Bake at 350° for 25 minutes. Sprinkle remaining ½ cup cheese over peppers; bake an additional 5 minutes or until cheese melts. Serve immediately. Yield: 6 servings (251 calories per serving).

PROTEIN 13.0 / FAT 10.2 / CARBOHYDRATE 27.9 / CHOLESTEROL 30 / IRON 3.0 / SODIUM 325 / CALCIUM 257

MOCK MEATBALLS WITH HORSERADISH SAUCE

1¾ cups cooked kidney beans
1 cup cooked pinto beans
1 cup fine, dry breadcrumbs
2 eggs
¼ teaspoon garlic powder
½ teaspoon pepper
½ teaspoon dry mustard
⅔ cup finely chopped onion
¼ cup finely chopped fresh mushrooms
½ cup skim milk
Vegetable cooking spray
Horseradish Sauce

Place kidney beans and pinto beans in a colander, and rinse under cold tap water 1 minute; set colander aside to let beans drain 1 minute.

Combine reserved beans and next 5 ingredients in container of electric blender or food processor; process until smooth. Stir in onion, mushrooms, and milk. Shape mixture into 40 balls, using 1 tablespoon mixture for each ball. Arrange on rack of a roasting pan coated with cooking spray. Bake at 350° for 15 minutes or until meatballs are browned. Serve immediately with Horseradish Sauce. Yield: 8 servings. Serving size: 5 meatballs plus 2 tablespoons sauce (186 calories per serving).

Horseradish Sauce:

1 (8-ounce) carton plain low-fat yogurt
1 egg, beaten
1 teaspoon grated fresh horseradish
⅛ teaspoon pepper
1 tablespoon lemon juice

Combine first 4 ingredients in top of a double boiler; stir well, and place over simmering water. Cook 3 minutes or until thickened, stirring frequently. Remove from heat, and stir in lemon juice. Yield: 1 cup.

PROTEIN 11.2 / FAT 3.5 / CARBOHYDRATE 27.5 / CHOLESTEROL 105 / IRON 2.5 / SODIUM 148 / CALCIUM 128

STUFFED EGGPLANT DELIGHT

2 medium eggplant
Vegetable cooking spray
1 tablespoon olive or vegetable oil
1 medium onion, chopped
1 medium-size green pepper, chopped
1 medium zucchini, diced
1 cup sliced fresh mushrooms
1 clove garlic, minced
1 medium tomato, chopped
1 (8-ounce) can no-salt-added tomato sauce
1 cup cooked brown rice (cooked without salt or fat)
1 cup (4 ounces) shredded part-skim mozzarella cheese
2 tablespoons unsalted sunflower kernels, toasted
1 teaspoon Italian seasoning
¼ cup grated Parmesan cheese

Wash eggplant and cut in half lengthwise. Remove pulp, leaving a ¼-inch-thick shell. Chop pulp, reserving 2 cups. (Reserve remaining pulp for use in other recipes; sprinkle with a small amount of lemon juice to prevent darkening, if desired.) Set eggplant shells aside.

Coat a large skillet with cooking spray; add oil. Place over medium-high heat until hot. Add onion and next 4 ingredients; sauté 5 minutes or until tender. Add 2 cups chopped eggplant, tomato, and tomato sauce. Cook, uncovered, over medium heat 15 minutes, stirring occasionally. Remove from heat. Stir in rice, mozzarella cheese, sunflower kernels, and seasoning.

Place reserved eggplant shells in a 13- x 9- x 2-inch baking dish coated with cooking spray. Spoon mixture evenly into shells; sprinkle with Parmesan cheese. Bake at 350° for 15 minutes or until thoroughly heated. Serve immediately. Yield: 4 servings (268 calories per serving).

PROTEIN 13.7 / FAT 12.4 / CARBOHYDRATE 27.5 / CHOLESTEROL 20 / IRON 2.1 / SODIUM 247 / CALCIUM 307

MEATLESS MAIN DISH PEA SALAD

1 (16-ounce) package small frozen English peas,
 thawed and drained
1 small head cauliflower, broken into flowerets
4 green onions, thinly sliced
1 (8-ounce) can sliced water chestnuts, drained
1 sweet red pepper, cut into julienne strips
2½ ounces Swiss cheese, cut into thin strips
3 hard-cooked eggs, chopped
½ cup reduced-calorie mayonnaise
¼ cup reduced-calorie buttermilk salad dressing
1 tablespoon grated Parmesan cheese
1 teaspoon lemon juice
Lettuce leaves

Combine thawed peas, cauliflower flowerets, sliced green onions, water chestnuts, sweet red pepper strips, Swiss cheese, and eggs in a large bowl, tossing gently. Combine mayonnaise, salad dressing, Parmesan cheese, and lemon juice in a small bowl; stir until well blended. Pour mayonnaise mixture over vegetable mixture, tossing gently. Cover salad and refrigerate 8 hours or overnight. To serve, spoon salad onto lettuce leaves. Yield: 6 servings (263 calories per serving).

PROTEIN 12.7 / FAT 15.0 / CARBOHYDRATE 23.5 / CHOLESTEROL 158 /
IRON 2.7 / SODIUM 413 / CALCIUM 183

MUSHROOM CAKES WITH FONTINA CHEESE SAUCE

1¼ cups low-fat cottage cheese
3 eggs, beaten
½ cup wheat germ, toasted
⅓ cup whole wheat breadcrumbs
3 tablespoons finely chopped mushrooms
1 tablespoon plus 1½ teaspoons finely chopped
 green onions
Fontina Cheese Sauce
Fresh parsley sprigs

Combine first 4 ingredients in container of an electric blender; process until smooth. Stir in mushrooms and green onions.

Place a large nonstick skillet over medium heat until hot. For each cake, spoon ⅓ cup batter onto hot skillet. Cook over medium heat, turning cakes when tops are bubbly and edges are browned. Repeat procedure until all batter is used. Serve with Fontina Cheese Sauce. Garnish with fresh parsley, and serve immediately.

Yield: 4 servings. Serving size: 2 cakes and 1 tablespoon sauce (238 calories per serving).

Fontina Cheese Sauce:

1 tablespoon unsalted margarine
1 tablespoon all-purpose flour
⅛ teaspoon white pepper
½ cup skim milk
2 tablespoons (½ ounce) shredded fontina cheese

Melt margarine in a heavy saucepan over low heat; add flour and white pepper. Cook 1 minute, stirring constantly. Gradually add milk, stirring with a wire whisk until smooth. Cook over medium heat until thickened and bubbly. Stir in cheese. Cook 1 minute or until cheese melts. Yield: ½ cup.

PROTEIN 21.7 / FAT 11.5 / CARBOHYDRATE 14.7 / CHOLESTEROL 216 /
IRON 2.4 / SODIUM 390 / CALCIUM 143

TOFU—A VERSATILE, ECONOMICAL MEAT SUBSTITUTE

As a meat substitute, tofu (soybean curd) bears consideration. Tofu has about one-third as much fat as meat (most is polyunsaturated), no cholesterol, and only a trace of sodium. Four ounces of tofu contain about 200 milligrams of calcium and 2.17 milligrams of iron. Combining it with pasta or cheese makes a dish with complete vegetable protein. And tofu is blessedly inexpensive.

Tofu acquires the flavor of other foods, so add it to almost any kind of dish. Cut it up for salads; cube it for stir-fry dishes and soups; or crumble it for entrées such as lasagna or Tofu Chalupas.

Tofu will keep its freshness in the refrigerator for about a week past its purchase date. Cover tofu with water in an airtight container, and change the water every day or two.

The mild flavor of tofu is enhanced by the spicy, Mexican flavors of jalapeño pepper, tomato, avocado, and cilantro in Tofu Chalupas—just one of the many ways to incorporate tofu (a protein-, iron-, and calcium-rich food) into your meal plans.

TOFU CHALUPAS

Vegetable cooking spray
⅓ cup finely chopped onion
1 (10½-ounce) package tofu, drained and crumbled
2 cloves garlic, crushed
2 tomatoes, seeded and chopped
1 jalapeño pepper, seeded and chopped
¼ teaspoon chili powder
¼ teaspoon ground cumin
½ teaspoon dried whole oregano
2 tablespoons chopped fresh cilantro
4 (6-inch) corn tortillas
½ cup shredded iceberg lettuce
½ medium avocado, peeled and chopped
¼ cup (1 ounce) shredded Cheddar cheese

Coat a large skillet with cooking spray; place over medium heat until hot. Add onion, and sauté until tender. Add tofu and garlic, and cook for 3 minutes, stirring constantly. Stir in tomatoes, pepper, chili powder, cumin, oregano, and cilantro, and continue to cook over medium heat, stirring frequently, until thoroughly heated.

Wrap tortillas in aluminum foil, and bake at 350° for 10 minutes or until thoroughly heated. Top each tortilla with one-fourth of lettuce, tofu mixture, avocado, and cheese. Serve immediately. Yield: 4 servings (216 calories per serving).

PROTEIN 11.7 / FAT 9.9 / CARBOHYDRATE 23.9 / CHOLESTEROL 7 / IRON 4.3 / SODIUM 120 / CALCIUM 221

ANGEL HAIR PATTIES

1 cup cooked angel hair pasta, chopped
(cooked without salt)
2 eggs, beaten
¼ cup (1 ounce) finely shredded Cheddar cheese
¼ cup finely shredded zucchini
¼ cup finely shredded carrots
¼ cup minced mushrooms
1 tablespoon skim milk
¼ cup all-purpose flour
⅛ teaspoon salt
¼ teaspoon onion powder
Vegetable cooking spray
1 teaspoon vegetable oil

Combine pasta, beaten eggs, cheese, zucchini, carrot, mushrooms, and skim milk in a medium bowl, stirring well. Add flour, salt, and onion powder to pasta mixture, stirring well. Divide mixture into 4 equal portions; shape each portion into a pattie. Refrigerate patties at least 2 hours.

Coat a medium skillet with cooking spray. Add oil; place over medium heat until hot. Add patties, and cook 3 minutes on each side or until golden brown. Drain on paper towels. Serve immediately. Yield: 2 servings (329 calories per serving).

PROTEIN 15.5 / FAT 13.1 / CARBOHYDRATE 36.2 / CHOLESTEROL 289 / IRON 2.6 / SODIUM 314 / CALCIUM 158

WALKERS WITH GOOD SOLES

Striding, trekking, hiking, racewalking—call it what you will, just as long as you wear a comfortable walking shoe when you do it. Walking shoes keep you on your feet longer with bigger payoffs. Even though walkers land with half the impact of a runner, they need even more cushioning in their shoes. A good shoe shouldn't only absorb the energy of the impact; it should return some of that energy back to the stride. It's the difference between jumping in sand or on a trampoline. Proper cushioning can propel you forward for the next stride.

Look for a sole at least ½-inch thick under the heel. Push your thumb into the bottom of the shoe; you should just be able to make a dent. Try them on; they should give you a little "push-off" with every step and offer good side-to-side support.

VEGETABLE-CHEESE CANNELLONI

1 (16-ounce) can no-salt-added whole tomatoes, undrained
1 (8-ounce) can no-salt-added tomato sauce
2 tablespoons tomato paste
1 clove garlic, crushed
¼ cup finely chopped green pepper
¼ cup finely chopped shallot
½ teaspoon dried whole basil
Vegetable cooking spray
12 cannelloni shells
1 cup shredded carrots
1 cup shredded zucchini
½ cup diced fresh mushrooms
2 tablespoons chopped fresh parsley
2 cups low-fat cottage cheese
1 egg, beaten
2 tablespoons grated Parmesan cheese
½ teaspoon dried whole basil
⅛ teaspoon ground nutmeg
⅛ teaspoon white pepper

Place whole tomatoes in container of electric blender; process until smooth. Pour into a medium saucepan. Stir in tomato sauce, tomato paste, garlic, green pepper, shallot, and basil. Bring to a boil; reduce heat, and simmer, uncovered, 20 minutes. Spread ½ cup tomato sauce mixture in a 13- x 9- x 2-inch baking dish lightly coated with cooking spray; set aside. Reserve remaining tomato sauce mixture.

Cook cannelloni shells according to package directions, omitting salt; drain, and set aside.

Coat a large skillet with cooking spray; place over medium-high heat until hot. Add carrots, zucchini, mushrooms, and parsley; sauté 2 to 3 minutes or until crisp-tender. Drain well on paper towels. Combine sautéed vegetables, cottage cheese, egg, Parmesan cheese, basil, nutmeg, and white pepper in a large mixing bowl; stir well.

Stuff cannelloni shells with vegetable-cheese mixture and place in baking dish. Spoon reserved tomato sauce mixture evenly over stuffed shells. Cover and bake at 375° for 20 minutes. Serve immediately. Yield: 6 servings (246 calories per serving).

PROTEIN 17.6 / FAT 3.4 / CARBOHYDRATE 36.2 / CHOLESTEROL 53 / IRON 2.1 / SODIUM 380 / CALCIUM 129

FETTUCCINE WITH HOT MEXI-BEAN SAUCE

1 (16-ounce) can pinto beans
Vegetable cooking spray
1 medium onion, chopped
1 clove garlic, minced
1 (14½-ounce) can no-salt-added stewed tomatoes, undrained
1 (10-ounce) can tomatoes, undrained and chopped
2 tablespoons chopped green chiles
1 tablespoon finely chopped fresh cilantro
1 teaspoon chili powder
½ teaspoon sugar
¼ teaspoon dried whole oregano, crushed
4 cups hot cooked fettuccine (cooked without salt)

Place pinto beans in a colander, and rinse under cold tap water 1 minute; set colander aside to let beans drain 1 minute.

Coat a large skillet with cooking spray; place over medium heat until hot. Add onion and garlic, and sauté until tender. Stir in tomatoes, green chiles, cilantro, chili powder, sugar, and oregano. Cover and bring to a boil; reduce heat, and simmer 15 minutes, stirring occasionally. Mash reserved pinto beans slightly, and stir into tomato mixture. Serve over hot cooked fettuccine. Yield: 4 servings (317 calories per serving).

PROTEIN 12.0 / FAT 1.6 / CARBOHYDRATE 64.2 / CHOLESTEROL 0 / IRON 3.6 / SODIUM 380 / CALCIUM 105

SPINACH LASAGNA ROLLS

8 lasagna noodles
2 (10-ounce) packages frozen chopped spinach, thawed
½ cup chopped onion
½ cup chopped fresh mushrooms
2 cloves garlic, minced
3 tablespoons dry, white vermouth
½ cup grated Parmesan cheese
½ cup (2 ounces) shredded part-skim mozzarella cheese
½ cup part-skim ricotta cheese
2 eggs, beaten
1 teaspoon dried whole basil
⅛ teaspoon pepper
Vegetable cooking spray
Chunky Tomato Sauce
Fresh basil leaves (optional)

Cook noodles according to package directions, omitting salt. Drain and set aside. Drain thawed spinach; squeeze out excess moisture between paper towels, and set aside.

Combine onion, mushrooms, garlic, and vermouth in a large skillet. Cook over medium heat until vegetables are tender. Transfer mixture to a large bowl. Add drained spinach, Parmesan cheese, and next 5 ingredients; stir well.

Spread ½ cup spinach mixture on each reserved lasagna noodle. Roll up jellyroll fashion, beginning at narrow end. Arrange rolls, seam side down, in a 12- x 8- x 2-inch baking dish coated with cooking spray. Cover and bake at 350° for 30 minutes. Slice each roll into thirds, and serve with 2 tablespoons Chunky Tomato Sauce. Garnish with fresh basil leaves, if desired. Yield: 8 servings (222 calories per serving).

Chunky Tomato Sauce:

Vegetable cooking spray
¼ cup finely chopped sweet red pepper
¼ cup shredded carrots
1 clove garlic, minced
½ teaspoon dried whole basil
¼ teaspoon dried marjoram
⅛ teaspoon freshly ground pepper
⅔ cup no-salt-added tomato sauce
2 tablespoons water

Coat a medium skillet with cooking spray. Place over medium-high heat until hot. Add sweet red pepper and next 5 ingredients. Sauté until vegetables are tender. Stir in tomato sauce and water. Bring to a boil. Cover; reduce heat, and simmer 5 minutes or until mixture is thickened. Yield: 1 cup.

PROTEIN 13.2 / FAT 5.9 / CARBOHYDRATE 29.6 / CHOLESTEROL 81 / IRON 2.9 / SODIUM 222 / CALCIUM 259

THREE CHEESE CASSEROLE

1 cup low-fat cottage cheese
½ (8-ounce) package Neufchâtel cheese, softened
2 eggs
¼ cup skim milk
1 cup (4 ounces) shredded extra-sharp Cheddar cheese
½ cup chopped green onions
⅛ teaspoon garlic powder
¼ teaspoon pepper
1 (5-ounce) package medium egg noodles (cooked without salt)
Vegetable cooking spray

Combine cottage cheese, Neufchâtel cheese, eggs, and milk in container of an electric blender; process until smooth. Combine cheese mixture with Cheddar cheese, onions, garlic powder, and pepper in a medium mixing bowl; mix well. Add cooked noodles; toss gently. Spoon mixture into a 10- x 6- x 2-inch baking dish coated with cooking spray. Bake at 350° for 20 minutes. Serve hot. Yield: 6 servings (284 calories per serving).

PROTEIN 17.3 / FAT 14.4 / CARBOHYDRATE 20.6 / CHOLESTEROL 151 / IRON 1.4 / SODIUM 375 / CALCIUM 210

POLENTA WITH SPANISH VEGETABLES

5 cups water, divided
1½ cups yellow cornmeal
⅛ teaspoon salt
¼ teaspoon red pepper
1 cup (4 ounces) shredded provolone cheese
Vegetable cooking spray
1 (9-ounce) package frozen artichoke hearts, thawed and quartered
1 small green pepper, seeded and thinly sliced
1 small sweet red pepper, seeded and thinly sliced
2 ounces fresh mushrooms, sliced
¼ cup chopped onion
1 clove garlic, minced
1 small tomato, chopped
1 teaspoon minced fresh cilantro
¼ teaspoon dried whole thyme
⅛ teaspoon chili powder
⅛ teaspoon ground cumin

Bring 4 cups water to a boil in a large Dutch oven. Combine cornmeal, remaining water, salt, and red pepper, stirring well. Add to boiling water, stirring with a wire whisk until well blended. Cook over medium heat, stirring frequently, 5 minutes or until mixture thickens. Stir in cheese. Remove from heat, and keep warm.

Coat a large skillet with cooking spray; place over medium heat until hot. Add artichokes, green pepper, sweet red pepper, mushrooms, onion, and garlic; sauté until vegetables are crisp-tender. Stir in tomato, cilantro, thyme, chili powder, and cumin; cook, stirring frequently, until thoroughly heated.

To serve, spoon 1 cup polenta mixture into 4 serving bowls; top each with ½ cup sautéed vegetables, and serve immediately. Yield: 4 servings (317 calories per serving).

PROTEIN 14.1 / FAT 8.8 / CARBOHYDRATE 46.2 / CHOLESTEROL 20 / IRON 2.9 / SODIUM 358 / CALCIUM 242

The tender little circles of pork in Pork Medallions with Sweet Peppers (page 156) are worth their weight in gold!

Meats

CHILI-STYLE ROAST

1 (4-pound) lean boneless round roast
Vegetable cooking spray
½ teaspoon salt
⅛ teaspoon red pepper
1 (8-ounce) can no-salt-added tomato
    sauce
½ cup water
¾ cup chopped onion
½ cup chopped green onions
2 cloves garlic, minced
2 tablespoons chili powder
1 teaspoon dried whole oregano

Trim excess fat from roast. Coat a Dutch oven with cooking spray; place over medium-high heat until hot. Add roast, and cook until browned on all sides. Sprinkle roast with salt and red pepper.

Combine tomato sauce and remaining ingredients in a small bowl; pour over roast. Cover; reduce heat, and simmer 2 to 2½ hours or until roast is tender. Yield: 12 servings (197 calories per serving).

PROTEIN 30.5 / FAT 6.1 / CARBOHYDRATE 3.6 / CHOLESTEROL 79 / IRON 3.0 / SODIUM 173 / CALCIUM 17

HERBED POT ROAST

1 (4½-pound) lean boneless rump roast
½ cup Burgundy or other dry red wine
½ cup tomato sauce
¼ cup vinegar
2 shallots, minced
1 tablespoon spicy hot mustard
1 teaspoon dried whole thyme
¼ teaspoon dried whole oregano
¼ teaspoon red pepper
1 bay leaf

Trim excess fat from roast. Place roast in a large shallow dish. Combine wine and next 7 ingredients, stirring with a wire whisk. Pour over roast. Add bay leaf. Cover and refrigerate 8 hours or overnight, turning roast occasionally.

Place roast, bay leaf, and marinade in a Dutch oven. Cover and bake at 350° for 2½ hours or until meat is tender.

Remove roast to a serving platter. Remove and discard bay leaf from marinade; skim off fat. Serve marinade with roast. Yield: 12 servings (189 calories per serving).

PROTEIN 30.2 / FAT 6.0 / CARBOHYDRATE 1.8 / CHOLESTEROL 79 / IRON 3.0 / SODIUM 132 / CALCIUM 12

POT ROAST WITH DILLED CARROT GRAVY

1 (4-pound) lean boneless rump roast
½ teaspoon pepper
Vegetable cooking spray
1 small onion, sliced
1 teaspoon beef-flavored bouillon granules
1 cup hot water
2 medium carrots, scraped and sliced
¼ cup low-fat sour cream
¼ teaspoon dried whole dillweed

Trim excess fat from roast. Rub pepper over entire surface of meat. Coat a Dutch oven with cooking spray; place over medium-high heat until hot. Add roast; cook until browned on all sides. Place onion slices on roast. Combine bouillon granules and water; pour over roast. Cover and bake at 350° for 2 hours. Add carrots; cover and bake an additional 30 minutes.

Transfer roast to a warm serving platter. Skim off fat from liquid in Dutch oven. Place carrots and ¼ cup of cooking liquid in container of electric blender. Process until smooth. Add sour cream and dillweed; process until combined. Serve Dilled Carrot Gravy with roast. Yield: 10 servings (191 calories per serving).

PROTEIN 29.2 / FAT 6.4 / CARBOHYDRATE 2.3 / CHOLESTEROL 78 / IRON 2.8 / SODIUM 108 / CALCIUM 19

Honey-Lime Marinated Flank Steak is grilled to perfection and garnished with fresh lime wedges.

HONEY-LIME MARINATED FLANK STEAK

1 (1½-pound) beef flank steak
⅓ cup lime juice
3 tablespoons honey
1 tablespoon catsup
1 clove garlic, minced
1 teaspoon Worcestershire sauce
½ teaspoon grated lime rind
Vegetable cooking spray
Lime wedges (optional)

Trim excess fat from steak, and place in a large shallow dish. Combine lime juice and next 5 ingredients, stirring well. Pour over steak. Cover and refrigerate 24 hours, turning steak occasionally.

Remove steak from marinade, reserving marinade. Coat grill with cooking spray. Grill steak 5 to 6 inches over hot coals 6 to 7 minutes on each side or until desired degree of doneness, basting frequently with reserved marinade. Cut diagonally across grain into thin slices to serve. Garnish with lime wedges, if desired. Yield: 6 servings (247 calories per serving).

PROTEIN 21.8 / FAT 12.8 / CARBOHYDRATE 11.0 / CHOLESTEROL 60 / IRON 2.2 / SODIUM 109 / CALCIUM 9

SAVORY SIRLOIN

1 (1-pound) lean boneless beef sirloin steak
¼ teaspoon dried whole rosemary, crushed
¼ teaspoon freshly ground pepper
Vegetable cooking spray
1 tablespoon margarine
1 tablespoon plain low-fat yogurt
1 tablespoon Dijon mustard
1 tablespoon Worcestershire sauce
1 tablespoon chopped fresh parsley

Trim excess fat from steak. Combine rosemary and pepper; sprinkle over steak. Coat a large skillet with cooking spray; add margarine, and place over medium heat until margarine melts. Add steak, and cook 6 minutes on each side or until desired degree of doneness. Remove steak from skillet; transfer to a serving platter, and keep warm.

Combine yogurt, mustard, and Worcestershire sauce in a small saucepan. Cook over low heat, stirring constantly, until thoroughly heated. (Do not boil.) Spoon sauce over warm steak. Sprinkle with parsley. Yield: 4 servings (190 calories per serving).

PROTEIN 24.4 / FAT 8.9 / CARBOHYDRATE 1.4 / CHOLESTEROL 69 / IRON 3.2 / SODIUM 250 / CALCIUM 22

LEMON-PEPPER STEAK CUTLETS

1 pound lean round steak
1 egg, beaten
1 teaspoon grated lemon rind
2 tablespoons fresh lemon juice
1 tablespoon water
½ cup soft whole wheat breadcrumbs
2 tablespoons all-purpose flour
½ teaspoon pepper
¼ teaspoon salt
Vegetable cooking spray

Trim excess fat from steak; place steak between 2 sheets of wax paper, and pound to ¼-inch thickness, using a meat mallet or rolling pin. Cut into serving-size pieces.

Combine egg, lemon rind, juice, and water in a small bowl, stirring well. Combine breadcrumbs, flour, pepper, and salt in a medium bowl, and mix well. Dip steak pieces in egg mixture, then dredge in breadcrumb mixture.

Coat a large non-stick skillet with cooking spray; place over medium-high heat until hot. Cook steaks 2½ minutes on each side or until desired degree of doneness. Yield: 4 servings (233 calories per serving).

PROTEIN 27.6 / FAT 8.6 / CARBOHYDRATE 10.3 / CHOLESTEROL 139 / IRON 3.0 / SODIUM 284 / CALCIUM 28

PICCADILLO ROUND STEAK

1½ pounds lean round steak
Vegetable cooking spray
1 medium onion, chopped
1 medium-size green pepper, seeded and chopped
1 clove garlic, minced
1 (15-ounce) can no-salt-added tomato sauce
1 tablespoon Worcestershire sauce
¼ teaspoon dried whole oregano
¼ teaspoon crushed red pepper
¼ teaspoon ground cinnamon
⅓ cup raisins
3 tablespoons sliced pimiento-stuffed olives

Trim excess fat from steak; cut steak into 1-inch pieces. Coat a large skillet with cooking spray; place over medium heat until hot. Add steak, and cook until browned on all sides. Remove steak, and drain on paper towels; wipe skillet dry with a paper towel.

Add onion, green pepper, and garlic to skillet; sauté until vegetables are tender. Return steak to skillet. Combine tomato sauce and next 4 ingredients; pour over steak. Cover; reduce heat, and simmer 1½ hours. Add raisins and sliced olives; simmer an additional 30 minutes or until steak is tender. Yield: 6 servings (228 calories per serving).

PROTEIN 25.6 / FAT 7.3 / CARBOHYDRATE 14.7 / CHOLESTEROL 70 / IRON 2.9 / SODIUM 155 / CALCIUM 21

SAUCY BEEF AND NOODLES

1 pound lean round steak (½-inch thick)
Vegetable cooking spray
1 teaspoon vegetable oil
2 cups sliced fresh mushrooms
½ cup chopped celery
½ cup chopped green onions
1 clove garlic, minced
2 (8-ounce) cans no-salt-added tomato sauce
⅓ cup Chablis or other dry white wine
1 tablespoon lemon juice
1 bay leaf
½ teaspoon dried whole oregano
¼ teaspoon dried whole rosemary, crushed
⅛ teaspoon pepper
3 cups hot cooked medium egg noodles (cooked without salt)

Trim excess fat from steak; cut meat into 1-inch pieces. Set aside.

Coat a Dutch oven with cooking spray; add oil, and place over medium-high heat until hot. Add reserved meat, and cook until browned. Remove meat, and drain on paper towels.

Drain Dutch oven, and wipe dry with a paper towel. Coat Dutch oven with cooking spray. Add mushrooms, celery, green onions, and garlic to Dutch oven. Sauté until vegetables are tender. Add reserved meat, tomato sauce and next 6 ingredients; stir well. Bring to a boil. Cover; reduce heat, and simmer 1 hour and 45 minutes or until meat is tender. Remove and discard bay leaf. Serve over hot cooked noodles. Yield: 6 servings (158 calories per serving plus 100 calories per ½ cup cooked noodles).

PROTEIN 20.9 / FAT 6.7 / CARBOHYDRATE 27.9 / CHOLESTEROL 71 / IRON 2.8 / SODIUM 66 / CALCIUM 27

BEEF AND SPINACH STIR-FRY

1 pound beef flank steak
½ cup boiling water
½ teaspoon beef-flavored bouillon granules
2 tablespoons reduced-sodium soy sauce
1 teaspoon sugar
1 teaspoon grated fresh gingerroot
¼ teaspoon crushed red pepper
Vegetable cooking spray
2 medium carrots, scraped and shredded
3 green onions with tops, cut into 1-inch pieces
½ pound fresh spinach leaves, coarsely chopped
3 cups hot cooked parboiled rice (cooked without salt or fat)

Trim excess fat from steak; partially freeze steak. Slice steak across grain into thin strips, and set aside.

Combine water and bouillon granules, stirring well. Add soy sauce, sugar, gingerroot, and red pepper. Stir well, and set aside.

Coat a wok with cooking spray. Allow to heat at medium-high (325°) for 2 minutes. Add carrots and green onions; stir-fry 2 minutes. Remove from wok, and set aside. Add reserved steak strips to wok; stir-fry 4 minutes or until desired degree of doneness. Add reserved soy sauce mixture. Bring to a boil. Cover; reduce heat, and simmer 4 minutes.

Return reserved vegetables and spinach to wok. Stir-fry 1 minute or until spinach wilts. Serve over hot cooked rice. Yield: 6 servings (157 calories per serving plus 93 calories per ½ cup cooked rice).

PROTEIN 18.6 / FAT 7.4 / CARBOHYDRATE 26.1 / CHOLESTEROL 38 / IRON 3.5 / SODIUM 329 / CALCIUM 69

AN ADEQUATE DAILY WATER SUPPLY—A NUTRITIONAL MUST

Water is an essential nutrient. We can live weeks without food, but only a few days without water. All chemical reactions in the body require water, and every cell of the body contains water. If a person weighs 150 pounds, 90 of those pounds are water.

In addition to water consumed from foods such as meats, fruits, and vegetables, we need 2 to 2½ quarts (8 to 10 glasses) of fluid daily. Other beverages count toward fulfilling total fluid requirements, but don't include coffee. Caffeine acts as a diuretic and promotes water loss.

ORIENTAL BEEF WITH PINEAPPLE

1 medium-size fresh pineapple
1 (1½-pound) lean round steak (about ½-inch thick)
¼ cup dry sherry
3 tablespoons reduced-sodium soy sauce
1 tablespoon cornstarch
1 tablespoon firmly packed brown sugar
¼ teaspoon crushed red pepper
Vegetable cooking spray
1 tablespoon vegetable oil
1 large sweet red pepper, seeded and cut into thin strips
4 green onions with tops, cut into 1-inch pieces
1 tablespoon minced fresh gingerroot

Peel and trim eyes from pineapple; remove core. Cut pineapple into 1-inch cubes. Set aside.

Trim excess fat from steak; partially freeze steak. Slice diagonally across the grain into 3- x ¼-inch strips. Combine sherry and next 4 ingredients; stir well. Add beef strips, tossing gently to coat. Cover, and let stand 20 minutes. Drain beef, reserving marinade.

Coat a wok with cooking spray; add oil. Heat at medium-high (325°) for 2 minutes. Add beef; stir-fry 3 minutes or until beef is no longer pink. Remove from wok, and set aside.

Add sweet red pepper, onions, and gingerroot to wok; stir-fry 2 minutes. Add beef, marinade, and reserved pineapple. Stir-fry 1 minute or until sauce thickens. Yield: 6 servings (268 calories per serving).

PROTEIN 26.3 / FAT 8.4 / CARBOHYDRATE 18.8 / CHOLESTEROL 66 / IRON 3.2 / SODIUM 359 / CALCIUM 21

STROGANOFF KABOBS

2 pounds lean boneless beef sirloin steak
1 (8-ounce) carton plain low-fat yogurt
2 tablespoons lemon juice
2 tablespoons Worcestershire sauce
2 cloves garlic, minced
¼ teaspoon celery salt
¼ teaspoon freshly ground pepper
16 large fresh mushrooms
2 medium onions, cut into 1-inch pieces
Vegetable cooking spray

Trim excess fat from steak, and cut steak into 1-inch cubes. Place cubes in a 12- x 8- x 2-inch baking dish. Combine yogurt and next 5 ingredients, stirring well; pour over steak. Cover and refrigerate 8 hours or overnight.

Remove steak cubes from marinade, reserving marinade. Alternate steak cubes, mushrooms, and onion pieces on 8 skewers. Brush kabobs with reserved marinade. Coat grill with cooking spray. Grill kabobs 4 to 5 inches over medium coals 12 to 14 minutes or until desired degree of doneness. Turn and baste kabobs frequently with reserved marinade. Yield: 8 servings (221 calories per serving).

PROTEIN 28.6 / FAT 8.1 / CARBOHYDRATE 7.5 / CHOLESTEROL 77 / IRON 3.5 / SODIUM 180 / CALCIUM 78

ITALIAN BEEF ROLLS

Vegetable cooking spray
½ cup shredded zucchini
¼ cup chopped onion
¼ cup chopped sweet red pepper
½ teaspoon dried Italian seasoning
6 beef cube steaks (about 1½ pounds)
1 (8-ounce) can no-salt-added tomato sauce
2 tablespoons Burgundy or other dry red wine
2 tablespoons chopped fresh parsley
½ teaspoon dried whole oregano
¼ teaspoon dried whole basil
¼ teaspoon garlic powder
1 cup (4 ounces) shredded part-skim mozzarella cheese

Coat a small skillet with cooking spray; place over medium heat until hot. Add zucchini, onion, and pepper, and sauté 2 to 3 minutes or until tender. Combine sautéed vegetables and Italian seasoning, stirring well.

Place 1 tablespoon vegetable mixture on each cube steak, spreading to within ½-inch of edge. Roll up each steak jellyroll fashion; secure with a wooden pick.

Wipe pan drippings from skillet with a paper towel; coat skillet with cooking spray. Place skillet over medium heat until hot. Add steak rolls; cook until browned on all sides.

Combine tomato sauce and next 5 ingredients; pour over steak rolls. Bring mixture to a boil; reduce heat; cover and simmer 1 hour or until steak is tender. Sprinkle with cheese; continue cooking just until cheese melts. Yield: 6 servings (218 calories per serving).

PROTEIN 30.0 / FAT 7.9 / CARBOHYDRATE 5.3 / CHOLESTEROL 72 / IRON 2.1 / SODIUM 158 / CALCIUM 139

ANEMIA AND THE ATHLETE

Nutrition plays a vital role in athletic performance. Studies show that serious athletes have an increased need for iron in their diets. Many lose iron due to sweat, blood loss from bowels, and blood-cell destruction associated with sustained impact (in areas like the feet in long-distance runners). An iron-poor diet can only compound the athlete's problem. This is especially true for endurance athletes, who have a tendency to develop low red blood cell counts and anemia.

Although anemia may cause fatigue, irritability, or poor performance, some people with mild anemia have no symptoms. For this reason, sports programs should provide nutritional counseling and periodic blood tests for anemia. Treatment is based on the cause of the anemia and may include iron supplements and a modified training routine. Athletes should not, however, take iron supplements without a physician's advice. Too much iron can deposit in the liver and cause damage.

BEEF AND CHILES CASSEROLE

Vegetable cooking spray
1 pound ground chuck
½ cup chopped green onions
1 (8-ounce) can no-salt-added tomato sauce
1½ teaspoons chili powder
⅛ teaspoon garlic powder
3 cups hot cooked egg noodles (cooked without salt)
1 cup low-fat cottage cheese
½ cup plain low-fat yogurt
1 (4-ounce) can chopped green chiles, drained
¾ cup (3 ounces) shredded Monterey Jack cheese

Coat a large skillet with cooking spray. Add meat and onions; cook until browned, stirring to crumble meat. Drain well; pat with paper towels to remove excess grease. Wipe pan drippings from skillet. Return meat to skillet; stir in tomato sauce, chili powder, and garlic powder. Cover and simmer 20 minutes, stirring occasionally. Set mixture aside.

Spoon cooked egg noodles in bottom of a 12- x 8- x 2-inch baking dish coated with cooking spray. Combine cottage cheese, yogurt, and chiles; spoon mixture over noodles. Spread reserved beef mixture over cottage cheese mixture. Cover and bake at 350° for 20 minutes. Remove from oven, and sprinkle with Monterey Jack cheese. Bake, uncovered, an additional 5 minutes or until cheese melts. Yield: 8 servings (271 calories per serving).

PROTEIN 21.3 / FAT 11.8 / CARBOHYDRATE 19.3 / CHOLESTEROL 65 / IRON 1.8 / SODIUM 222 / CALCIUM 138

BURGERS STUFFED WITH THREE CHEESES

1½ pounds ground chuck
2 tablespoons minced onion
¼ teaspoon salt
¼ teaspoon dried whole thyme
⅛ teaspoon pepper
1 ounce crumbled blue cheese
1 ounce Neufchâtel cheese, softened
¼ cup (1 ounce) shredded Swiss cheese
Vegetable cooking spray

Combine ground chuck, onion, salt, thyme, and pepper in a medium bowl; stir well. Divide mixture into 12 thin patties. Combine cheeses, stirring well. Top 6 patties each with about 1 tablespoon cheese mixture. Top with remaining 6 patties, and seal edges.

Coat rack of a broiler pan with cooking spray. Place patties on rack in broiler pan. Broil patties 6 inches from heating element 4 minutes on each side or until desired degree of doneness. Drain patties well on paper towels. Transfer to a warm serving platter. Yield: 6 servings (261 calories per serving).

PROTEIN 25.4 / FAT 17.5 / CARBOHYDRATE 0.7 / CHOLESTEROL 81 / IRON 2.3 / SODIUM 236 / CALCIUM 83

ITALIAN LINGUINE RING

Vegetable cooking spray
¾ pound ground chuck
¾ cup chopped onion
¾ cup sliced fresh mushrooms
½ cup chopped celery
¼ cup chopped green pepper
1 clove garlic, minced
1 (14½-ounce) can whole tomatoes, undrained and chopped
1 (8-ounce) can no-salt-added tomato sauce
¾ teaspoon dried whole oregano
½ teaspoon dried whole marjoram
¼ teaspoon salt
8 ounces linguine
¼ cup (1 ounce) shredded part-skim mozzarella cheese
¼ cup grated Parmesan cheese
1 tablespoon margarine, melted
¼ cup finely chopped fresh parsley

Coat a large skillet with cooking spray; place over medium heat until hot. Add meat, onion, mushrooms, celery, green pepper, and garlic; cook over medium heat, stirring frequently, until meat is browned and vegetables are tender. Drain well on paper towels. Wipe pan drippings from skillet.

Return meat mixture to skillet. Stir in tomatoes, tomato sauce, oregano, marjoram, and salt. Bring mixture to a boil; reduce heat, and simmer, uncovered, 15 minutes, stirring frequently.

Cook linguine according to package directions, omitting salt; drain. Combine linguine, cheeses, margarine, and parsley in a large bowl, stirring well. Press mixture into a 4-cup ring mold coated with cooking spray; let stand 5 minutes.

To serve, unmold linguine onto serving platter; spoon sauce into center of ring. Serve immediately. Yield: 8 servings (252 calories per serving).

PROTEIN 15.3 / FAT 8.4 / CARBOHYDRATE 29.1 / CHOLESTEROL 30 / IRON 2.6 / SODIUM 280 / CALCIUM 96

MEATBALLS IN SHERRIED DIJON SAUCE

1 pound ground chuck
1 slice whole wheat bread, crumbled
¼ cup minced onion
2 teaspoons Dijon mustard
⅛ teaspoon salt
Dash of pepper
Vegetable cooking spray
Sherried Dijon Sauce
3 cups hot cooked noodles (cooked without salt)

Combine ground chuck, breadcrumbs, onion, mustard, salt, and pepper in a medium bowl; mix well. Shape into meatballs, using 1 tablespoon mixture for each meatball. Arrange meatballs on rack of a broiler pan coated with cooking spray. Broil 6 inches from heat 5 minutes; turn meatballs, and broil an additional 5 minutes or until browned. Drain well on paper towels.

Add meatballs to Sherried Dijon Sauce, stirring gently. Serve over hot cooked noodles. Yield: 6 servings (195 calories per serving plus 100 calories per ½-cup cooked noodles).

Sherried Dijon Sauce:

½ teaspoon beef-flavored bouillon granules
¼ cup hot water
1 tablespoon margarine
2 tablespoons all-purpose flour
½ cup water
¼ cup skim milk
2 tablespoons minced fresh parsley
1 tablespoon dry sherry
1 tablespoon Dijon mustard

Dissolve bouillon granules in hot water, and set aside.

Melt margarine in a heavy saucepan over low heat; add flour, stirring until smooth. Cook 1 minute, stirring constantly. Gradually add ½ cup water, milk, and reserved bouillon mixture; cook over medium heat, stirring constantly with a wire whisk, until thickened and bubbly. Add parsley, sherry, and mustard, stirring until smooth. Yield: 1 cup plus 1 tablespoon.

PROTEIN 19.4 / FAT 12.8 / CARBOHYDRATE 24.3 / CHOLESTEROL 72 / IRON 2.4 / SODIUM 291 / CALCIUM 34

ORIENTAL MEAT LOAF ROLL

1 (10-ounce) package frozen chopped
  spinach
¼ pound fresh mushrooms, finely
  chopped
½ cup finely chopped water chestnuts
1 pound ground chuck
1 cup soft whole wheat breadcrumbs
1 egg, beaten
2 tablespoons minced onion
2 tablespoons reduced-sodium soy
  sauce
1 teaspoon ground ginger
Vegetable cooking spray

Cook spinach according to package directions, omitting salt; drain well. Combine spinach, mushrooms, and water chestnuts; set aside.

Combine ground chuck, breadcrumbs, egg, onion, soy sauce, and ginger, stirring well. Shape mixture into a 12- x 10-inch rectangle on a sheet of wax paper coated with cooking spray. Spread reserved spinach mixture over top, leaving a 1-inch margin around edges. Roll up jellyroll fashion, beginning at short end and lifting wax paper to facilitate rolling procedure. Pinch edges and ends together to seal; transfer roll, seam side down, to rack of a roasting pan coated with cooking spray.

Bake at 350° for 50 to 60 minutes. Let stand 10 minutes before cutting into slices. Yield: 6 servings (217 calories per serving).

PROTEIN 19.5 / FAT 10.5 / CARBOHYDRATE 12.5 / CHOLESTEROL 92 / IRON 2.9 / SODIUM 321 / CALCIUM 90

LIVER WITH SAUTÉED VEGETABLES

3 tablespoons all-purpose flour
¼ teaspoon red pepper
⅛ teaspoon salt
1 pound thinly sliced beef liver
Vegetable cooking spray
1 medium-size sweet yellow pepper, seeded
  and cut into ¼-inch-wide strips
3 green onions, cut into 1-inch pieces
12 cherry tomatoes, cut in half

Combine first 3 ingredients in a medium bowl, stirring well. Dredge liver in flour mixture. Coat a large skillet with cooking spray, and place over medium-high heat until hot. Add liver, and cook 2 minutes on each side or until browned. Transfer to a warm serving platter. Set aside, and keep warm.

Wipe skillet with a paper towel. Recoat skillet with cooking spray. Add yellow pepper and green onions to skillet; sauté over medium heat 2 minutes. Add tomatoes, and sauté an additional 1 minute.

Arrange sautéed vegetables over reserved liver, and serve immediately. Yield: 4 servings (179 calories per serving).

PROTEIN 22.2 / FAT 4.5 / CARBOHYDRATE 11.9 / CHOLESTEROL 331 / IRON 6.5 / SODIUM 138 / CALCIUM 18

VEAL ROAST

1 (3½-pound) lean boneless veal roast,
  rolled and tied
1 clove garlic, split
1 tablespoon Dijon mustard
1 teaspoon dried whole dillweed
⅛ teaspoon pepper
Vegetable cooking spray
1 teaspoon vegetable oil
1 medium onion, chopped
1 cup sliced fresh mushrooms
½ cup water
¼ cup Chablis or other dry white wine
½ teaspoon beef-flavored bouillon granules

Unroll roast, and trim excess fat; rub roast thoroughly with cut side of garlic. Retie roast. Combine mustard, dillweed, and pepper; rub over entire surface of roast.

Coat a large ovenproof Dutch oven with cooking spray; add oil, and place over medium-high heat until hot. Add veal roast, and cook until browned on all sides, turning occasionally. Add remaining ingredients.

Cover and bake at 325° for 1 hour and 15 minutes, basting frequently with pan juices. Remove string before slicing. Yield: 12 servings (167 calories per serving).

PROTEIN 19.8 / FAT 8.5 / CARBOHYDRATE 1.6 / CHOLESTEROL 70 / IRON 3.2 / SODIUM 147 / CALCIUM 17

CALIFORNIA VEAL CUTLETS

1 pound veal cutlets
3 tablespoons all-purpose flour, divided
Vegetable cooking spray
2 teaspoons margarine
½ cup water
½ teaspoon chicken-flavored bouillon granules
2 tablespoons unsweetened orange juice
½ teaspoon dried whole tarragon
8 thin avocado slices
1 small orange, divided into 12 sections
Fresh tarragon sprig (optional)

Trim excess fat from cutlets. Place cutlets between 2 sheets of wax paper; flatten to ⅛-inch thickness, using a meat mallet or rolling pin. Dredge cutlets in 2 tablespoons flour.

Coat a large skillet with cooking spray; add margarine. Place over medium-high heat until hot. Add cutlets; cook 2 minutes on each side or until browned. Remove from skillet, and drain on paper towels; set aside. Wipe skillet dry with a paper towel. Add remaining flour, water, bouillon granules, orange juice, and dried whole tarragon to skillet. Cook, stirring constantly, 2 minutes or until thickened. Add cutlets; cook until thoroughly heated. Transfer to a platter; top with avocado slices and orange sections. Garnish with fresh tarragon sprig, if desired. Yield: 4 servings (237 calories per serving).

PROTEIN 18.4 / FAT 13.3 / CARBOHYDRATE 11.4 / CHOLESTEROL 60 / IRON 3.2 / SODIUM 150 / CALCIUM 29

LEMON-GARLIC VEAL

1 pound veal cutlets (¼-inch thick)
3 tablespoons lemon juice
1 teaspoon minced fresh rosemary or ¼ teaspoon dried whole rosemary
1 clove garlic, minced
½ teaspoon pepper
Vegetable cooking spray
2 teaspoons margarine
1 tablespoon minced fresh parsley

Trim excess fat from cutlets; cut cutlets into 4 serving-size pieces. Place cutlets between 2 sheets of wax paper; flatten to ⅛-inch thickness using a meat mallet or rolling pin. Place in a shallow dish.

Combine lemon juice, rosemary, garlic, and pepper; pour over cutlets. Cover and marinate in refrigerator 8 hours. Drain, discarding marinade.

Coat a large skillet with cooking spray; add margarine. Place over medium-high heat until margarine melts. Add cutlets, and cook 1 minute on each side or until browned.

Transfer to a serving platter, and sprinkle with parsley. Serve immediately. Yield: 4 servings (155 calories per serving).

PROTEIN 16.9 / FAT 8.7 / CARBOHYDRATE 1.5 / CHOLESTEROL 60 / IRON 2.7 / SODIUM 100 / CALCIUM 15

VEAL STROGANOFF

½ (12-ounce) package medium egg noodles
1 pound veal cutlets
¼ cup all-purpose flour
¼ teaspoon paprika
¼ teaspoon pepper
Vegetable cooking spray
2 teaspoons vegetable oil
¼ cup Chablis or other dry white wine
2 cups sliced fresh mushrooms
1 tablespoon chopped fresh chives
1 (8-ounce) carton plain low-fat yogurt
½ cup low-fat sour cream
1 tablespoon plus 1½ teaspoons cornstarch
¼ teaspoon salt

Cook noodles according to package directions, omitting salt; drain, and set aside.

Trim excess fat from cutlets; cut cutlets into 2- x ½-inch strips. Combine flour, paprika, and pepper in a shallow dish. Dredge veal strips in flour mixture.

Coat a large skillet with cooking spray; add oil, and place over medium-high heat until hot. Add strips to skillet, and cook 2 to 3 minutes or until browned on all sides. Remove from skillet, and drain on paper towels; set aside. Add wine, mushrooms, and chives to skillet; cover and cook 3 minutes. Stir in yogurt, sour cream, cornstarch, and salt. Return strips to skillet. Cook until thoroughly heated. Spoon veal mixture over reserved noodles. Yield: 6 servings (134 calories per serving plus 165 calories per ½-cup cooked noodles).

PROTEIN 18.5 / FAT 10.5 / CARBOHYDRATE 31.6 / CHOLESTEROL 77 / IRON 3.1 / SODIUM 186 / CALCIUM 110

GRILLED VEAL CHOPS WITH ARUGULA

⅓ cup unsweetened orange juice
1 tablespoon vegetable oil
⅛ teaspoon white pepper
4 (5-ounce) lean loin veal chops (¾-inch thick)
Vegetable cooking spray
1 teaspoon margarine
2 teaspoons grated orange rind
2 teaspoons unsweetened orange juice
¼ pound arugula, washed and drained

Combine ⅓ cup orange juice, oil, and pepper, stirring well. Trim away excess fat from chops; coat veal well with orange juice mixture. Grill over medium coals 5 minutes on each side.

Baste frequently with orange juice mixture. Transfer to a serving platter, and keep warm.

Coat a large skillet with cooking spray; add margarine, and place over medium heat until hot. Stir in orange rind and 2 teaspoons orange juice. Remove stems from arugula and discard. Add leaves to skillet, and cook, stirring constantly, just until wilted (about 10 seconds). Place arugula on a serving platter, and top with warm veal chops. Serve immediately. Yield: 4 servings (262 calories per serving).

PROTEIN 23.7 / FAT 16.2 / CARBOHYDRATE 3.8 / CHOLESTEROL 89 / IRON 3.1 / SODIUM 85 / CALCIUM 38

Arugula is a green vegetable with a distinctive, slightly bitter flavor. Grilled Veal Chops with Arugula definitely make it worth a try!

BAVARIAN VEAL SHANKS

4 (5-ounce) veal shanks
Vegetable cooking spray
¾ cup light beer
¼ cup water
1 teaspoon beef-flavored bouillon granules
1 teaspoon prepared horseradish
1 clove garlic, minced
⅛ teaspoon pepper
1 large onion, sliced
1 bay leaf

Trim excess fat from shanks. Coat a large skillet with cooking spray; place over medium-high heat until hot. Add shanks; cook 3 minutes on each side or until browned. Drain; transfer to a 3-quart casserole. Add remaining ingredients. Cover and bake at 325° for 1½ hours. Remove and discard bay leaf before serving. Yield: 4 servings (296 calories per serving).

PROTEIN 36.0 / FAT 12.9 / CARBOHYDRATE 5.4 / CHOLESTEROL 124 / IRON 4.6 / SODIUM 219 / CALCIUM 32

MUSTARD-SAUCED VEAL PATTIES

1½ pounds ground veal
1½ teaspoons lite lemon and pepper seasoning salt
½ teaspoon dried whole chervil
Vegetable cooking spray
¼ cup plus 2 tablespoons Chablis or other dry white wine
¼ cup water
3 tablespoons prepared mustard
1 tablespoon plus 1 teaspoon Worcestershire sauce
2 tablespoons chopped fresh parsley (optional)

Combine first 3 ingredients in a medium bowl; mix well. Shape mixture into 6 (1-inch-thick) patties.

Coat a large skillet with cooking spray; place over medium-high heat until hot. Cook patties 5 minutes on each side or until desired degree of doneness. Remove from skillet; drain well on paper towels. Set aside, and keep warm.

Wipe skillet with a paper towel; add wine, water, mustard, and Worcestershire sauce. Cook over low heat, stirring just until blended. Add reserved patties to skillet, spooning sauce over top. Continue to cook over low heat until thoroughly heated. Remove from heat, and sprinkle with chopped parsley, if desired. Yield: 6 servings (145 calories per serving).

PROTEIN 17.2 / FAT 7.2 / CARBOHYDRATE 1.9 / CHOLESTEROL 60 / IRON 2.8 / SODIUM 250 / CALCIUM 21

ZESTY GINGERED LAMB

1 (3½-pound) boneless leg of lamb
½ cup lemon juice
¼ cup reduced-sodium soy sauce
2 tablespoons Dijon mustard
2 tablespoons honey
3 tablespoons minced fresh gingerroot
1 clove garlic, minced
¼ teaspoon freshly ground pepper
Vegetable cooking spray

Trim excess fat from leg of lamb. Combine lemon juice and next 6 ingredients in a large dish or roasting pan. Place leg of lamb in marinade, turning to coat well. Cover and refrigerate 8 hours or overnight, turning occasionally.

Remove lamb from marinade, reserving marinade. Coat rack of a broiler pan with cooking spray. Place lamb on rack. Insert meat thermometer into thickest part of lamb. Bake, uncovered, at 325° for 1½ to 2½ hours or until meat thermometer registers 140° (rare) or 160° (medium). Baste frequently with marinade. Let lamb stand at room temperature 10 minutes before slicing. Yield: 12 servings (151 calories per serving).

PROTEIN 20.2 / FAT 5.1 / CARBOHYDRATE 4.8 / CHOLESTEROL 69 / IRON 1.7 / SODIUM 343 / CALCIUM 14

ROSEMARY-GRILLED LAMB CHOPS

6 (6-ounce) lean lamb loin chops (1-inch thick)
¼ cup Chablis or other dry white wine
2 tablespoons water
1 tablespoon dried whole rosemary
1 tablespoon lemon juice
1 tablespoon Worcestershire sauce
2 teaspoons Dijon mustard
1 clove garlic, minced
Vegetable cooking spray

Trim excess fat from chops. Place chops in a large shallow dish. Combine wine and next 6 ingredients, stirring well. Pour over chops; cover and refrigerate 2 hours, turning occasionally.

Remove chops from marinade, reserving marinade. Coat grill with cooking spray. Grill chops 5 to 6 inches over medium coals 35 minutes or until desired degree of doneness, turning and basting frequently with reserved marinade. Yield: 6 servings (165 calories per serving).

PROTEIN 24.1 / FAT 6.2 / CARBOHYDRATE 1.7 / CHOLESTEROL 85 / IRON 1.9 / SODIUM 134 / CALCIUM 21

LEMON AND PINEAPPLE LAMB CHOPS

6 (5-ounce) lamb chops (1-inch thick)
1 (8-ounce) can unsweetened pineapple tidbits, undrained
¼ cup lemon juice
2 tablespoons minced onion
2 tablespoons honey
¼ teaspoon salt
¼ teaspoon dry mustard
¼ teaspoon crushed red pepper
⅛ teaspoon ground ginger
Vegetable cooking spray
1 medium-size sweet red pepper, seeded and chopped
2 teaspoons cornstarch
2 tablespoons cold water

Trim excess fat from chops; place chops in a large shallow dish. Drain pineapple, reserving juice; set pineapple aside. Combine pineapple juice, lemon juice, and next 6 ingredients; stir well. Pour marinade over chops. Cover and refrigerate 2 hours.

Remove chops from marinade, reserving marinade. Coat a large nonstick skillet with cooking spray; place over medium heat until hot. Add chops, and cook 4 minutes on each side or until browned. Drain on paper towels. Wipe skillet dry with a paper towel. Return chops to skillet. Add reserved pineapple, reserved marinade, and sweet red pepper. Bring to a boil. Cover; reduce heat, and simmer 20 minutes.

Remove lamb chops using a slotted spoon; place on a warm platter. Combine cornstarch and water, stirring well. Add to mixture in skillet, stirring well. Cook until mixture is thickened and bubbly. Spoon over warm lamb chops. Yield: 6 servings (243 calories per serving).

PROTEIN 30.4 / FAT 7.6 / CARBOHYDRATE 12.4 / CHOLESTEROL 106 / IRON 2.5 / SODIUM 174 / CALCIUM 20

LAMB CHOPS WITH TARRAGON-TOMATO SAUCE

6 (6-ounce) lean lamb loin chops (1-inch thick)
Vegetable cooking spray
⅛ teaspoon pepper
1 (8-ounce) can no-salt-added tomato sauce
2 tablespoons dry, white vermouth
¾ teaspoon dried whole tarragon
⅛ teaspoon garlic powder
3 cups hot cooked parboiled rice (cooked without salt or fat)

Trim excess fat from chops. Coat a large skillet with cooking spray. Place over medium-high heat until hot. Add chops, and cook 4 minutes on each side or until browned. Remove chops from skillet, and drain well on paper towels. Sprinkle chops with pepper. Wipe skillet dry with a paper towel.

Combine tomato sauce and next 3 ingredients, stirring well. Return chops to skillet. Pour tomato sauce mixture over lamb chops. Bring to a boil. Cover; reduce heat, and simmer 20 minutes or until chops are tender, turning occasionally. Serve over hot cooked rice. Yield: 6 servings (171 calories per serving plus 93 calories per ½-cup cooked rice).

PROTEIN 26.1 / FAT 6.0 / CARBOHYDRATE 23.8 / CHOLESTEROL 85 / IRON 2.4 / SODIUM 69 / CALCIUM 27

LAMB CURRY WITH APRICOTS

1 (6-ounce) package dried apricots
2 cups hot water
Vegetable cooking spray
1 pound lean boneless lamb, cut into 1-inch cubes
1 medium onion, chopped
2 cloves garlic, minced
1 teaspoon chicken-flavored bouillon granules
1 cup hot water
1 teaspoon ground coriander
½ teaspoon ground cumin
½ teaspoon ground cinnamon
½ teaspoon ground ginger
½ teaspoon ground turmeric
⅛ teaspoon red pepper
⅛ teaspoon ground cardamom
2 cups hot cooked parboiled rice (cooked without salt or fat)

Combine apricots and 2 cups hot water in a small bowl; set aside.

Coat a Dutch oven with cooking spray. Add lamb, and cook, stirring frequently, until browned on all sides. Remove lamb, and drain on paper towels. Add onion and garlic to Dutch oven, and sauté until tender. Return lamb to Dutch oven. Combine bouillon granules and 1 cup hot water; add to Dutch oven. Add coriander and next 6 ingredients. Bring to a boil; cover, reduce heat, and simmer 30 minutes.

Drain apricots; add to lamb mixture, and simmer an additional 30 minutes. Serve over hot cooked rice. Yield: 6 servings (152 calories per serving plus 93 calories per ½-cup cooked rice).

PROTEIN 18.6 / FAT 4.4 / CARBOHYDRATE 33.3 / CHOLESTEROL 57 / IRON 3.3 / SODIUM 316 / CALCIUM 42

SPICY ORANGE-LAMB STIR-FRY

1 pound lamb cutlets
¼ cup water
3 tablespoons dry sherry
2 tablespoons reduced-sodium soy sauce
1 teaspoon sugar
½ teaspoon crushed red pepper
2 teaspoons cornstarch
Vegetable cooking spray
1 teaspoon vegetable oil
1 (8-ounce) can water chestnuts, drained
1 medium-size sweet red pepper, seeded and cut into cubes
4 green onions with tops, cut into 1-inch pieces
1 tablespoon grated orange rind
1 tablespoon minced fresh gingerroot
2 cups hot cooked regular rice (cooked without salt or fat)

Trim excess fat from cutlets; cut cutlets into thin strips, and set aside. Combine water, sherry, soy sauce, sugar, and crushed red pepper in a large bowl. Stir well. Add reserved strips. Cover and let stand 20 minutes.

Drain strips, reserving marinade. Combine marinade and cornstarch, stirring until smooth. Set aside.

Coat a wok or skillet with cooking spray; add oil. Allow to heat at medium-high (325°) for 2 minutes. Add strips; stir-fry 5 minutes. Remove strips from wok, and set aside. Add water chestnuts and next 4 ingredients to wok; stir-fry 1 minute. Return strips to wok. Add reserved marinade. Cook, stirring constantly, until thickened. Serve over hot cooked rice. Yield: 4 servings (182 calories per serving plus 118 calories per ½-cup cooked rice).

PROTEIN 20.4 / FAT 6.1 / CARBOHYDRATE 36.4 / CHOLESTEROL 60 / IRON 3.2 / SODIUM 362 / CALCIUM 29

Spicy Orange-Lamb Stir-Fry utilizes the simplicity and speed of wok cookery for a unique approach to lamb. Pick up the chopsticks, and enjoy!

GRECIAN LAMB-STUFFED EGGPLANT

2 (¾-pound) eggplant
1 pound lean ground lamb
1 cup chopped onion
½ cup chopped green pepper
¼ cup chopped fresh parsley
2 cloves garlic, minced
1 (8-ounce) can no-salt-added tomato
  sauce
3 tablespoons raisins
2 tablespoons Burgundy or other dry
  red wine
¼ teaspoon ground cinnamon
¼ teaspoon dried whole thyme
⅛ teaspoon pepper
3 tablespoons grated Parmesan cheese

Wash eggplant; wrap in aluminum foil. Bake at 350° for 1 hour. Remove foil; let cool. Slice each eggplant in half lengthwise; scoop out pulp, leaving ¼-inch-thick shells. Set shells aside.

Position knife blade in food processor bowl; add pulp. Process until smooth; set aside.

Combine ground lamb, onion, green pepper, parsley, and garlic in a large skillet. Cook over medium heat until lamb is browned, stirring to crumble. Remove lamb mixture from skillet, and drain well in a colander. Wipe skillet dry with a paper towel, and return lamb mixture to skillet. Add reserved eggplant pulp, tomato sauce, raisins, wine, cinnamon, thyme, and pepper; stir well. Bring mixture to a boil. Cover; reduce heat, and simmer 10 minutes.

Place reserved shells in a large shallow baking dish. Spoon lamb mixture into shells. Cover and bake at 350° for 10 minutes. Uncover; sprinkle with cheese, and bake an additional 5 minutes or until cheese melts. Yield: 4 servings (282 calories per serving).

PROTEIN 29.0 / FAT 7.5 / CARBOHYDRATE 26.1 / CHOLESTEROL 88 / IRON 3.8 / SODIUM 154 / CALCIUM 150

GRILLED LAMB PATTIES WITH YOGURT SAUCE

1 pound lean ground lamb
¼ cup chopped fresh mint leaves
1 clove garlic, minced
1 teaspoon grated lemon rind
¼ teaspoon salt
⅛ teaspoon freshly ground pepper
Vegetable cooking spray
Yogurt Sauce

Combine lamb, mint leaves, garlic, lemon rind, salt, and pepper; mix well. Shape into 4 patties, 1-inch thick.

Coat grill with cooking spray. Grill patties 4 to 6 inches over hot coals 6 minutes on each side or until desired degree of doneness. Serve each patty with 3 tablespoons Yogurt Sauce. Yield: 4 servings (180 calories per serving).

Yogurt Sauce:

½ cup plain low-fat yogurt
¼ cup diced cucumber
2 tablespoons minced onion
Dash of white pepper

Combine all ingredients; stir well. Cover; chill thoroughly. Yield: ¾ cup.

PROTEIN 25.7 / FAT 6.4 / CARBOHYDRATE 3.2 / CHOLESTEROL 87 / IRON 2.0 / SODIUM 228 / CALCIUM 72

NO LINK BETWEEN CAFFEINE AND BENIGN BREAST LUMPS

Women with fibrocystic breast disease who have been concerned about their daily coffee consumption don't need to be, according to a National Cancer Institute study of 3,300 women. The study found no link between caffeine consumption and development of benign breast lumps.

A flavorful ribbon of jalapeño peppers darts through Jalapeño Pork Roast.

JALAPEÑO PORK ROAST

1 (2½-pound) lean boneless pork loin roast, rolled
    and tied
¼ cup chopped pickled jalapeño peppers
1 (8-ounce) bottle reduced-calorie Italian salad
    dressing
1 (6-ounce) can frozen unsweetened orange juice
    concentrate, thawed and undiluted
Jalapeño pepper (optional)
Fresh cilantro sprigs (optional)

Untie roast, and trim excess fat. Sprinkle inside of roast with chopped jalapeño peppers. Retie roast, and place in a shallow baking dish. Combine salad dressing and orange juice concentrate; stir well, and pour over roast. Cover and marinate in refrigerator 8 hours or overnight, turning roast occasionally.

Remove roast from marinade, reserving marinade. Place on a rack in a roasting pan, and insert a meat thermometer, if desired. Place in a 450° oven. Reduce heat to 350°, and bake 1 hour and 45 minutes or until meat thermometer registers 170°. Baste frequently with reserved marinade.

Transfer roast to a cutting board, and let stand 10 minutes. Remove string; cut roast into ½-inch slices. Garnish with jalapeño pepper and cilantro, if desired. Yield: 10 servings (227 calories per serving).

PROTEIN 26.6 / FAT 8.7 / CARBOHYDRATE 8.9 / CHOLESTEROL 80 /
IRON 0.8 / SODIUM 325 / CALCIUM 12

GRILLED MARINATED PORK CHOPS

4 (6-ounce) lean center loin pork chops
  (¾-inch thick)
1 (6-ounce) can unsweetened pineapple juice
2 tablespoons reduced-sodium soy sauce
2 cloves garlic, minced
Vegetable cooking spray
Fresh parsley sprigs

Trim excess fat from chops; place chops in a shallow baking dish. Combine juice, soy sauce, and garlic, stirring well; pour over chops. Cover and marinate in refrigerator 8 hours or overnight, turning occasionally.

Remove chops from marinade, reserving marinade. Arrange chops on a grill coated with cooking spray. Grill 5 to 6 inches over medium coals 15 minutes or until chops are tender, turning and basting frequently with marinade.

Transfer to a platter; garnish with parsley. Yield: 4 servings (236 calories per serving).

PROTEIN 24.9 / FAT 11.1 / CARBOHYDRATE 7.3 / CHOLESTEROL 77 / IRON 1.1 / SODIUM 350 / CALCIUM 14

PORK CHOPS AU POIVRE

4 (6-ounce) lean center loin pork chops (¾-inch
  thick)
2 tablespoons cracked black pepper
Vegetable cooking spray
¼ cup Cognac

Trim excess fat from chops. Rub chops on all sides with pepper; let stand at room temperature 30 minutes. Place on rack of a broiler pan coated with cooking spray. Broil 4 to 5 inches from heating element 15 minutes on each side or until desired degree of doneness.

Transfer chops to a hot platter. Place Cognac in a small saucepan; heat just until warm. Pour over steak, and ignite with a long match. After flames die down, serve immediately. Yield: 4 servings (247 calories per serving).

PROTEIN 24.4 / FAT 11.1 / CARBOHYDRATE 2.1 / CHOLESTEROL 77 / IRON 1.8 / SODIUM 60 / CALCIUM 19

PORK MEDALLIONS WITH SWEET PEPPERS

¼ cup all-purpose flour
¼ teaspoon salt
¼ teaspoon dried whole basil
⅛ teaspoon pepper
1 pound pork medallions
Vegetable cooking spray
1 teaspoon vegetable oil
1 small sweet red pepper, sliced
1 small sweet yellow pepper, sliced
1 small green pepper, sliced
2 teaspoons minced shallot
⅓ cup dry, white vermouth
1 teaspoon cornstarch
½ teaspoon dried whole sage

Combine flour, salt, basil, and ⅛ teaspoon pepper in a small bowl; mix well. Dredge pork medallions well in flour mixture.

Coat a large skillet with cooking spray; add oil and place over medium-high heat until hot. Add medallions, and cook 2 minutes on each side until browned. Transfer medallions to a serving platter, and keep warm.

Wipe skillet with a paper towel; coat with cooking spray, and place over medium heat until hot. Add peppers and shallot; cook, stirring frequently, until crisp-tender.

Combine vermouth, cornstarch, and sage; add to skillet, and bring to a boil. Reduce heat, and cook just until thickened. Spoon mixture over pork, and serve immediately. Yield: 4 servings (221 calories per serving).

PROTEIN 27.5 / FAT 5.9 / CARBOHYDRATE 13.5 / CHOLESTEROL 83 / IRON 2.8 / SODIUM 210 / CALCIUM 20

SPICED PORK

1 (1¼-pound) lean boneless pork
  shoulder
2 tablespoons vinegar
1 teaspoon ground cumin
1 teaspoon ground turmeric
¼ teaspoon garlic powder
Dash of pepper
Vegetable cooking spray
1 teaspoon vegetable oil
½ cup unsweetened orange
  juice
¼ cup water
¾ teaspoon cornstarch
1 tablespoon water
1 tablespoon minced fresh
  cilantro
2 cups hot cooked orzo (cooked
  without salt)

Trim excess fat from pork; cut into ½-inch cubes. Combine vinegar, cumin, turmeric, garlic powder, and pepper in a zip top heavy-duty plastic bag. Place pork in bag, and seal tightly, turning bag to coat each side thoroughly. Refrigerate 1 hour.

Remove pork from marinade, and drain. Coat a large skillet with cooking spray; add oil, and place over medium-high heat until hot. Add pork, and cook, stirring frequently, until evenly browned on all sides. Stir in orange juice and ¼ cup water; cover and simmer 30 minutes or until pork is tender.

Dissolve cornstarch in 1 tablespoon water, and stir into mixture. Cook, stirring frequently, until thickened. Remove from heat, and stir in cilantro and orzo. Serve immediately. Yield: 4 servings (297 calories per serving).

PROTEIN 23.7 / FAT 14.3 / CARBOHYDRATE 17.0 / CHOLESTEROL 82 /
IRON 2.4 / SODIUM 67 / CALCIUM 21

CAJUN STUFFED PEPPERS

6 medium-size sweet red peppers
1 pound ground lean pork
⅔ cup chopped celery
½ cup chopped onion
½ cup chopped green pepper
1 clove garlic, minced
1 bay leaf
1 (8-ounce) can no-salt-added tomato
  sauce
1 medium tomato, peeled, seeded,
  and chopped
¼ cup grated Parmesan cheese
¾ teaspoon dried whole thyme
¼ teaspoon crushed red pepper
¼ teaspoon pepper

Cut a slice from the top of each sweet red pepper, reserving tops; remove seeds. Place peppers in boiling water; boil 5 minutes. Drain, and set aside.

Combine ground pork, celery, onion, green pepper, garlic, and bay leaf in a large skillet. Cook over medium-high heat until meat is browned, stirring to crumble. Drain meat mixture in a colander; pat dry with paper towels to remove excess fat. Remove and discard bay leaf. Wipe skillet dry with a paper towel.

Return meat mixture to skillet. Add tomato sauce and remaining ingredients; stir well. Bring to a boil. Reduce heat; simmer, uncovered, 5 minutes.

Spoon ½ cup meat mixture into each reserved pepper; arrange peppers, cut side up, in a 10- x 6- x 2-inch baking dish. Top with reserved pepper tops. Bake at 350° for 25 minutes or until thoroughly heated. Yield: 6 servings (213 calories per serving).

PROTEIN 19.0 / FAT 10.2 / CARBOHYDRATE 11.5 / CHOLESTEROL 56 /
IRON 2.4 / SODIUM 129 / CALCIUM 73

 ## CORPORATE FITNESS YIELDS HIGH DIVIDENDS

More employers are encouraging fitness, and early data indicates they may reap rewards in the form of lower health-care costs. A study reported in *The Wall Street Journal* found these costs were 114 percent more for sedentary people than for those who engaged in physical activity equivalent to walking up 15 flights of stairs or walking one-and-a-half miles a week.

CRUSTLESS HAM QUICHE

1 (8-ounce) can unsweetened pineapple tidbits, undrained
1 small onion, chopped
1 small green pepper, chopped
1 cup finely chopped lean cooked ham
¾ cup (3 ounces) shredded Swiss cheese
4 eggs, beaten
½ cup skim milk
1 teaspoon dry mustard
⅛ teaspoon red pepper
Vegetable cooking spray

Drain pineapple, reserving juice; set pineapple aside.

Combine pineapple juice, onion, and green pepper in a skillet; cook over medium heat until vegetables are tender and liquid evaporates. Remove from heat; stir in pineapple, ham, and cheese. Set aside.

Combine eggs, milk, mustard, and red pepper in a large bowl; beat until well blended. Add reserved pineapple mixture; mix well. Pour into a 9-inch quiche dish or pieplate coated with cooking spray. Bake at 350° for 35 minutes or until a knife inserted off-center comes out clean. Let stand 10 minutes before serving. Cut into wedges, and serve warm. Yield: 6 servings (178 calories per serving).

PROTEIN 14.2 / FAT 9.3 / CARBOHYDRATE 9.3 / CHOLESTEROL 208 / IRON 1.5 / SODIUM 375 / CALCIUM 191

HAM TACOS WITH JICAMA SALSA

8 ounces ground lean cooked ham
3 tablespoons (¾ ounce) shredded Cheddar cheese
3 tablespoons (¾ ounce) shredded Monterey Jack cheese
10 taco shells
Jicama Salsa

Combine ground ham and cheeses, stirring well. Spoon 2 tablespoons mixture into each taco shell; top each taco with 1 tablespoon Jicama Salsa. Yield: 10 servings (110 calories per serving).

Jicama Salsa:

½ cup shredded jicama
¼ cup chopped tomato
1 tablespoon green onions
1 clove garlic, crushed
1 tablespoon lime juice
1½ teaspoons white wine vinegar
⅛ teaspoon chili powder

Combine all ingredients in a small bowl; stir well. Cover and let stand at room temperature 2 hours. Yield: ⅔ cup.

PROTEIN 6.8 / FAT 5.6 / CARBOHYDRATE 7.8 / CHOLESTEROL 16 / IRON 0.8 / SODIUM 365 / CALCIUM 36

 WINNING WITH PORK

Pork producers raise leaner animals than in years past. Today's pork is about 50 percent leaner than it was in the '60s. Some lean cuts of pork have less saturated fat than some cuts of beef. Three ounces of lean pork provide plenty of nutrients, more minerals and B vitamins than poultry, and calories that fall under 200.

The way to win with pork is to limit the use of highly processed, high-fat sausage and bacon. Instead, choose lean cuts with little internal marbling, and be sure to trim all excess fat before cooking. Fat represents less than 30 percent of total calories in the tenderloin used to make colorful Pork Medallions with Sweet Peppers (page 156).

Arroz con Pollo (page 160), Spanish and Mexican in origin, means "rice with chicken." The rice obtains its golden yellow color from saffron, a spice made from the dried, golden-orange stigmas of an autumn-flowering crocus.

ROAST CHICKEN WITH YOGURT GRAVY

1 (3½-pound) broiler fryer, skinned
½ small lemon, cut into wedges
¼ cup water
⅓ cup reduced-calorie Italian salad
   dressing
⅛ teaspoon pepper
Yogurt Gravy

Remove giblets and neck from chicken, and reserve for other uses. Trim excess fat from chicken. Rinse chicken with cold water, and pat dry. Place lemon wedges in cavity of chicken. Close cavity with skewers, and truss. Lift wingtips up and over back, tucking under bird securely. Place chicken, breast side up, on a rack in a roasting pan. Pour ¼ cup water in bottom of pan. Set aside.

Combine salad dressing and pepper, stirring well. Brush half of dressing mixture over entire surface of chicken. Bake chicken, uncovered, at 375° for 1 hour and 15 minutes or until drumsticks move up and down easily and juices run clear. Baste frequently with remaining dressing mixture during cooking. Remove and discard lemon wedges.

Transfer chicken to a serving platter, and top with Yogurt Gravy. Yield: 6 servings (218 calories per serving).

Yogurt Gravy:

1 tablespoon plus 2 teaspoons reduced-calorie
   Italian salad dressing
1 tablespoon all-purpose flour
½ teaspoon chicken-flavored bouillon
   granules
¼ cup water
1 (8-ounce) carton plain low-fat yogurt

Combine salad dressing, flour, and bouillon granules in a small bowl to form a smooth paste. Place ¼ cup water in a small saucepan. Stir in dressing paste. Cook over medium heat, stirring constantly, until thickened and bubbly. Stir yogurt into mixture. Cook, stirring constantly, until gravy is thoroughly heated. (Do not boil.) Yield: 1 cup.

PROTEIN 29.5 / FAT 7.6 / CARBOHYDRATE 6.5 / CHOLESTEROL 86 / IRON 1.3 / SODIUM 298 / CALCIUM 91

ARROZ CON POLLO

1 (3½-pound) broiler fryer, cut up and skinned
Vegetable cooking spray
1 teaspoon vegetable oil
2 cups water
1 (14½-ounce) can no-salt-added stewed tomatoes,
   undrained and chopped
1 cup chopped onion
2 teaspoons chicken-flavored bouillon granules
1 clove garlic, minced
1 medium-size jalapeño pepper, minced
¼ teaspoon powdered saffron
⅛ teaspoon pepper
1 cup regular rice, uncooked
¼ cup sliced pimiento-stuffed olives, drained
2 tablespoons lime juice

Trim excess fat from chicken. Rinse chicken with cold water; pat dry. Coat a 12-inch skillet with cooking spray; add oil, and place over medium-high heat until hot. Add chicken, and cook 4 minutes on each side or until browned. Remove chicken; drain on paper towels.

Wipe skillet with a paper towel; recoat with cooking spray. Add chicken to skillet. Combine water and next 7 ingredients; pour over chicken. Cover and cook over medium heat 15 minutes. Add rice; cover and cook over medium heat 20 minutes or until tender. Remove from heat, and stir in olives; sprinkle with lime juice. Yield: 6 servings (347 calories per serving).

PROTEIN 30.7 / FAT 8.8 / CARBOHYDRATE 34.5 / CHOLESTEROL 84 / IRON 2.8 / SODIUM 358 / CALCIUM 54

BAKED CHICKEN WITH WINTER VEGETABLES

⅓ pound fresh brussels sprouts
2 medium tomatoes, cut into wedges
⅓ pound carrots, scraped and cut into ¼-inch
   diagonal slices
1 (8-ounce) acorn squash, peeled and cubed
¼ cup chopped onion
1 teaspoon dried whole basil
½ teaspoon dry mustard
¼ teaspoon salt
¼ teaspoon pepper
1 (3½-pound) broiler fryer, cut up and skinned

Remove discolored leaves from brussels sprouts. Cut off stem ends; wash sprouts thoroughly. Cut a shallow X in the base of each sprout. Combine sprouts, tomatoes, carrots, squash, onion, basil, mustard, salt, and pepper in a large bowl; toss well. Set aside.

Trim excess fat from chicken. Rinse chicken with cold water; pat dry. Place chicken in a browning bag prepared according to package directions. Place reserved vegetable mixture in bag around chicken. Seal bag according to package directions, cutting slits in top of bag. Place bag in a 13- x 9- x 2-inch baking dish; bake at 350° for 1 hour or until chicken and vegetables are tender. Yield: 8 servings (165 calories per serving).

PROTEIN 21.7 / FAT 5.4 / CARBOHYDRATE 7.0 / CHOLESTEROL 63 / IRON 1.4 / SODIUM 148 / CALCIUM 38

ORANGE SKILLET CHICKEN

1 (3½-pound) broiler fryer, cut up
  and skinned
Vegetable cooking spray
2 teaspoons vegetable oil
¼ cup brandy
¾ cup unsweetened orange juice
½ cup water
¼ teaspoon salt
⅛ teaspoon white pepper
¼ cup Grand Marnier or other
  orange-flavored liqueur
¼ cup reduced-calorie orange
  marmalade
1 teaspoon lemon juice
2 teaspoons cornstarch
1 tablespoon water

Trim excess fat from chicken. Rinse chicken with cold water; pat dry. Coat a large skillet with cooking spray; add oil, and place over medium-high heat until hot. Add chicken and cook until lightly browned on all sides. Remove chicken; drain on paper towels.

Wipe skillet with a paper towel. Return chicken to skillet. Add brandy, and heat just until warm (do not boil). Ignite brandy with a long-handled match. When flames die, add

orange juice, ½ cup water, salt, and pepper, stirring well. Cover; reduce heat, and simmer 20 minutes. Add Grand Marnier, marmalade, and lemon juice. Cover and simmer 10 minutes, basting occasionally. Remove chicken to a serving platter, and keep warm.

Combine cornstarch and 1 tablespoon water, stirring until blended. Pour cornstarch mixture into chicken liquid; cook over medium-high heat, stirring constantly, until thickened. Remove from heat, and spoon orange juice mixture over chicken. Serve immediately. Yield: 8 servings (209 calories per serving).

PROTEIN 20.6 / FAT 6.4 / CARBOHYDRATE 8.3 / CHOLESTEROL 63 / IRON 0.9 / SODIUM 134 / CALCIUM 13

CHINESE CHICKEN BARBECUE

4 chicken breast halves (about 1½ pounds),
  skinned
½ cup reduced-calorie catsup
2 tablespoons firmly packed brown
  sugar
2 tablespoons reduced-sodium soy
  sauce
½ teaspoon ground ginger
1 clove garlic, minced
Vegetable cooking spray
Minced fresh parsley (optional)

Trim excess fat from chicken. Rinse chicken with cold water, and pat dry. Place chicken in a 10- x 6- x 2-inch baking dish. Combine catsup, brown sugar, soy sauce, ginger, and garlic, stirring well. Pour over chicken, turning chicken to coat well. Cover and marinate in refrigerator at least 2 hours.

Remove chicken from marinade, reserving marinade. Place chicken on a rack in a roasting pan coated with cooking spray. Brush chicken with 2 tablespoons marinade.

Bake at 350° for 40 minutes, basting with marinade every 20 minutes. Transfer to a serving platter, and sprinkle chicken with minced parsley, if desired. Yield: 4 servings (193 calories per serving).

PROTEIN 27.8 / FAT 3.1 / CARBOHYDRATE 10.3 / CHOLESTEROL 74 / IRON 1.2 / SODIUM 365 / CALCIUM 21

COLD GRILLED CHICKEN WITH EXOTIC FRUIT

8 boneless chicken breast halves (2 pounds), skinned
¾ cup unsweetened pineapple juice
¼ cup reduced-sodium soy sauce
2 tablespoons lime juice
1 clove garlic, minced
8 mesquite chips
Vegetable cooking spray
Blueberry Sauce
1 medium star fruit, sliced
2 medium kiwifruit, peeled and sliced
8 medium-size fresh strawberries

Trim excess fat from chicken. Rinse chicken with cold water, and pat dry. Place chicken in a shallow container. Combine pineapple juice, soy sauce, lime juice, and garlic, stirring well. Pour over chicken; cover and marinate in refrigerator 8 hours or overnight, turning occasionally. Drain; reserve marinade.

Cover mesquite chips with water, and soak 30 minutes. Drain chips, and place directly on medium coals. Coat grill with cooking spray. Grill chicken 4 to 5 inches over medium-hot coals 5 minutes on each side or until chicken is tender, basting once with reserved marinade. Remove chicken from grill, and chill thoroughly.

Spoon 2 tablespoons Blueberry Sauce onto 8 individual serving plates. Place each chicken breast half in Blueberry Sauce. Top each serving with 1 slice of star fruit, 2 slices of kiwifruit, and 1 strawberry. Yield: 8 servings (198 calories per serving).

Blueberry Sauce:

1 cup fresh blueberries
2 tablespoons water
2 tablespoons crème de cassis
1 teaspoon lemon juice

Combine blueberries, water, and crème de cassis in a small saucepan. Bring to a boil; reduce heat, and simmer 1 to 2 minutes. Remove from heat, and cool. Transfer mixture to container of electric blender or food processor; process until smooth. Stir in lemon juice. Cover and chill thoroughly. Yield: 1 cup.

PROTEIN 27.1 / FAT 3.3 / CARBOHYDRATE 12.9 / CHOLESTEROL 70 /
IRON 1.2 / SODIUM 354 / CALCIUM 28

Hot outside? Serve Cold Grilled Chicken with Exotic Fruit.

CRANBERRY CHICKEN CUTLETS

4 boneless chicken breast halves (1 pound), skinned
¼ cup all-purpose flour
⅛ teaspoon salt
¼ teaspoon pepper
Vegetable cooking spray
1 tablespoon margarine
¾ cup cranberry juice cocktail
⅓ cup fresh or frozen cranberries, thawed
⅛ teaspoon ground cinnamon
Dash of ground cloves
2 tablespoons cold water
2 teaspoons cornstarch
1 teaspoon sugar

Trim excess fat from chicken. Rinse chicken with cold water, and pat dry. Place chicken between 2 sheets of wax paper; flatten to ¼-inch thickness, using a meat mallet or rolling pin. Combine flour, salt, and pepper; stir well. Dredge chicken in flour mixture.

Coat a large skillet with cooking spray; add margarine, and place over medium-high heat until margarine melts. Add chicken, and cook 3 minutes on each side or until browned. Remove chicken from skillet, and drain well on paper towels. Transfer chicken to a serving platter, and keep warm.

Combine cranberry juice cocktail, cranberries, cinnamon, and cloves in a small saucepan. Bring to a boil; reduce heat, and simmer, uncovered, 2 minutes or until cranberries burst. Combine water, cornstarch, and sugar, stirring until blended. Pour cornstarch mixture into cranberry mixture; cook over medium-high heat, stirring constantly, until mixture thickens. Remove from heat, and spoon sauce over chicken. Serve immediately. Yield: 4 servings (235 calories per serving).

PROTEIN 26.7 / FAT 5.9 / CARBOHYDRATE 17.1 / CHOLESTEROL 70 / IRON 1.2 / SODIUM 170 / CALCIUM 19

FRUIT-STUFFED CHICKEN ROLLS

½ cup cored, peeled, sliced Granny Smith apple
½ cup mixed dried fruit bits
⅓ cup Chablis or other dry white wine
⅓ cup peach brandy
¼ cup unsweetened apple juice
4 boneless chicken breast halves (1 pound), skinned
Vegetable cooking spray
2 teaspoons margarine
3 tablespoons skim milk
⅛ teaspoon salt
¼ teaspoon pepper

Combine apple and dried fruit in a small bowl; set aside. Combine wine, brandy, and apple juice in a saucepan; bring to a boil. Boil 2 minutes, stirring occasionally. Pour over reserved fruit mixture; let stand at room temperature 1 to 2 hours.

Trim excess fat from chicken. Rinse chicken with cold water, and pat dry. Place chicken between 2 sheets of wax paper; flatten to ¼-inch

thickness, using a meat mallet or rolling pin. Set aside.

Drain fruit mixture, reserving marinade. Spoon ¼ cup fruit mixture onto center of each chicken breast half; roll up lengthwise, tucking edges under. Secure with wooden picks.

Coat a large skillet with cooking spray; add margarine, and place over medium-high heat until margarine melts. Add chicken rolls, and cook until browned on all sides. Add ¼ cup reserved marinade. Cover; reduce heat, and simmer 45 minutes or until chicken is tender. Transfer chicken to a serving platter, and keep warm. Add remaining marinade to skillet; bring to a boil and boil 2 minutes. Reduce heat and stir in skim milk; simmer 5 minutes. Stir in salt and pepper. Spoon sauce over chicken. Yield: 4 servings (268 calories per serving).

PROTEIN 26.8 / FAT 4.9 / CARBOHYDRATE 15.2 / CHOLESTEROL 71 / IRON 1.3 / SODIUM 177 / CALCIUM 32

GRECIAN-GRILLED CHICKEN

4 boneless chicken breast halves (1 pound), skinned
¼ cup fresh lemon juice
3 tablespoons olive oil
2 cloves garlic, crushed
½ teaspoon dried whole oregano
¼ teaspoon salt
¼ teaspoon pepper
Vegetable cooking spray

Trim excess fat from chicken. Rinse chicken with cold water, and pat dry. Place chicken in a 10- x 6- x 2-inch baking dish, and set aside.

Combine lemon juice and next 5 ingredients in a small bowl; stir well. Pour lemon juice marinade over reserved chicken. Cover and refrigerate 2 hours.

Remove chicken from marinade, reserving marinade in baking dish. Coat grill with cooking spray. Grill chicken 4 to 5 inches over medium-hot coals 15 minutes or until chicken is tender, turning and basting with reserved marinade frequently during grilling. Yield: 4 servings (233 calories per serving).

PROTEIN 25.9 / FAT 13.1 / CARBOHYDRATE 2.0 / CHOLESTEROL 70 / IRON 1.0 / SODIUM 208 / CALCIUM 21

INDIAN-STYLE CHICKEN BREASTS

4 boneless chicken breast halves (1 pound), skinned
1 (8-ounce) carton plain low-fat yogurt
½ teaspoon curry powder
½ teaspoon paprika
½ teaspoon grated fresh gingerroot
⅛ teaspoon ground cardamom
Vegetable cooking spray
2 tablespoons chutney

Trim excess fat from chicken. Rinse chicken with cold water, and pat dry. Place chicken in a shallow baking dish. Combine yogurt, curry powder, paprika, gingerroot, and cardamom, stirring well. Spoon over chicken, turning chicken to coat well. Cover and marinate in refrigerator 8 hours or overnight, turning occasionally.

Remove chicken from marinade, brushing off excess marinade. Arrange chicken on rack of a roasting pan coated with cooking spray. Broil 6 inches from heating element 4 minutes on each side or until tender.

Transfer to a serving platter, and top each chicken breast half with 1½ teaspoons chutney. Yield: 4 servings (195 calories per serving).

PROTEIN 28.8 / FAT 3.9 / CARBOHYDRATE 9.6 / CHOLESTEROL 74 / IRON 1.1 / SODIUM 118 / CALCIUM 121

RED MEAT OR POULTRY?

Poultry is lower in fat and cholesterol than red meat—unless it's fried. The passion of Americans for fried chicken, however, diminishes as people strive to eat a low-fat diet. They discover that chicken can be "anything cuisine." Dressed up with a gourmet sauce as in the recipes on this page or cut up for a quick stir-fry or summer salad, chicken takes center stage at any meal on any occasion. More budget-wise than beef, poultry is usually half the price pound for pound.

Do remember, however, that red meat has some nutritional superiority over poultry. Poultry has only about 10 to 15 percent of the vitamin B_{12} found in red meat and much less zinc. And beef is one of the best sources of usable iron, containing twice the amount of iron found in poultry.

Enjoy the low-fat, low-cholesterol benefits of poultry, but keep moderate portions of lean red meat in your menu plans to benefit from its unique bounty of nutrients.

MANDARIN CHICKEN BREASTS

4 boneless chicken breast halves (1 pound), skinned
Vegetable cooking spray
2 teaspoons vegetable oil
1 (11-ounce) can unsweetened mandarin oranges, undrained
2 tablespoons firmly packed brown sugar
1 teaspoon prepared mustard
3 tablespoons reduced-calorie catsup
1 tablespoon vinegar
1 teaspoon cornstarch
½ teaspoon ground cinnamon
⅛ teaspoon ground cloves

Trim excess fat from chicken. Rinse chicken with cold water, and pat dry. Coat a large skillet with cooking spray; add oil. Place skillet over medium-high heat until hot. Add chicken to skillet; cook 2 to 3 minutes on each side or until lightly browned.

Drain oranges, reserving juice. Set oranges aside. Combine juice and remaining ingredients; stir well, and pour over chicken in skillet. Cover and simmer 30 minutes. Add reserved mandarin oranges, and simmer an additional 5 minutes or until chicken is tender. Transfer to a serving platter, and serve immediately. Yield: 4 servings (216 calories per serving).

PROTEIN 25.8 / FAT 5.3 / CARBOHYDRATE 14.1 / CHOLESTEROL 70 / IRON 1.5 / SODIUM 89 / CALCIUM 23

SOUTHWESTERN CHICKEN KIEV

3 tablespoons margarine, softened
3 tablespoons (¾ ounce) shredded Monterey Jack cheese with jalapeño peppers
2 tablespoons minced fresh cilantro
1 teaspoon minced onion
¼ teaspoon garlic powder
Dash of pepper
6 boneless chicken breast halves (1½ pounds), skinned
⅓ cup fine, dry breadcrumbs
½ teaspoon chili powder
¼ cup skim milk
Vegetable cooking spray
3 cups finely shredded iceberg lettuce
1 large tomato, cut into 8 wedges
Fresh cilantro sprigs

The spicy, hot Southwestern flavors of jalapeño peppers and cilantro are tempered with the mild flavor of chicken, crisp shredded lettuce, and fresh tomato slices in this palate-pleasing Southwestern Chicken Kiev.

Combine first 6 ingredients in a small bowl; stir well. Shape mixture into a 3- x 2-inch stick. Cover and freeze 30 minutes or until firm.

Trim excess fat from chicken. Rinse chicken with cold water, and pat dry. Place chicken between 2 sheets of wax paper; flatten to ¼-inch thickness, using a meat mallet or rolling pin.

Remove margarine stick from freezer, and cut crosswise into 6 portions; place one portion in center of each chicken breast half. Fold long sides of chicken over margarine; fold ends over, and secure with wooden picks.

Combine breadcrumbs and chili powder. Dip each chicken breast half in skim milk, and coat with breadcrumb mixture. Place chicken, seam side up, in a 12- x 8- x 2-inch baking dish coated with cooking spray. Bake at 400° for 15 minutes; turn chicken rolls, and bake an additional 15 minutes or until chicken is tender.

To serve, place shredded lettuce on a serving platter. Top with chicken, and garnish with tomato wedges and cilantro sprigs. Yield: 6 servings (240 calories per serving).

PROTEIN 28.4 / FAT 10.2 / CARBOHYDRATE 7.6 / CHOLESTEROL 74 / IRON 1.5 / SODIUM 202 / CALCIUM 71

CHICKEN SPAGHETTI

1 pound chicken breast halves,
  skinned
5 cups water
3 ounces uncooked spaghetti
1 tablespoon margarine
1 tablespoon all-purpose flour
2 tablespoons skim milk
⅛ teaspoon pepper
Vegetable cooking spray
⅓ cup chopped onion
¼ cup chopped celery
¼ cup chopped green pepper
1 clove garlic, minced
1 (14½-ounce) can no-salt-added stewed
  tomatoes, undrained
⅛ teaspoon crushed red pepper
¼ cup (1 ounce) shredded Cheddar cheese

Trim excess fat from chicken. Rinse chicken with cold water, and pat dry. Place chicken in a small Dutch oven; add water, and bring to a boil. Cover; reduce heat, and simmer 20 minutes or until chicken is tender. Remove chicken from broth; cool, and reserve ½ cup broth. Bone chicken, and cut meat into bite-size pieces; set aside.

Cook spaghetti according to package directions, omitting salt; drain well, and set aside.

Melt margarine in a small saucepan; add flour, stirring until smooth. Cook 1 minute, stirring constantly. Gradually stir in skim milk and ½ cup reserved chicken broth. Cook over medium heat, stirring constantly, until thickened and bubbly. Stir in pepper. Remove milk mixture from heat, and set aside.

Coat a large skillet with cooking spray, and place over medium heat until hot. Add onion, celery, green pepper, and garlic; sauté until tender. Stir in tomatoes, red pepper, and reserved milk mixture. Stir in reserved spaghetti and chicken.

Spoon into a 1½-quart casserole coated with cooking spray. Cover and bake at 350° for 20 minutes. Uncover, and sprinkle with shredded cheese; bake an additional 5 minutes or until cheese melts. Yield: 4 servings (270 calories per serving).

PROTEIN 23.1 / FAT 7.5 / CARBOHYDRATE 27.0 / CHOLESTEROL 53 / IRON 2.2 / SODIUM 147 / CALCIUM 114

A piping hot salad? Yes! Stir-Fried Chicken Salad is a simple-to-prepare change of pace. The crunch of fresh lettuce and vegetables is still there, but the high calories are gone—only 161 calories per serving.

SPICY CHICKEN STRIP CASSEROLE

1 pound boneless chicken breast halves,
  skinned
Vegetable cooking spray
2 teaspoons vegetable oil
1 cup frozen whole kernel corn, thawed
  and drained
½ cup thinly sliced onion
½ cup no-salt-added tomato sauce
2 tablespoons water
1½ teaspoons minced fresh cilantro
1 teaspoon chili powder
½ medium-size green pepper, seeded
  and chopped
2 tablespoons plus 1½ teaspoons reduced-calorie
  no-salt-added chili sauce
½ cup (2 ounces) shredded Monterey Jack cheese
  with jalapeño peppers

Trim excess fat from chicken. Rinse chicken with cold water, and pat dry. Cut chicken into 3- x ½-inch strips. Coat a large skillet with cooking spray; add oil. Place over medium-high heat until hot. Add chicken strips, and cook 4 minutes or until chicken is browned, stirring frequently. Remove chicken from skillet, and drain on paper towels.

Combine chicken strips, corn, onion, tomato sauce, water, cilantro, chili powder, green pepper, and chili sauce in a large bowl; stir well. Spoon mixture into a 1½-quart casserole coated with cooking spray. Cover and bake at 350° for 35 minutes. Uncover; sprinkle with cheese, and bake an additional 5 minutes or until cheese melts. Yield: 4 servings (268 calories per serving).

PROTEIN 31.0 / FAT 9.7 / CARBOHYDRATE 14.2 / CHOLESTEROL 81 / IRON 1.4 / SODIUM 159 / CALCIUM 126

drain well on paper towels.

Add sweet red pepper, snow peas, and onion to wok; stir-fry 2 minutes. Return chicken to wok; add lettuce, and stir-fry until thoroughly heated. Serve immediately. Yield: 6 servings (161 calories per serving).

PROTEIN 18.7 / FAT 3.7 / CARBOHYDRATE 13.1 / CHOLESTEROL 47 / IRON 1.8 / SODIUM 114 / CALCIUM 39

STIR-FRIED CHICKEN SALAD

1 pound boneless chicken breast halves, skinned
2 tablespoons honey
1 tablespoon dark corn syrup
2 teaspoons cornstarch
1 teaspoon grated orange rind
1 tablespoon unsweetened orange juice
2 teaspoons reduced-sodium soy sauce
¼ teaspoon grated fresh gingerroot
Dash of red pepper
Vegetable cooking spray
2 teaspoons peanut oil
1 small sweet red pepper, thinly sliced
2 ounces fresh snow peas
1 green onion, thinly sliced
6 cups romaine lettuce

Trim excess fat from chicken. Rinse chicken with cold water, and pat dry. Cut chicken into ¼-inch strips; set aside.

Combine honey and next 7 ingredients in a medium bowl; stir well. Add reserved chicken, tossing to coat. Cover and marinate in refrigerator at least 30 minutes. Drain.

Coat a wok with cooking spray; add peanut oil, and heat at medium-high (325°) until hot. Add chicken strips, and stir-fry 2 minutes or until chicken is done. Remove chicken strips, and

CHICKEN THIGHS MARENGO

6 chicken thighs (2 pounds), skinned
½ teaspoon salt
¼ teaspoon pepper
Vegetable cooking spray
2 teaspoons olive oil
1 cup sliced fresh mushrooms
4 green onions, sliced
1 clove garlic, minced
½ cup Chablis or other dry white wine
¼ teaspoon dried whole thyme or 1 teaspoon chopped fresh thyme
2 medium tomatoes, cut into wedges
1 tablespoon minced fresh parsley

Trim excess fat from chicken. Rinse chicken with cold water, and pat dry. Place chicken in a shallow container. Sprinkle with salt and pepper.

Coat a large skillet with cooking spray; add oil. Place over medium-high heat until hot. Add chicken to skillet; cook 2 to 3 minutes on each side or until lightly browned. Remove chicken from skillet, and drain on paper towels.

Wipe skillet dry with a paper towel. Recoat skillet with cooking spray; place over medium-high heat until hot. Add mushrooms and cook 2 minutes, stirring frequently. Remove mushrooms from skillet, and set aside.

Recoat skillet with cooking spray. Place over medium-high heat until hot. Add onions and garlic; sauté 1 minute. Stir in wine and thyme. Add reserved chicken. Bring mixture to a boil. Cover; reduce heat, and simmer 25 minutes. Add reserved mushrooms and tomato wedges; simmer 2 minutes or until thoroughly heated. Sprinkle with parsley, and serve immediately. Yield: 6 servings (175 calories per serving).

PROTEIN 18.6 / FAT 9.2 / CARBOHYDRATE 3.9 / CHOLESTEROL 65 / IRON 1.4 / SODIUM 262 / CALCIUM 20

APRICOT CHICKEN THIGHS

½ cup apricot nectar
¼ cup dry sherry
2 tablespoons reduced-sodium soy sauce
1 tablespoon lemon juice
1 tablespoon prepared mustard
½ teaspoon ground ginger
6 chicken thighs (2 pounds), skinned
12 dried apricot halves

Combine first 6 ingredients, mixing well. Set aside.

Trim excess fat from chicken. Rinse chicken with cold water, and pat dry. Place chicken in a 12- x 8- x 2-inch baking dish. Pour reserved apricot nectar mixture over chicken. Cover and bake at 350° for 45 minutes. Uncover, and place apricot halves in apricot nectar mixture. Continue baking, uncovered, 15 minutes or until chicken is tender.

Remove chicken to a warmed serving platter, discarding apricot nectar mixture. Garnish each thigh with 2 apricot halves. Serve immediately. Yield: 6 servings (192 calories per serving).

PROTEIN 18.8 / FAT 7.7 / CARBOHYDRATE 8.5 / CHOLESTEROL 65 / IRON 1.3 / SODIUM 290 / CALCIUM 16

SCAMPI-STYLE CHICKEN THIGHS

4 chicken thighs (1½ pounds), skinned
⅓ cup freshly squeezed lemon juice
2 tablespoons minced fresh parsley
2 tablespoons Chablis or other dry white wine
1 tablespoon margarine, melted
1 tablespoon olive oil
1 clove garlic, minced
⅛ teaspoon onion powder
⅛ teaspoon paprika
Vegetable cooking spray
Lemon wedges (optional)
Fresh parsley sprigs (optional)

Trim excess fat from chicken. Rinse chicken with cold water, and pat dry. Place chicken in a shallow container. Pour lemon juice over chicken, and let stand 20 minutes.

Combine parsley and next 6 ingredients in a small bowl; stir well. Coat rack of a broiler pan with cooking spray. Remove chicken from lemon juice, discarding lemon juice. Arrange chicken on rack, and brush with parsley mixture. Broil 6 inches from heating element 4 minutes on each side or until tender.

Transfer chicken to a serving platter. Garnish with lemon wedges and parsley, if desired. Yield: 4 servings (218 calories per serving).

PROTEIN 19.4 / FAT 14.3 / CARBOHYDRATE 2.6 / CHOLESTEROL 70 / IRON 1.1 / SODIUM 100 / CALCIUM 16

CRISPY DRUMSTICKS

8 chicken drumsticks (2½ pounds), skinned
1½ cups dry whole wheat breadcrumbs
¼ cup grated Parmesan cheese
2 tablespoons minced fresh parsley
¼ teaspoon garlic powder
⅛ teaspoon pepper
⅓ cup skim milk
Vegetable cooking spray

Rinse chicken with cold water, and pat dry. Combine breadcrumbs and next 4 ingredients, stirring well. Dip drumsticks in milk. Dredge in breadcrumb mixture, coating well. Place drumsticks in a 10- x 6- x 2-inch baking dish coated with cooking spray. Bake at 350° for 1 hour or until tender. Yield: 4 servings (286 calories per serving).

PROTEIN 37.3 / FAT 8.7 / CARBOHYDRATE 13.4 / CHOLESTEROL 110 / IRON 2.1 / SODIUM 343 / CALCIUM 135

LITTLE CHICKEN CASSEROLES

4 cups chopped, cooked chicken breast (skinned before cooking and cooked without salt)
¼ cup sherry
1 tablespoon plus 1½ teaspoons margarine
1 tablespoon plus 1½ teaspoons all-purpose flour
1 cup plus 2 tablespoons skim milk
Vegetable cooking spray
½ pound fresh mushrooms, sliced
2 tablespoons chopped fresh parsley
⅛ teaspoon poultry seasoning
½ cup (2 ounces) shredded Provolone cheese
Paprika

Combine chicken and sherry in a zip top heavy-duty plastic bag; seal tightly. Turn bag to coat chicken thoroughly. Let stand 1 hour.

Melt margarine in a large heavy saucepan over low heat; add flour, stirring until smooth. Cook 1 minute, stirring constantly. Gradually add milk; cook over medium heat, stirring constantly, until thickened and bubbly. Remove from heat, and stir in chicken and sherry. Set chicken mixture aside.

Coat a small skillet with cooking spray; place over medium heat until hot. Add mushrooms and sauté 3 to 5 minutes or until tender. Stir mushrooms, parsley, and poultry seasoning into reserved chicken mixture.

Divide chicken mixture evenly into 4 (10-ounce) custard cups or ramekins coated with cooking spray. Bake at 375° for 20 minutes or until thoroughly heated. Remove from oven; sprinkle with cheese and paprika. Bake an additional 5 minutes. Yield: 4 servings (260 calories per serving).

PROTEIN 34.0 / FAT 8.9 / CARBOHYDRATE 6.6 / CHOLESTEROL 87 / IRON 1.7 / SODIUM 213 / CALCIUM 148

CHICKEN ÉTOUFFÉE

Vegetable cooking spray
1 large onion, chopped
1 small green pepper, chopped
½ small sweet red pepper, chopped
2 stalks celery, chopped
1 clove garlic, minced
2 tablespoons margarine
2 tablespoons all-purpose flour
3 cups chopped, cooked chicken breast (skinned before cooking and cooked without salt)
¾ cup water
¾ teaspoon chicken-flavored bouillon granules
½ teaspoon dried whole thyme
¼ teaspoon salt
¼ teaspoon red pepper
Dash of hot sauce
2 cups hot cooked parboiled rice (cooked without salt or fat)
1 tablespoon chopped fresh parsley

Coat a large skillet with cooking spray; place over medium heat until hot. Add onion and next 4 ingredients, and sauté until tender. Remove vegetables from skillet; set aside.

Place margarine and flour in large skillet; cook over low heat 5 minutes, stirring constantly, until mixture is the color of a copper penny. Return vegetables to skillet. Add chicken and next 6 ingredients; simmer 2 minutes or until thoroughly heated. Serve over hot cooked rice. Sprinkle with parsley. Yield: 8 servings (182 calories per serving).

PROTEIN 18.0 / FAT 5.0 / CARBOHYDRATE 15.0 / CHOLESTEROL 45 / IRON 1.5 / SODIUM 352 / CALCIUM 32

CHINESE CHICKEN-STUFFED PEPPERS

4 large sweet red peppers
Vegetable cooking spray
1 tablespoon sesame oil
1 clove garlic, minced
1 teaspoon minced fresh gingerroot
½ cup finely chopped carrots
¼ cup thinly sliced green onions
1 cup finely chopped, cooked chicken breast (skinned before cooking and cooked without salt)
1 cup cooked regular rice (cooked without salt or fat)
½ cup frozen English peas, thawed and drained
1 egg, beaten
1 tablespoon plus 1½ teaspoons reduced-sodium soy sauce
⅛ teaspoon salt

Cut a ½-inch-thick slice from the side of each pepper, reserving slices; remove seeds. Place peppers in boiling water; boil 5 minutes. Drain and set aside.

Coat a large skillet or wok with cooking spray; add oil, and place over medium heat until hot. Add garlic and gingerroot; stir-fry 30 seconds. Add carrots and green onions; stir-fry 2 minutes. Remove from heat. Add chicken and remaining ingredients, stirring well.

Spoon ¾ cup mixture into each reserved pepper. Top with reserved pepper slices. Arrange peppers, cut side up, in a 10- x 6- x 2-inch baking dish. Cover and bake at 350° for 30 minutes or until thoroughly heated. Yield: 4 servings (231 calories per serving).

PROTEIN 16.4 / FAT 6.7 / CARBOHYDRATE 25.7 / CHOLESTEROL 98 / IRON 3.1 / SODIUM 366 / CALCIUM 37

CHICKEN SPOONBREAD

Vegetable cooking spray
⅓ cup shredded carrots
¼ cup finely chopped fresh mushrooms
2 tablespoons finely chopped onion
1 cup skim milk
1 cup water
1 teaspoon chicken-flavored bouillon granules
½ cup cornmeal
3 eggs, separated
½ teaspoon baking powder
⅛ teaspoon salt
¼ teaspoon pepper
2 cups chopped, cooked chicken breast (skinned before cooking and cooked without salt)
1 tablespoon chopped fresh parsley
½ cup (2 ounces) shredded American cheese

Coat a large skillet with cooking spray; place over medium-high heat until hot. Add carrots, mushrooms, and onion; sauté until mushrooms are tender. Set aside.

Combine milk, water, and bouillon in a large saucepan; cook over medium heat just until boiling. Stir in cornmeal; reduce heat, and cook until thickened. Remove from heat.

Beat egg yolks until thick and lemon colored. Add egg yolks, baking powder, salt, pepper, chicken, parsley, and sautéed vegetables to cornmeal mixture; stir well. Beat egg whites (at room temperature) until stiff. Gently fold into chicken mixture. Spoon into a 2-quart casserole coated with cooking spray. Bake, uncovered, at 375° for 40 minutes. Sprinkle with cheese; bake 5 minutes or until cheese melts. Yield: 8 servings (143 calories per serving).

PROTEIN 16.8 / FAT 4.1 / CARBOHYDRATE 8.8 / CHOLESTEROL 133 / IRON 1.1 / SODIUM 274 / CALCIUM 119

SPAGHETTI WITH CHICKEN LIVERS

Vegetable cooking spray
1 teaspoon vegetable oil
¾ pound chicken livers, quartered
½ pound fresh mushrooms, sliced
1 large onion, chopped
1 small green pepper, seeded and chopped
2 cloves garlic, minced
2 (8-ounce) cans no-salt-added tomato sauce
1 (6-ounce) can no-salt-added tomato paste
1 teaspoon dried whole basil
½ teaspoon dried whole oregano
¼ teaspoon black pepper
⅛ teaspoon crushed red pepper
4 cups hot cooked spaghetti (cooked without salt)
¼ cup grated Parmesan cheese

Coat a large skillet with cooking spray; add oil, and place over medium heat until hot. Add chicken livers, and cook 5 minutes or until browned, stirring occasionally. Remove chicken livers; set aside.

Recoat skillet with cooking spray. Add mushrooms, onion, green pepper, and garlic; sauté until tender. Stir in tomato sauce, tomato paste, basil, oregano, black pepper, and red pepper. Cover; reduce heat, and simmer 20 minutes, stirring occasionally. Stir in reserved chicken livers; cook 1 minute or until thoroughly heated. Serve over hot cooked spaghetti; sprinkle with Parmesan cheese. Yield: 8 servings (235 calories per serving).

PROTEIN 17.0 / FAT 4.2 / CARBOHYDRATE 32.4 / CHOLESTEROL 270 / IRON 5.3 / SODIUM 93 / CALCIUM 66

CONSIDER LIVER: A BOUNTY OF VITAMINS, MINERALS—AND CHOLESTEROL

As an ideal source of various vitamins and minerals, liver ranks right up there with dark green vegetables, whole grains, milk, and meats. Two to 3 ounces of liver provide considerable amounts of iron, vitamins A, C, B_6, B_{12}, folate, niacin, riboflavin, and thiamin. Liver is also relatively low in total fat and saturated fat.

Beyond liver's store of nutrients, however, is its high cholesterol content. Three ounces of liver have 372 milligrams of cholesterol, well over 100 percent of the recommended daily intake. For this reason, the American Heart Association recommends only one serving of liver per month, like well-spiced Spaghetti with Chicken Livers.

OFF WITH THE SKIN—AND FAT

Most of the fat in poultry is concentrated in the skin, under the skin, and near the tail. Removing this fat before cooking reduces calories by about 50 percent. Use these simple procedures to remove the skin before preparing Garlic-Sage Roasted or Raspberry-Grilled Cornish Hens:
- Rinse hens with cold water, and pat dry.
- Place hens, cavity side down, on a wooden cutting board. Use kitchen shears or a sharp knife to cut skin down the middle of each breast.
- Pull skin to each side of hens and then over each leg. Remove skin from legs.
- Snip skin around wings. Pull skin over each wing and remove.
- Turn hen over; use a sharp knife to remove remaining skin on backs.

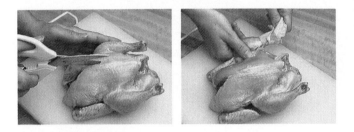

GARLIC-SAGE ROASTED CORNISH HENS

4 (1-pound, 6-ounce) cornish hens, skinned
2 cloves garlic, crushed
¼ teaspoon dried whole sage or 1 teaspoon minced fresh sage
2 teaspoons olive oil
⅛ teaspoon coarse salt
Pepper

Remove giblets from hens, and reserve for other uses. Rinse hens with cold water, and pat dry. Lift wingtips up and over back so they are tucked under hen. Close cavities, and tie leg ends together with string; set aside.

Combine garlic and next 3 ingredients; spread on hens. Sprinkle lightly with pepper. Place hens, breast side up, in a shallow roasting pan.

Bake at 350° for 1 hour, basting often with pan drippings. Split hens lengthwise to serve. Yield: 8 servings (222 calories per serving).

PROTEIN 32.1 / FAT 9.3 / CARBOHYDRATE 0.3 / CHOLESTEROL 99 / IRON 1.4 / SODIUM 132 / CALCIUM 19

RASPBERRY-GRILLED CORNISH HENS

4 (1-pound, 6-ounce) cornish hens, skinned
⅔ cup low-sugar red raspberry spread
⅓ cup crème de cassis
1 tablespoon firmly packed brown sugar
½ teaspoon ground ginger
Vegetable cooking spray

Remove giblets from hens; reserve for other use. Rinse hens with cold water, and pat dry. Split hens lengthwise, using an electric knife.

Combine raspberry spread and next 3 ingredients in a small saucepan; cook over medium heat until thoroughly heated. (Do not boil.)

Coat grill with cooking spray. Grill hens 6 inches over medium-hot coals 20 to 30 minutes, turning and basting hens with warm glaze mixture every 5 minutes. Yield: 8 servings (247 calories per serving).

PROTEIN 32.1 / FAT 8.2 / CARBOHYDRATE 6.5 / CHOLESTEROL 99 / IRON 1.4 / SODIUM 96 / CALCIUM 19

TURKEY YAKI TORI

½ cup rice wine
¼ cup Sauterne
2 tablespoons firmly packed brown sugar
2 tablespoons reduced-sodium soy sauce
1 pound boneless turkey breast, skinned
1 small green pepper, seeded and cut into 1-inch pieces
4 green onions with tops, cut into 1-inch pieces

Combine first 4 ingredients in a saucepan. Bring to a boil; reduce heat, and simmer, uncovered, 5 minutes. Remove from heat; let cool.

Rinse turkey with cold water, and pat dry. Cut into 1-inch cubes. Place cubes in a shallow container. Pour cooled marinade over turkey. Cover; refrigerate 8 hours or overnight.

Drain turkey, reserving marinade. Alternate turkey cubes, green pepper, and onions on four 12-inch wooden skewers. Grill 5 to 6 inches from hot coals 10 to 12 minutes or until desired degree of doneness. Turn and brush turkey and vegetables frequently with reserved marinade. Yield: 4 servings (173 calories per serving).

PROTEIN 23.6 / FAT 2.6 / CARBOHYDRATE 12.5 / CHOLESTEROL 52 / IRON 1.7 / SODIUM 345 / CALCIUM 33

Lemon-Grilled Turkey Breast has a distinctive hickory-smoked flavor.

LEMON-GRILLED TURKEY BREAST

¼ cup lemon juice
2 tablespoons vegetable oil
2 cloves garlic, crushed
1 teaspoon dried whole dillweed
½ teaspoon grated lemon rind
½ teaspoon paprika
½ teaspoon pepper
1 (4-pound) boneless turkey breast, skinned
Hickory chips
Vegetable cooking spray

Combine first 7 ingredients in a small bowl, stirring well. Set aside.

Rinse turkey with cold water, and pat dry. Roll turkey loosely, securing any loose pieces with string. Brush turkey with half of reserved lemon juice mixture. Set aside remaining lemon juice mixture.

Prepare charcoal fire in commercial meat smoker; let fire burn 15 to 20 minutes. Soak hickory chips in water 15 minutes, and place chips on coals. Place water pan in smoker; fill pan with water.

Place turkey on rack coated with cooking spray. Insert meat thermometer, if desired. Cover with smoker lid; cook 8 hours or until meat thermometer registers 185°, basting turkey with remaining lemon juice mixture after 4 hours. Refill water pan with water, and add additional charcoal as needed.

Transfer turkey breast to a cutting board; remove string. Slice turkey. Tranfer turkey slices to a serving platter. Yield: 14 servings (156 calories per serving).

PROTEIN 25.9 / FAT 4.8 / CARBOHYDRATE 0.7 / CHOLESTEROL 60 / IRON 1.3 / SODIUM 56 / CALCIUM 19

BEING FRANK ON FRANKS

All-beef, all-chicken, or all-turkey—the 5 billion hot dogs typically consumed by Americans between Memorial Day and Labor Day are high in saturated fat. It's true that a 1-ounce chicken or turkey frank averages 40 percent less fat than its beef or pork counterpart, but look what happens when roasted turkey breast is compared to the processed frank:

	Calories	Fat	Sodium
Roast Turkey Breast (1 ounce)	45	.9 g	18 mg
Turkey Frank (1 ounce)	65	5.4 g	248 mg

Turkey breast, naturally low in fat and sodium, is nutritionally superior to the turkey frank, whose fat content is over 70 percent of total calories. The sodium level is about thirteen times that of turkey breast. Enjoy a hot dog at the ball game, but when it comes to nutritious summertime fare, a turkey breast sandwich or the delicious turkey dishes on these pages have them beat.

ROAST TURKEY WITH FENNEL STUFFING

¼ teaspoon chicken-flavored bouillon granules
¼ cup water
3 small fennel bulbs
Vegetable cooking spray
1 teaspoon margarine
1 small onion, thinly sliced
¼ teaspoon salt
¼ teaspoon pepper
1 (4-pound) boneless turkey breast, skinned
½ cup Chablis or other dry white wine
1 bay leaf

Combine bouillon granules and water; set aside.

Wash fennel; remove top stems, bottom, and tough outer portions. Slice bulbs crosswise into thin strips. Coat a large skillet with cooking spray; add margarine, and place over medium-high heat until hot. Add onion; sauté 10 minutes or until tender. Add fennel, reserved bouillon mixture, salt, and pepper. Cover; reduce heat, and simmer mixture 20 minutes or until fennel is tender. Uncover, and continue cooking until liquid evaporates.

Rinse turkey with cold water, and pat dry. Lay turkey breast flat. Pat fennel mixture evenly over turkey, keeping 1 inch from edges. Roll turkey breast starting at long end, and secure with string. Insert meat thermometer into turkey breast, if desired, making sure thermometer end touches meat. Place in a browning bag prepared according to package directions. Pour wine over turkey; add bay leaf. Place in a shallow roasting pan. Bake at 325° for 2 hours or until meat thermometer registers 185°. Remove and discard bay leaf before serving. Yield: 12 servings (179 calories per serving).

PROTEIN 31.4 / FAT 3.8 / CARBOHYDRATE 3.3 / CHOLESTEROL 70 / IRON 2.6 / SODIUM 130 / CALCIUM 66

HUNTER'S TURKEY CUTLETS

8 turkey breast cutlets (1 pound)
Vegetable cooking spray
1 teaspoon vegetable oil
¾ pound small fresh mushrooms
2 medium shallots, thinly sliced
1 medium clove garlic, thinly sliced
1 large tomato, peeled, seeded, and chopped
1 (8-ounce) can no-salt-added tomato paste
⅔ cup Chablis or other dry white wine
¼ teaspoon pepper
1 tablespoon minced fresh parsley

Rinse turkey with cold water, and pat dry. Coat a large skillet with cooking spray; add oil, and place over medium heat until hot. Add turkey; cook 2 minutes on each side or until lightly browned. Drain well on paper towels. Wipe skillet with a paper towel.

Remove stems from mushrooms; reserve for other uses. Recoat skillet with cooking spray, and place over medium heat until hot. Add mushroom caps, shallots, and garlic to skillet; sauté until tender. Return turkey to skillet, and add tomato. Combine tomato paste, wine, and pepper; stir well, and add to skillet. Cover and simmer 10 minutes or until turkey is tender. Remove from heat; sprinkle with parsley. Yield: 4 servings (239 calories per serving).

PROTEIN 30.8 / FAT 4.5 / CARBOHYDRATE 20.0 / CHOLESTEROL 61 / IRON 3.5 / SODIUM 90 / CALCIUM 57

DILL-DIJON TURKEY PATTIES

1 (1-pound) package raw ground turkey, thawed
2¼ teaspoons dried whole dillweed, divided
Vegetable cooking spray
1 tablespoon margarine
½ pound fresh mushrooms, sliced
2 green onions, sliced
¼ cup Chablis or other dry white wine
2 tablespoons water
1 tablespoon Dijon mustard
2 tablespoons low-fat sour cream

Combine turkey and ¼ teaspoon dillweed in a bowl; stir well. Shape mixture into 4 (¾-inch-thick) patties.

Coat a large skillet with cooking spray; place over medium heat until hot. Add patties, and cook 5 to 7 minutes on each side or until browned. Remove patties, and drain on paper towels; transfer to a platter.

Wipe skillet dry with a paper towel. Recoat skillet with cooking spray; add margarine, and place over medium heat until margarine melts. Add mushrooms and onions, and sauté until tender. Stir in wine, water, mustard, sour cream, and remaining 2 teaspoons dillweed, blending well. Return patties to skillet and cook until thoroughly heated. Yield: 4 servings (205 calories per serving).

PROTEIN 26.6 / FAT 8.5 / CARBOHYDRATE 4.7 / CHOLESTEROL 67 / IRON 2.6 / SODIUM 212 / CALCIUM 48

TURKEY LOAF WITH MUSTARD SAUCE

2 (1-pound) packages raw ground
    turkey, thawed
2 cups soft whole wheat breadcrumbs
½ cup shredded carrot
¼ cup finely chopped onion
2 eggs, beaten
1 tablespoon minced fresh parsley
1½ teaspoons dry mustard
½ teaspoon pepper
Vegetable cooking spray
Fresh dill sprigs (optional)
Mustard Sauce

Combine first 8 ingredients in a large bowl; stir well. Place mixture on a broiler rack coated with cooking spray, and shape into a slightly rounded loaf. (Mixture will be soft.) Bake at 350° for 1 hour and 10 minutes or until meat is no longer pink. Transfer loaf to a serving platter, and garnish with dill sprigs, if desired. Serve with 2 tablespoons Mustard Sauce per serving. Yield: 10 servings (229 calories per serving).

Mustard Sauce:

1 cup reduced-calorie mayonnaise
3 tablespoons water
2 tablespoons lemon juice
1 tablespoon plus 1 teaspoon Dijon mustard
1 teaspoon dried whole dillweed

Combine all ingredients in a small saucepan, stirring well. Cook over low heat, stirring constantly, 2 minutes or until thoroughly heated. Yield: 1⅓ cups.

PROTEIN 22.7 / FAT 11.5 / CARBOHYDRATE 7.9 / CHOLESTEROL 115 / IRON 1.8 / SODIUM 354 / CALCIUM 39

Light summer salads made from light ingredients: Nouvelle Tossed Salad (page 179), composed of a curly endive, radicchio, and arugula; Pasta-Stuffed Tomatoes (page 182); and Oriental Fruit Salad (page 178), a tempting combination of litchis, tangerines, fresh pineapple, and water chestnuts.

Salads & Salad Dressings

MULLED WINE MOLD

2 cups Burgundy or other dry red wine
2 cups unsweetened red grape juice
1½ cups unsweetened orange juice
1 medium-size orange, thinly sliced
3 (3-inch) sticks cinnamon
2 tablespoons firmly packed brown sugar
1 teaspoon whole allspice
1 teaspoon whole cloves
4 envelopes unflavored gelatin
1½ cups cold water
1 (16-ounce) can peach halves in light syrup,
   drained and chopped
1 (8-ounce) can unsweetened crushed pineapple,
   drained
1 small banana, sliced
Vegetable cooking spray

Combine first 8 ingredients in a large saucepan. Bring to a boil. Reduce heat, and simmer, uncovered, 15 minutes. Strain orange slices and spices from wine mixture. Return wine mixture to saucepan.

Sprinkle unflavored gelatin over cold water; let stand 3 minutes. Add gelatin mixture to saucepan. Cook over low heat, stirring until gelatin dissolves. Chill until the consistency of unbeaten egg white. Fold in chopped peaches, pineapple, and banana slices. Pour into an 8-cup mold coated with cooking spray. Cover and chill until firm. Unmold onto a serving platter. Yield: 16 servings (73 calories per serving).

PROTEIN 2.1 / FAT 0.1 / CARBOHYDRATE 16.9 / CHOLESTEROL 0 / IRON 0.6 / SODIUM 7 / CALCIUM 25

MIXED BERRIES WITH RASPBERRY VINAIGRETTE

1 cup fresh blackberries
1 cup fresh blueberries
1 cup fresh raspberries
1 cup fresh strawberries, washed and hulled
½ cup strawberry nectar
2 tablespoons raspberry vinegar
1 tablespoon vegetable oil

Combine berries, tossing gently. Combine strawberry nectar, raspberry vinegar, and vegetable oil; stir well. Pour over berries; toss gently. Cover and chill 1 hour. Yield: 8 servings (59 calories per serving).

PROTEIN 0.5 / FAT 2.0 / CARBOHYDRATE 10.7 / CHOLESTEROL 0 / IRON 0.5 / SODIUM 1 / CALCIUM 14

FRUIT KABOB SALAD WITH RUBY DRESSING

1 small banana, peeled and cut into 8 pieces
8 medium-size fresh strawberries, washed and hulled
8 medium-size fresh kumquats
1 medium kiwifruit, peeled and cut into 4 slices
Ruby Dressing
Red leaf lettuce

Alternate bananas, strawberries, and kumquats with kiwifruit on 4 skewers. Brush each skewer of fruit with equal amounts of Ruby Dressing. Chill fruit skewers thoroughly, if desired, and serve on a lettuce-lined platter. Yield: 4 servings (86 calories per serving).

Ruby Dressing:

2 tablespoons reduced-calorie strawberry spread
2 tablespoons cranberry juice cocktail
¼ teaspoon ground cinnamon
½ teaspoon lemon juice

Combine all ingredients in a non-aluminum saucepan, stirring well. Cook mixture over low heat, stirring constantly, until strawberry spread melts. Remove from heat, and cool. Yield: about 3 tablespoons.

PROTEIN 1.1 / FAT 0.5 / CARBOHYDRATE 21.3 / CHOLESTEROL 0 / IRON 0.8 / SODIUM 5 / CALCIUM 37

Luncheon Lilies are ripe melons filled with a mango, honeydew, and strawberry-studded cottage cheese mixture. Serve with frosted green and red grapes for an impressive fruit salad.

LUNCHEON LILIES

2 (2-ounce) bunches seedless green grapes
2 (2-ounce) bunches seedless red grapes
1 egg white
2 teaspoons sugar
1¼ cups low-fat cottage cheese
½ cup sliced fresh strawberries
½ cup finely chopped fresh mango
½ cup finely chopped fresh honeydew
¼ teaspoon coconut extract
2 small cantaloupes (1¼ pounds each)

Place grape bunches on a large wire rack. Beat egg white just until frothy. Using a soft pastry brush, paint the grapes with the beaten egg white. Immediately sprinkle with sugar, and set aside to dry at least 2½ hours in a cool place (do not refrigerate).

Combine cottage cheese, strawberries, mango, honeydew, and coconut extract; toss gently. Cover and chill at least 1 hour.

Cut cantaloupes in half crosswise, and scoop out seeds. Cut a thin slice from bottom of each half to sit flat, if necessary. Using a sharp knife or a V-shaped cutter, wedge the top edge of each cantaloupe half. Spoon ½ cup chilled cottage cheese mixture into each cantaloupe half.

Transfer to a large serving platter, and garnish platter with reserved frosted grapes. Yield: 4 servings (249 calories per serving).

PROTEIN 13.8 / FAT 2.7 / CARBOHYDRATE 46.7 / CHOLESTEROL 6 / IRON 1.1 / SODIUM 330 / CALCIUM 97

PEACH MELBA SALAD CUPS

2 (6-ounce) peaches, halved and pitted
1 tablespoon lime juice, divided
½ cup fresh raspberries
2 tablespoons unsweetened peach nectar
¼ teaspoon almond extract
Curly leaf lettuce leaves (optional)

Carefully scoop out pulp from peach halves, leaving a ¼-inch-thick shell. Chop pulp, and set aside. Brush peach shells with 2 teaspoons lime juice to prevent browning. Set aside.

Combine reserved chopped pulp, raspberries, peach nectar, 1 teaspoon lime juice, and almond extract in a small bowl. Toss gently to coat. Spoon 3 tablespoons peach-raspberry mixture into each peach shell. Serve on curly leaf lettuce leaves, if desired. Yield: 4 servings (37 calories per serving).

PROTEIN 0.6 / FAT 0.2 / CARBOHYDRATE 9.2 / CHOLESTEROL 0 / IRON 0.4 / SODIUM 1 / CALCIUM 10

ORIENTAL FRUIT SALAD

1 (11-ounce) can litchis, rinsed and drained
3 tangerines, peeled and sectioned
1 cup cubed fresh pineapple
1 (8-ounce) can sliced water chestnuts, drained
2 tablespoons unsweetened pineapple juice
2 tablespoons lime juice
1 tablespoon honey
½ teaspoon grated lime rind
½ teaspoon almond extract
1 fresh pineapple boat (optional)

Combine first 4 ingredients in a large bowl; stir well to combine. Combine pineapple juice, lime juice, honey, rind, and extract in a small bowl, stirring until well blended. Pour dressing over fruit mixture. Toss gently; cover and chill thoroughly. Spoon salad into pineapple boat to serve, if desired. Yield: 6 servings (77 calories per serving).

PROTEIN 0.9 / FAT 0.3 / CARBOHYDRATE 19.6 / CHOLESTEROL 0 / IRON 0.5 / SODIUM 4 / CALCIUM 13

BROCCOLI-GARBANZO BEAN SALAD

1 (19-ounce) can garbanzo beans
¼ cup red wine vinegar with garlic
¼ cup water
1 tablespoon vegetable oil
1 teaspoon dried whole oregano
½ teaspoon dried whole basil
¼ teaspoon dried whole tarragon
¼ teaspoon pepper
Dash of red pepper
½ pound cherry tomatoes, halved
3 green onions with tops, chopped
2½ cups broccoli flowerets

Place garbanzo beans in a colander, and rinse under cold tap water 1 minute; set colander aside to let beans drain 1 minute.
Combine vinegar and next 7 ingredients, stirring well; set aside. Combine reserved beans, tomatoes, and green onions; toss gently. Add reserved dressing mixture, and toss lightly to coat well. Cover and chill 2 hours. Add broccoli, tossing gently. Cover and chill 30 minutes. Yield: 6 servings (97 calories per serving).

PROTEIN 4.5 / FAT 3.9 / CARBOHYDRATE 13.1 / CHOLESTEROL 0 / IRON 1.3 / SODIUM 105 / CALCIUM 47

SUMMERTIME SLAW

½ pound cabbage, chopped
½ cup chopped cucumber
½ cup chopped tomato
⅓ cup tomato juice
2 tablespoons cider vinegar
1 teaspoon sugar
½ teaspoon salt
½ teaspoon dried whole dillweed
¼ teaspoon pepper

Combine cabbage, cucumber, and tomato in a large bowl. Toss gently. Combine tomato juice and remaining ingredients, stirring with a wire whisk. Pour tomato juice mixture over cabbage mixture. Toss gently to coat well. Cover and chill thoroughly. Yield: 6 servings (16 calories per serving).

PROTEIN 0.6 / FAT 0.1 / CARBOHYDRATE 3.8 / CHOLESTEROL 0 / IRON 0.4 / SODIUM 250 / CALCIUM 18

WARM CHINESE CABBAGE SALAD

1 large head Chinese cabbage
½ cup sliced green onions
¼ cup rice wine vinegar
2 tablespoons vegetable oil
1 teaspoon Worcestershire sauce
¼ teaspoon pepper

Combine cabbage and green onions in a large bowl. Combine remaining ingredients in a small saucepan. Bring to a boil. Boil 1 minute. Remove from heat, and pour hot mixture over cabbage. Toss lightly. Serve immediately. Yield: 4 servings (98 calories per serving).

PROTEIN 1.9 / FAT 7.1 / CARBOHYDRATE 8.9 / CHOLESTEROL 0 / IRON 1.0 / SODIUM 40 / CALCIUM 75

NOUVELLE TOSSED SALAD

1 clove garlic, split
7 cups torn curly endive
3 cups torn radicchio
2 cups arugula leaves
3 tablespoons vinegar
2 tablespoons walnut oil
¼ teaspoon salt-free herb and
    spice seasoning
⅛ teaspoon pepper
Tomato rose (optional)

Rub a large salad bowl with garlic. Discard garlic. Combine endive, radicchio, and arugula in salad bowl, and toss well. Cover and chill thoroughly.

Combine vinegar, oil, seasoning, and pepper in a jar; cover tightly, and shake vigorously. Pour over chilled salad, and toss well. Garnish with tomato rose, if desired. Yield: 12 servings (30 calories per serving).

PROTEIN 0.6 / FAT 2.4 / CARBOHYDRATE 1.9 / CHOLESTEROL 0 / IRON 0.4 / SODIUM 9 / CALCIUM 28

MEXICAN DINNER SALAD

2 cups torn red leaf lettuce
2 cups torn romaine lettuce
1 cup cubed avocado
1 cup jicama, peeled and cut into
    ¼-inch strips
4 fresh tomatillos, husked and
    chopped
¼ cup tomato juice with green
    chiles
1 tablespoon red wine vinegar
2 teaspoons vegetable oil
¼ teaspoon sugar

Combine first 5 ingredients in a large bowl; set aside. Combine tomato juice, vinegar, oil, and sugar in a small bowl, mixing well. Pour dressing over salad, and toss well. Serve immediately. Yield: 6 servings (59 calories per serving).

PROTEIN 1.3 / FAT 4.2 / CARBOHYDRATE 4.8 / CHOLESTEROL 0 / IRON 0.6 / SODIUM 61 / CALCIUM 15

HOMINY SALAD

1 (15½-ounce) can golden hominy, drained
¼ cup sliced green onions
3 tablespoons red wine vinegar
3 tablespoons water
1 tablespoon vegetable oil
¼ teaspoon salt
¼ teaspoon pepper
2 cups torn iceberg lettuce
1 cup sliced celery
¼ cup sliced pimiento
2 tablespoons sliced ripe olives

Combine first 7 ingredients in a large bowl, stirring well. Cover and chill 2 hours. Add lettuce, celery, pimiento, and olives just before serving; toss gently. Yield: 6 servings (65 calories per serving).

PROTEIN 1.0 / FAT 3.1 / CARBOHYDRATE 8.4 / CHOLESTEROL 0 / IRON 0.6 / SODIUM 254 / CALCIUM 20

LEMON-MUSHROOM SALAD

½ pound fresh mushrooms, sliced
¼ cup water
3 tablespoons freshly squeezed lemon juice
2 tablespoons plus ½ teaspoon vegetable oil
1 tablespoon plus 1 teaspoon Dijon mustard
½ teaspoon sugar
¼ teaspoon dried whole tarragon
1 small lemon, cut into 4 slices
Lettuce leaves
1 medium tomato, cut into 8 slices

Place mushrooms in a large shallow container. Combine water and next 5 ingredients in a small bowl, stirring with a wire whisk. Pour mixture over mushrooms. Add lemon slices. Cover and marinate in refrigerator 4 hours, stirring occasionally.

Drain mushrooms, reserving marinade and lemon slices. Place ½ cup mushrooms on individual lettuce-lined salad plates. Spoon 1 tablespoon reserved marinade over each salad. Garnish each salad with 2 tomato slices and 1 reserved lemon slice. Yield: 4 servings (104 calories per serving).

PROTEIN 1.9 / FAT 8.1 / CARBOHYDRATE 7.8 / CHOLESTEROL 0 / IRON 1.1 / SODIUM 156 / CALCIUM 14

BAKED POTATO SALAD

2 large baking potatoes (1 pound)
½ cup diced celery
1 (2-ounce) jar sliced pimiento, drained
1 tablespoon plus 1½ teaspoons reduced-calorie
  mayonnaise
2 tablespoons low-fat sour cream
¾ teaspoon prepared horseradish mustard
¾ teaspoon celery seeds
⅛ teaspoon pepper
1 tablespoon plus 1 teaspoon minced fresh chives

Scrub potatoes thoroughly; bake at 400° for 45 minutes or until done. Allow potatoes to cool completely. Cut potatoes in half lengthwise; carefully scoop out pulp, leaving shells intact. Chop pulp; set pulp and shells aside.

Combine celery and next 6 ingredients in a medium mixing bowl; gently fold in reserved potato pulp.

Spoon ½ cup potato mixture into each reserved potato shell; cover and chill thoroughly. Sprinkle with chives before serving. Yield: 4 servings (125 calories per serving).

PROTEIN 3.4 / FAT 2.7 / CARBOHYDRATE 22.8 / CHOLESTEROL 5 / IRON 1.9 / SODIUM 87 / CALCIUM 40

SWEET POTATO AMBROSIA SALAD

3 medium-size sweet potatoes (1½ pounds)
1 cup cubed fresh pineapple, well drained
1 medium orange, sectioned and well drained
2 tablespoons low-fat sour cream
2 tablespoons plain non-fat yogurt
2 tablespoons reduced-calorie mayonnaise
1 tablespoon plus 1½ teaspoons grated coconut
1 tablespoon honey
½ teaspoon grated orange rind
1 tablespoon unsweetened orange juice
¼ teaspoon coconut extract
⅛ teaspoon salt
Fresh mint sprig (optional)

Wrap sweet potatoes in aluminum foil; bake at 400° for 45 minutes or until tender. Cool completely. Remove and discard skin; cut potatoes into cubes. Combine sweet potatoes, pineapple, and orange sections in a serving bowl; toss gently, and set aside.

Combine sour cream and remaining ingredients, except mint, in a small bowl, stirring well. Pour over reserved sweet potato mixture; toss gently. Cover and chill 2 hours. Garnish with mint, if desired. Yield: 8 servings (120 calories per serving).

PROTEIN 1.8 / FAT 2.4 / CARBOHYDRATE 23.8 / CHOLESTEROL 3 / IRON 0.6 / SODIUM 78 / CALCIUM 34

SPAGHETTI SQUASH SALAD

1 (2-pound) spaghetti squash
2 medium tomatoes, seeded and chopped
1 medium cucumber, seeded and chopped
½ cup chopped purple onion
½ cup chopped green pepper
¼ cup reduced-calorie Italian salad dressing
¼ cup reduced-calorie mayonnaise

Wash spaghetti squash, and cut in half lengthwise; remove and discard seeds. Place squash, cut side down, in a Dutch oven; add 2 inches water. Cover, and bring to a boil; reduce heat and simmer 20 minutes or until tender. Drain squash, and cool. Remove spaghetti-like strands using a fork; press excess moisture from squash using paper towels. Discard squash shells.

Combine spaghetti squash, tomatoes, cucumber, purple onion, and green pepper in a large bowl. Combine salad dressing and mayonnaise, stirring well. Pour over vegetable mixture, and toss gently. Cover and chill at least 2 hours. Yield: 12 servings (39 calories per serving).

PROTEIN 0.8 / FAT 1.6 / CARBOHYDRATE 6.0 / CHOLESTEROL 2 / IRON 0.4 / SODIUM 93 / CALCIUM 15

TOMATO-ARTICHOKE SALAD

1 (9-ounce) package frozen artichoke hearts
2 medium tomatoes, chopped
2 tablespoons olive oil
1 tablespoon red wine vinegar with garlic
¼ teaspoon sugar
¼ teaspoon dried whole basil
¼ teaspoon dried whole oregano
¼ teaspoon dried whole dillweed

Cook artichoke hearts according to package directions, omitting salt; drain, and cool.

Combine artichoke hearts and tomatoes in a medium bowl. Combine remaining ingredients in a jar; cover tightly and shake vigorously. Pour over vegetables, tossing lightly. Cover and marinate in refrigerator 8 hours or overnight. Serve, using a slotted spoon. Yield: 8 servings (50 calories per serving).

PROTEIN 1.2 / FAT 3.6 / CARBOHYDRATE 4.2 / CHOLESTEROL 0 / IRON 0.4 / SODIUM 18 / CALCIUM 10

VEGETARIAN CHEF SALAD

¼ cup reduced-calorie mayonnaise
¼ cup plain non-fat yogurt
2 tablespoons white wine vinegar
1 teaspoon dry mustard
¼ teaspoon sugar
¼ teaspoon salt
¼ teaspoon pepper
2 cups hot cooked brown rice (cooked without salt or fat)
1 pound fresh broccoli
½ pound fresh mushrooms, sliced
1 medium tomato, seeded and chopped
¾ cup coarsely grated carrot
4 ounces Swiss cheese, cut into julienne strips
4 ounces Cheddar cheese, cut into cubes

Combine first 7 ingredients, stirring well. Pour over hot cooked rice in a large bowl; stir well, and set aside to cool.

Trim off large leaves of broccoli; remove stalks, and reserve for use in other recipes. Place broccoli flowerets in a vegetable steamer. Place steamer over boiling water. Cover and steam 5 minutes or until crisp-tender.

Add broccoli, mushrooms, chopped tomato, grated carrot, and cheeses to reserved rice mixture; toss gently to mix thoroughly. Cover and chill at least 2 hours. Yield: 8 servings (209 calories per serving).

PROTEIN 10.7 / FAT 11.2 / CARBOHYDRATE 17.2 / CHOLESTEROL 31 / IRON 1.0 / SODIUM 273 / CALCIUM 276

PICNIC VEGETABLE SALAD

1 (16-ounce) can pinto beans
2 cups seeded, diced tomato
½ cup diced cucumber
½ cup chopped green pepper
½ cup chopped onion
½ cup chopped celery
¼ cup plain non-fat yogurt
¼ cup reduced-calorie mayonnaise
⅓ cup (1½ ounces) shredded sharp Cheddar cheese
3 tablespoons chopped fresh parsley

Place pinto beans in a colander, and rinse under cold tap water 1 minute; set colander aside to let beans drain 1 minute.

Combine beans and next 5 ingredients in a large bowl, stirring well. Combine yogurt and mayonnaise. Pour over vegetables; toss lightly until well coated. Chill at least 2 hours. Sprinkle with cheese and parsley before serving. Yield: 10 servings (76 calories per serving).

PROTEIN 3.3 / FAT 3.4 / CARBOHYDRATE 8.7 / CHOLESTEROL 7 / IRON 0.7 / SODIUM 84 / CALCIUM 62

EGG FLOWERS

6 hard-cooked eggs, peeled
1 tablespoon prepared mustard
½ teaspoon sugar
1 tablespoon Neufchâtel cheese
⅛ teaspoon white pepper
1 teaspoon white wine vinegar
½ teaspoon dried whole dillweed
1 teaspoon diced pimiento
Lettuce leaves
Paprika

Slice eggs in half lengthwise, and carefully remove yolks. Mash yolks, and stir in next 7 ingredients. Divide mixture into 6 equal portions; shape into balls, and chill 1 hour. Slice each egg white half into 4 equal wedges; arrange egg white wedges spoke-fashion on individual lettuce leaf-lined plates. Roll each ball in paprika and place in center of whites. Yield: 6 servings (86 calories per serving).

PROTEIN 6.3 / FAT 6.0 / CARBOHYDRATE 1.3 / CHOLESTEROL 275 / IRON 1.2 / SODIUM 107 / CALCIUM 33

LAYERED PASTA SALAD

6 ounces multicolored fusilli pasta
½ cup red wine vinegar
3 tablespoons grated Parmesan cheese
3 tablespoons olive oil
2 tablespoons dried whole basil
1 tablespoon dried chervil
1 tablespoon water
2 teaspoons garlic powder
5 ounces fresh spinach, shredded
1 cup sliced fresh mushrooms
2 medium tomatoes, seeded and chopped
¾ cup chopped celery
½ cup chopped green onions
3 tablespoons chopped fresh parsley

Cook pasta according to package directions, omitting salt; drain, and set aside. Combine vinegar and next 6 ingredients, stirring well. Pour ½ cup vinegar mixture over reserved cooked pasta. Toss gently. Set aside remaining vinegar mixture.

Layer reserved cooked pasta, spinach, mushrooms, tomatoes, celery, onions, and parsley in order listed in a large salad bowl. Pour remaining vinegar mixture over salad. (Do not toss.) Cover salad and chill 2 hours. Yield: 10 servings (125 calories per serving).

PROTEIN 3.9 / FAT 4.9 / CARBOHYDRATE 16.5 / CHOLESTEROL 1 / IRON 1.5 / SODIUM 52 / CALCIUM 60

PASTA-STUFFED TOMATOES

4 small tomatoes
1 cup cooked small bow-tie pasta (cooked without salt)
½ cup frozen English peas, thawed and drained
2 tablespoons chopped sweet red pepper
1 tablespoon sliced ripe olives
3 tablespoons reduced-calorie ranch dressing
Paprika (optional)

Cut off top of each tomato; scoop out pulp, leaving shells intact. Reserve pulp for use in other recipes. Invert tomato shells on paper towels to drain. Set aside.

Combine pasta, peas, sweet red pepper, olives, and ranch dressing; stir well. Spoon ½ cup mixture into each reserved tomato shell. Cover and chill thoroughly. Sprinkle with paprika before serving, if desired. Yield: 4 servings (115 calories per serving).

PROTEIN 3.5 / FAT 4.1 / CARBOHYDRATE 20.1 / CHOLESTEROL 0 / IRON 1.2 / SODIUM 43 / CALCIUM 18

SEASHELL SALAD

4 ounces small shell macaroni
⅓ cup plain low-fat yogurt
2 teaspoons lemon juice
2 teaspoons olive oil
½ teaspoon dried whole dillweed
¼ teaspoon salt
⅛ teaspoon garlic powder
⅛ teaspoon white pepper
1 cup frozen English peas, thawed and drained
½ cup thinly sliced cauliflower flowerets
¼ cup finely chopped celery
¼ cup shredded carrots
8 lettuce leaves

Cook macaroni according to package directions, omitting salt. Drain; rinse with cold water, and drain again. Cover and chill.

Combine yogurt, lemon juice, olive oil, dillweed, salt, garlic powder, and pepper, stirring with a wire whisk. Cover and chill. Combine peas, cauliflower, celery, and carrots; toss gently. Add reserved macaroni and yogurt mixture. Toss gently to coat. Cover and chill thoroughly. Serve on lettuce leaves. Yield: 8 servings (89 calories per serving).

PROTEIN 3.6 / FAT 1.6 / CARBOHYDRATE 15.1 / CHOLESTEROL 1 / IRON 0.9 / SODIUM 108 / CALCIUM 35

CHILLED CAJUN RED BEANS AND RICE

1 (15-ounce) can red kidney beans
⅓ cup reduced-calorie Italian
  salad dressing
3 tablespoons water
2 tablespoons vinegar
½ teaspoon paprika
¼ teaspoon red pepper
¼ teaspoon dried whole thyme
¼ teaspoon dried whole oregano
⅛ teaspoon pepper
1 cup cooked parboiled rice (cooked
  without salt or fat), chilled
¾ cup sliced celery
¾ cup chopped onion
¾ cup chopped tomato

Place kidney beans in a colander, and rinse under cold tap water 1 minute; set colander aside to let beans drain 1 minute.

Combine dressing and next 7 ingredients in a jar; cover tightly, and shake vigorously. Chill dressing 2 hours.

Combine reserved kidney beans, reserved chilled dressing, and remaining ingredients; toss gently. Cover and refrigerate 8 hours or overnight. Yield: 8 servings (67 calories per serving).

PROTEIN 2.8 / FAT 0.2 / CARBOHYDRATE 13.6 / CHOLESTEROL 0 /
IRON 0.9 / SODIUM 162 / CALCIUM 25

GARDEN TABBOULEH

¾ cup bulgur wheat
1½ cups hot water
3 tablespoons white wine vinegar
2 tablespoons sliced green onions
2 tablespoons sliced radishes
2 tablespoons chopped carrots
2 tablespoons chopped zucchini
1½ teaspoons vegetable oil
¼ teaspoon salt
1 medium tomato, chopped
2 tablespoons chopped fresh parsley
6 lettuce leaves

Place bulgur in a medium-size bowl; add hot water, and let stand 1 hour. Drain well. Stir in vinegar and next 6 ingredients. Cover and chill thoroughly. Before serving, stir in chopped tomato and parsley. Serve on lettuce leaves. Yield: 6 servings (96 calories per serving).

PROTEIN 2.9 / FAT 1.6 / CARBOHYDRATE 18.2 / CHOLESTEROL 0 /
IRON 1.1 / SODIUM 105 / CALCIUM 16

STIR-FRY FAJITA SALAD

1 pound beef flank steak
2 tablespoons lime juice
1 tablespoon vinegar
1½ teaspoons vegetable oil
⅛ teaspoon salt
¼ teaspoon pepper
1 clove garlic, sliced
1 tablespoon minced fresh cilantro
Vegetable cooking spray
1 tablespoon vegetable oil
1 medium-size sweet red pepper, sliced
2 medium-size green chiles, seeded
  and chopped
¾ cup sliced green onions
2 cups peeled, seeded, and chopped tomato
3 cups torn leaf lettuce
3 cups torn romaine lettuce

Trim excess fat from steak; place in a shallow dish. Combine lime juice and next 6 ingredients, stirring well; pour over steak. Cover and marinate in refrigerator 8 hours or overnight, turning occasionally.

Partially freeze steak; slice meat diagonally across grain into thin strips, and set aside.

Coat a wok or skillet with cooking spray; add oil. Allow to heat at medium-high (325°) for 2 minutes. Add sweet red pepper, chiles, and green onions; stir-fry 2 minutes. Remove vegetables from wok, and set aside.

Add half of reserved steak to wok; stir-fry 3 to 5 minutes; remove from wok, and repeat procedure with remaining steak.

Return reserved vegetables and steak to wok; add tomato, and stir-fry 1 minute. Remove wok from heat, and add lettuce, stirring constantly for 1 minute or until lettuce wilts. Serve immediately. Yield: 6 servings (192 calories per serving).

PROTEIN 16.9 / FAT 10.9 / CARBOHYDRATE 7.4 / CHOLESTEROL 38 /
IRON 2.7 / SODIUM 115 / CALCIUM 29

Salade Niçoise, a lightened classic from the South of France, is made with water-packed tuna.

SALADE NIÇOISE

1 (6½-ounce) can water-packed white tuna
½ cup reduced-calorie Italian salad dressing
2 teaspoons dried whole tarragon
4 small new potatoes, unpeeled
2 tablespoons Chablis or other dry white wine
1 clove garlic, crushed
½ pound fresh green beans
4 cups torn Bibb lettuce
½ small purple onion
1 large tomato, cut into wedges
1 hard-cooked egg, sliced
4 pitted ripe olives, sliced in half lengthwise

Place tuna in a colander, and rinse under cold water 1 minute; set colander aside to let tuna drain 1 minute.

Combine dressing and tarragon; stir well, and set aside.

Arrange potatoes in a vegetable steamer. Place over boiling water in a saucepan. Cover and steam 15 minutes or until potatoes are tender. Set aside to cool. Slice potatoes, and combine with wine and garlic. Toss gently. Cover and chill 2 hours.

Wash beans; trim ends, and remove strings. Cook beans, covered, in a small amount of boiling water 5 minutes or until crisp-tender; drain. Combine beans and ¼ cup reserved dressing mixture. Toss gently; cover, and chill 30 minutes.

Place lettuce on 4 serving plates. Cut onion into thin slices; separate into rings. Arrange onion over lettuce. Drain chilled potatoes, discarding liquid. Arrange over onion slices. Drain chilled beans, discarding liquid. Arrange beans, tomato wedges, reserved tuna, egg, and olives on top of onions. Pour remaining reserved dressing mixture evenly over salads. Yield: 4 servings (243 calories per serving).

PROTEIN 16.6 / FAT 3.0 / CARBOHYDRATE 38.4 / CHOLESTEROL 89 / IRON 4.1 / SODIUM 397 / CALCIUM 74

RINSING TUNA

Duke University scientists conducted a study to determine whether or not rinsing canned foods would reduce the sodium. They found that rinsing tuna fish under cold tap water for 1 minute reduced the level of sodium by 80 percent. When canned green beans were rinsed, the effects were less dramatic—a reduction of 41 percent. Use this rinsing technique to reduce sodium in the classic salad entrée Salade Niçoise.

COBB SALAD

3 cups torn romaine lettuce
2 cups torn curly endive
1 cup torn watercress
2 cups thinly sliced, cooked chicken (skinned before cooking and cooked without salt)
1 large tomato, thinly sliced
½ medium avocado
2 hard-cooked eggs, sliced
2 tablespoons plus 2 teaspoons crumbled Roquefort cheese
3 tablespoons plus 2 teaspoons water
2 tablespoons lemon juice
2 tablespoons vegetable oil
1 teaspoon dry mustard
1 teaspoon white wine vinegar
⅛ teaspoon pepper

Combine first 3 ingredients; toss well. Divide salad greens among 4 individual serving plates. Arrange chicken over salad greens. Arrange tomato, avocado, and egg slices over salads. Sprinkle 2 teaspoons cheese over each salad.

Combine remaining ingredients in a jar; cover tightly, and shake vigorously. Top each salad with 2 tablespoons dressing. Yield: 4 servings (287 calories per serving).

PROTEIN 22.1 / FAT 18.8 / CARBOHYDRATE 8.5 / CHOLESTEROL 186 / IRON 2.4 / SODIUM 282 / CALCIUM 140

CAJUN CATFISH SALAD

2 cups water
1 small lemon, sliced
½ teaspoon salt, divided
2 (12-ounce) pan-dressed catfish
1 cup sliced celery
1 cup chopped tomato
2 tablespoons chopped green onions
¼ cup chopped green pepper
¼ cup reduced-calorie mayonnaise
¼ cup plain low-fat yogurt
¼ teaspoon dried whole oregano
¼ teaspoon dried whole thyme
⅛ teaspoon white pepper
8 curly leaf lettuce leaves

Combine water, lemon, and ¼ teaspoon salt in a fish poacher or large skillet; bring to a boil, and add catfish. Cover; reduce heat, and simmer 20 minutes or until catfish flakes easily when tested with a fork.

Remove catfish from poacher or skillet carefully. Remove skin and bones from catfish; flake fish with a fork.

Combine fish, remaining ¼ teaspoon salt, celery, tomato, green onions, and green pepper; stir well. Combine mayonnaise and next 4 ingredients. Add to fish mixture, tossing gently. Cover and chill 2 hours.

To serve, spoon ½ cup mixture onto 8 individual lettuce-lined salad plates. Yield: 8 servings (125 calories per serving).

PROTEIN 16.1 / FAT 4.8 / CARBOHYDRATE 4.3 / CHOLESTEROL 50 / IRON 0.8 / SODIUM 275 / CALCIUM 53

CRAWFISH SALAD IN PAPAYA CUPS

¼ cup reduced-calorie mayonnaise
¼ cup plain non-fat yogurt
2 teaspoons unsweetened pineapple juice
¼ teaspoon curry powder
¼ teaspoon reduced-sodium soy sauce
1 pound cooked crawfish tails, peeled, deveined, rinsed, and coarsely chopped
1 cup diced celery
3 medium papayas
1 teaspoon lime juice
6 lettuce leaves
3 tablespoons sliced almonds, toasted

Combine mayonnaise, yogurt, pineapple juice, curry powder, and soy sauce in a large bowl, stirring until well blended. Add crawfish and celery, tossing gently to mix well; cover and chill thoroughly.

Cut papayas in half with a sharp knife; remove and discard seeds. Peel each half. Cut a thin slice from bottom of each half to sit flat, if necessary. Brush each half with lime juice; place each half on a lettuce-lined plate. Spoon ½ cup crawfish mixture into each papaya half. Top with toasted almonds. Yield: 6 servings (156 calories per serving).

PROTEIN 13.3 / FAT 4.8 / CARBOHYDRATE 15.5 / CHOLESTEROL 53 / IRON 1.5 / SODIUM 271 / CALCIUM 125

CREAMY ORANGE-NUTMEG DRESSING

1 (8-ounce) carton plain low-fat yogurt
3 tablespoons unsweetened orange juice
1 tablespoon honey
½ teaspoon grated orange rind
¼ teaspoon ground nutmeg

Combine all ingredients, stirring with a wire whisk until well blended. Cover and chill thoroughly. Serve with fresh fruit. Yield: 1 cup (14 calories per tablespoon).

PROTEIN 0.8 / FAT 0.2 / CARBOHYDRATE 2.4 / CHOLESTEROL 1 /
IRON 0.0 / SODIUM 10 / CALCIUM 26

POPPY SEED DRESSING

1 tablespoon cornstarch
1 teaspoon sugar
½ teaspoon dry mustard
1 cup water
3 tablespoons honey
3 tablespoons vinegar
1 tablespoon poppy seeds

Combine cornstarch, sugar, and mustard in a small non-aluminum saucepan. Stir in water, honey, and vinegar; bring to a boil. Reduce heat to medium, and cook, stirring constantly, until thickened and bubbly. Remove from heat, and cool slightly. Stir in poppy seeds. Cover and chill thoroughly. Serve with fresh fruit. Yield: 1⅓ cups (14 calories per tablespoon).

PROTEIN 0.1 / FAT 0.2 / CARBOHYDRATE 3.2 / CHOLESTEROL 0 /
IRON 0.1 / SODIUM 0 / CALCIUM 6

Poppy Seed Dressing (left) is a wonderful accompaniment to fresh fruit salads. A crisp mix of salad greens will leap to life with the addition of Raspberry Vinegar (rear) or chunky Tomatillo Dressing (page 188) spiced with cilantro and chervil.

RUM FRUIT DRESSING

½ cup pear nectar
1 tablespoon dark rum
1 teaspoon lime juice
¼ teaspoon ground nutmeg

Combine all ingredients, stirring well. Cover and chill thoroughly. Serve with fresh fruit. Yield: ½ cup (13 calories per tablespoon).

PROTEIN 0.1 / FAT 0.1 / CARBOHYDRATE 2.1 / CHOLESTEROL 0 /
IRON 0.0 / SODIUM 0 / CALCIUM 1

RASPBERRY VINEGAR

1½ cups white wine vinegar
½ cup Chambord or other raspberry-flavored liqueur
2 sprigs fresh dillweed

Combine vinegar and liqueur in a small non-aluminum saucepan; bring to a boil. Reduce heat, and simmer 5 minutes. Let cool.

Place dillweed in a wide-mouth glass jar. Pour vinegar mixture over dillweed, and cover. Let stand at room temperature for 24 hours. Serve with salad greens. Yield: 2 cups (13 calories per tablespoon).

PROTEIN 0.0 / FAT 0.0 / CARBOHYDRATE 1.0 / CHOLESTEROL 0 /
IRON 0.0 / SODIUM 1 / CALCIUM 0

BURGUNDY DRESSING

¾ cup red wine vinegar
¼ cup Burgundy or other dry red wine
2 tablespoons sugar
¼ cup vegetable oil
¼ teaspoon salt
½ teaspoon pepper

Combine vinegar, wine, and sugar in a medium saucepan. Bring to a boil. Cover; reduce heat, and simmer 5 minutes. Remove from heat. Let cool to room temperature. Stir in remaining ingredients. Cover and refrigerate 8 hours or overnight. Stir well before serving with salad greens or assorted raw vegetables. Yield: 1¼ cups (31 calories per tablespoon).

PROTEIN 0.0 / FAT 2.7 / CARBOHYDRATE 1.4 / CHOLESTEROL 0 /
IRON 0.0 / SODIUM 30 / CALCIUM 1

CREAMY COUNTRY DRESSING

½ cup plain non-fat yogurt
¼ cup reduced-calorie mayonnaise
2 tablespoons low-fat buttermilk
1 clove garlic, minced
½ teaspoon white wine Worcestershire sauce
¼ teaspoon white wine vinegar
¼ teaspoon lemon juice
¼ teaspoon celery seeds
¼ teaspoon pepper
Dash of hot sauce

Combine all ingredients in a small bowl; stir with a wire whisk until well blended. Cover and chill thoroughly. Serve with salad greens. Yield: 1 cup (16 calories per tablespoon).

PROTEIN 0.5 / FAT 1.1 / CARBOHYDRATE 1.0 / CHOLESTEROL 1 / IRON 0.0 / SODIUM 36 / CALCIUM 18

 ## TOMATILLO: THE TOMATO'S MEXICAN COUSIN

Those who are familiar with Mexican cuisine, already know the distinct acidic flavor of the tomatillo (also called the Mexican tomato). This small, hard, green fruit with a papery outer husk is used most often in cooked sauces. The husks are pulled off before using. You'll find tomatillos at the supermarket fresh or canned (often labeled *tomatillo entero*). Give the simplest salads "South-of-the-Border" flair with Tomatillo Dressing. Each flavorful tablespoon has only 11 calories.

TOMATILLO DRESSING

½ pound fresh tomatillos
3 tablespoons loosely packed fresh cilantro
1 tablespoon vegetable oil
1 teaspoon dried chervil
¼ teaspoon salt
1 clove garlic
1 teaspoon lime juice

Place tomatillos on a baking sheet; bake at 450° for 10 minutes. Remove from oven; cool. Remove husks; rinse tomatillos.

Position knife blade in food processor bowl; add tomatillos and remaining ingredients. Process until smooth. Cover and chill thoroughly. Serve with lettuce, sliced tomatoes, or cucumbers. Yield: 1 cup (11 calories per tablespoon).

PROTEIN 0.2 / FAT 0.9 / CARBOHYDRATE 0.8 / CHOLESTEROL 0 / IRON 0.1 / SODIUM 38 / CALCIUM 3

FRESH TOMATO DRESSING

1 medium tomato, seeded and chopped
2 tablespoons olive oil
2 tablespoons cider vinegar
2 tablespoons chopped shallot
1 tablespoon chopped fresh parsley
1 small clove garlic
¼ teaspoon dried whole basil
¼ teaspoon salt
¼ teaspoon paprika
4 drops hot sauce

Combine all ingredients in container of electric blender or food processor; process until smooth. Cover and chill thoroughly. Serve with lettuce, sliced tomatoes, or cucumbers. Yield: ¾ cup (25 calories per tablespoon).

PROTEIN 0.2 / FAT 2.3 / CARBOHYDRATE 1.2 / CHOLESTEROL 0 / IRON 0.1 / SODIUM 50 / CALCIUM 4

Have a taste for something sweet? Fruit and Cheese Spread (page 196), accompanied by an asssortment of fresh fruit dippers, is sure to satisfy. For light, nutritious snacking, try our savory Herbed Ham and Cheese Spread (page 196), served with fresh raw vegetables.

Sandwiches & Snacks

ARTICHOKE-OLIVE SANDWICHES ON RYE

1 (14-ounce) can artichoke hearts, drained
   and chopped
½ cup (2 ounces) shredded Cheddar
   cheese
⅓ cup reduced-calorie mayonnaise
2 tablespoons minced green onions
2 tablespoons chopped ripe olives
¼ teaspoon curry powder
6 slices thinly sliced rye bread

Combine first 6 ingredients, stirring well. Toast bread on one side. Spread ½ cup artichoke mixture on untoasted side of each slice of bread. Place on a baking sheet, and broil 6 inches from heating element 3 minutes or until browned. Yield: 6 servings (159 calories per serving).

PROTEIN 5.7 / FAT 7.6 / CARBOHYDRATE 18.7 / CHOLESTEROL 14 / IRON 1.1 / SODIUM 347 / CALCIUM 107

BREAKFAST PITA SANDWICHES

Vegetable cooking spray
½ cup thinly sliced fresh mushrooms
¼ cup chopped onion
¼ cup chopped green pepper
3 eggs, beaten
¼ cup low-fat cottage cheese
⅛ teaspoon pepper
¼ cup (1 ounce) shredded Cheddar
   cheese
2 (6-inch) whole wheat pita bread rounds,
   cut in half crosswise

Coat a medium skillet with cooking spray; place over medium heat until hot. Add mushrooms, onion, and green pepper to skillet; sauté until tender.

Combine eggs, cottage cheese, and pepper in a small bowl; pour over vegetables. Cook over medium heat, stirring often, until eggs are firm but still moist. Stir in cheese. Spoon ½ cup mixture into each pita half. Serve immediately. Yield: 4 servings (143 calories per serving).

PROTEIN 9.4 / FAT 7.2 / CARBOHYDRATE 9.3 / CHOLESTEROL 214 / IRON 1.5 / SODIUM 154 / CALCIUM 96

BLUE CHEESE AND VEGETABLE SANDWICHES

¾ cup fresh sliced broccoli flowerets
¾ cup fresh sliced cauliflower flowerets
⅓ cup sliced radishes
1 medium carrot, shredded
⅓ cup chopped green pepper
3 tablespoons minced onion
¼ cup reduced-calorie mayonnaise
2 tablespoons low-fat sour cream
¼ cup (1 ounce) crumbled blue cheese
2 (2½-ounce) hard dinner rolls

Combine first 9 ingredients in a medium bowl, tossing well to coat vegetables.

Cut top ⅓ from each roll; scoop out center, leaving a ½-inch-thick shell. (Reserve breadcrumbs for another use.) Divide vegetable mixture among shells. Cover with remaining roll top; cut each roll in half crosswise to serve. Yield: 4 servings (176 calories per serving).

PROTEIN 5.4 / FAT 8.0 / CARBOHYDRATE 21.2 / CHOLESTEROL 14 / IRON 1.1 / SODIUM 384 / CALCIUM 77

CHEESY ZUCCHINI OPEN-FACE SANDWICHES

Vegetable cooking spray
2 cups shredded zucchini
1 cup (4 ounces) shredded part-skim mozzarella
   cheese
¼ cup minced onion
2 tablespoons chopped ripe olives
2 tablespoons reduced-calorie mayonnaise
¼ teaspoon dried Italian seasoning
3 whole wheat English muffins, split
1 medium tomato, cut into 6 thin slices
2 tablespoons grated Parmesan cheese

Coat a large skillet with cooking spray; place over medium-high heat until hot. Add zucchini, and sauté 3 minutes. Remove from heat, and drain well. Press zucchini between paper towels to remove excess moisture.

Combine zucchini and next 5 ingredients in a medium bowl. Stir well. Place English muffin halves on a baking sheet. Spread zucchini mixture evenly over each half, and top with 1 tomato slice. Sprinkle 1 teaspoon Parmesan cheese over each tomato slice.

Broil 6 inches from heating element 2 minutes or until cheese is melted. Yield: 6 servings (174 calories per serving).

PROTEIN 8.8 / FAT 6.2 / CARBOHYDRATE 21.2 / CHOLESTEROL 15 / IRON 1.4 / SODIUM 330 / CALCIUM 213

PITAS WITH FRUITED SLAW

2 cups shredded cabbage
1 cup shredded carrots
1 (11-ounce) can mandarin oranges in light syrup, drained
2 ounces toasted sunflower kernels
2 tablespoons raisins
⅓ cup plain low-fat yogurt
½ medium banana
2 tablespoons reduced-calorie mayonnaise
2 tablespoons unsweetened orange juice
1 teaspoon lemon juice
3 (6-inch) whole wheat pita bread rounds, cut in half crosswise
6 curly leaf lettuce leaves

Combine first 5 ingredients in a large bowl. Combine yogurt, banana, mayonnaise, and juices in container of electric blender or food processor; process until smooth. Add yogurt mixture to cabbage mixture, tossing well.

Line each pita round half with a lettuce leaf. Spoon ½ cup mixture into each pita half, and serve immediately. Yield: 6 servings (295 calories per serving).

PROTEIN 7.6 / FAT 9.8 / CARBOHYDRATE 43.9 / CHOLESTEROL 2 / IRON 3.0 / SODIUM 64 / CALCIUM 108

CALIFORNIA SANDWICHES

2 tablespoons reduced-calorie mayonnaise
2 tablespoons plain low-fat yogurt
1 tablespoon unsweetened orange juice
1 tablespoon minced onion
1 teaspoon prepared horseradish
1 medium orange, peeled, sectioned, and chopped
¾ cup chopped cooked chicken breast (skinned before cooking and cooked without salt)
¼ cup chopped avocado
4 curly leaf lettuce leaves
4 slices thinly sliced whole wheat bread, toasted

Combine first 5 ingredients; stir until well blended. Cover and chill thoroughly.

Combine orange, chicken, and avocado. Place one lettuce leaf on each bread slice. Spread fruit-chicken mixture evenly over lettuce leaves. Top with reserved mayonnaise mixture. Yield: 4 servings (186 calories per serving).

PROTEIN 12.3 / FAT 7.2 / CARBOHYDRATE 19.9 / CHOLESTEROL 26 / IRON 1.3 / SODIUM 217 / CALCIUM 64

 CROISSANTS AND BREAD: NOT CREATED EQUAL

The buttery croissant is no longer limited to gourmet food shops. At the supermarket it keeps company with white, wheat, and rye breads. Stuffed with ham and cheese, it appears as a sandwich in the frozen food section. The finest restaurants—and the fastest—feature "sandwich" variety croissants on their menus.

Even though the croissant functions as bread instead of pastry when served as a sandwich, it cannot be considered a substitute for bread. A plain croissant has 272 calories and about 17 grams of fat. That means over 50 percent of the total calories are fat. Two slices of whole wheat bread, by comparison, have 122 calories and 1.6 grams of fat. By the time high-fat fillings such as eggs, cheese, bacon,

and sausage are added to croissants, calories can reach over 500 and fat (mostly saturated), over 40 grams. The sodium level follows suit, increasing from 384 milligrams in a plain croissant to as high as 1,053 milligrams if it is filled with cheese and cured meat—not a nutritional bargain.

When you become weary of morning toast and noontime rye, try low-fat bagels or English muffins. One bagel (made without egg) has 161 calories and only 1.5 grams of fat. English muffins vary, but can have as little as 149 calories and .8 grams of fat. At dinnertime? Present a basket of Herbed Dinner Rolls (page 109), made flavorful with Italian seasoning, garlic powder, and Parmesan cheese. Each roll has only 70 calories and 1.4 grams of fat.

CHICKEN-AND-PEPPERS SANDWICHES

4 boneless chicken breast halves (1 pound), skinned
2 tablespoons lemon juice
2 tablespoons water
2 tablespoons olive oil
1 teaspoon dried whole basil
1 teaspoon dried whole oregano
1 clove garlic, crushed
Dash of pepper
Vegetable cooking spray
½ cup (2 ounces) shredded part-skim mozzarella cheese
3 tablespoons finely chopped green pepper
3 tablespoons finely chopped sweet red pepper
2 tablespoons finely chopped onion
4 curly leaf lettuce leaves
2 whole wheat hamburger buns, split

Trim excess fat from chicken breast halves. Place chicken between 2 sheets of wax paper, and flatten to ¼-inch thickness, using a meat mallet or rolling pin.

Place chicken breast halves in a shallow container. Combine lemon juice and next 6 ingredients, stirring well. Pour over chicken. Cover and marinate in refrigerator 2 hours.

Remove chicken from marinade, reserving marinade. Arrange chicken on a grill coated with cooking spray. Grill 6 inches over hot coals 15 minutes, turning and basting with reserved marinade every 5 minutes. Remove chicken from grill, and sprinkle with cheese. Set chicken aside, and keep warm.

Coat a medium skillet with cooking spray. Place over medium heat until hot. Add green pepper, sweet red pepper, and onion. Sauté 2 minutes or until tender. Remove from heat.

Place lettuce leaves on 4 bun halves. Place reserved chicken on lettuce leaves. Top each bun half with 2 tablespoons pepper mixture. Yield: 4 servings (318 calories per serving).

PROTEIN 32.0 / FAT 13.9 / CARBOHYDRATE 15.5 / CHOLESTEROL 87 / IRON 2.0 / SODIUM 137 / CALCIUM 139

Colorful Chicken-and-Peppers Sandwiches, served on whole wheat bun halves and topped with sweet red and green peppers, are oozing with melted mozzarella cheese. Are you convinced Cooking Light cuisine is delicious?

POLYNESIAN HAM POCKETS

¾ cup chopped lean cooked ham
1 (8-ounce) can unsweetened pineapple tidbits, drained
½ cup (2 ounces) shredded Swiss cheese
2 green onions, chopped
1 tablespoon plus 1 teaspoon reduced-calorie mayonnaise
¼ teaspoon ground ginger
2 (6-inch) whole wheat pita bread rounds, cut in half crosswise
4 curly leaf lettuce leaves
¼ cup alfalfa sprouts

Combine first 6 ingredients in a medium bowl. Cover and chill thoroughly.

Spoon ½ cup chilled mixture into each pita round half; add lettuce leaves, and top with alfalfa sprouts. Yield: 4 servings (163 calories per serving).

PROTEIN 10.8 / FAT 7.2 / CARBOHYDRATE 13.5 / CHOLESTEROL 29 / IRON 1.2 / SODIUM 392 / CALCIUM 161

GRILLED FISH SANDWICHES

3 tablespoons reduced-calorie mayonnaise
1 tablespoon minced onion
2 teaspoons dill pickle relish
½ teaspoon prepared mustard
2 flounder fillets (¾ pound)
Vegetable cooking spray
2 tablespoons lemon juice
1 teaspoon Worcestershire sauce
1 teaspoon vegetable oil
⅛ teaspoon paprika
Lettuce leaves
4 hamburger buns, split and toasted
4 tomato slices

Combine first 4 ingredients in a small bowl; stir well. Cover and chill.

Rinse fillets with cold water, and pat dry. Cut each fillet in half crosswise; place in a wire grilling basket coated with cooking spray. Set aside. Combine lemon juice, Worcestershire, oil, and paprika in a small bowl, stirring well. Brush lemon juice mixture over fish in grilling basket. Grill fish 6 inches over medium coals 5

minutes on each side or until fish flakes easily when tested with a fork; baste frequently with remaining lemon juice mixture during grilling.

To serve, place one lettuce leaf on bottom of each bun. Top each with a fillet and tomato slice. Spread each with 1 tablespoon reserved mayonnaise mixture. Cover with tops of buns. Yield: 4 servings (253 calories per serving).

PROTEIN 18.0 / FAT 8.4 / CARBOHYDRATE 25.4 / CHOLESTEROL 59 / IRON 1.7 / SODIUM 319 / CALCIUM 38

FIBER FROM PILLS

Fiber pills designed to capitalize on our need for more fiber and our desire to lose weight are of little, if any, benefit. These pills will reduce little more than the money in your pocketbook. The prescribed five pills before meals only supply about 2.5 grams of fiber, as much as one apple. The suggested daily fiber intake is at least 25 grams each day.

CURRIED SHRIMP SANDWICHES

1½ quarts water
½ pound uncooked small shrimp
¾ cup frozen English peas, thawed and drained
2 green onions, chopped
¼ cup sliced water chestnuts, drained and chopped
3 tablespoons reduced-calorie mayonnaise
1 teaspoon lemon juice
½ teaspoon curry powder
Dash of red pepper
6 hamburger buns, split and toasted

Bring water to a boil; add shrimp, and reduce heat. Cook 3 minutes. Drain well, and rinse with cold water. Let shrimp cool; peel, devein, and coarsley chop.

Combine shrimp and next 7 ingredients in a medium bowl, tossing lightly to coat. Cover and chill thoroughly.

To serve, spoon ⅓ shrimp mixture over each bun. Cover with top half of bun. Yield: 6 servings (203 calories per serving).

PROTEIN 9.5 / FAT 5.8 / CARBOHYDRATE 27.6 / CHOLESTEROL 58 / IRON 1.7 / SODIUM 228 / CALCIUM 45

CRUNCHY TUNA POCKETS

1 (6½-ounce) can water-packed white tuna
1½ cups shredded cabbage
¼ cup shredded carrots
¼ cup diced celery
¼ cup diced green pepper
¼ cup chopped pecans, toasted
¼ cup plus 2 tablespoons reduced-calorie
  mayonnaise
1 teaspoon lemon juice
¼ teaspoon dried whole dillweed
3 (6-inch) pita bread rounds, cut in half crosswise
Celery leaves (optional)

Place tuna in a colander; rinse under cold tap water 1 minute. Set colander aside to let tuna drain 1 minute.

Combine tuna and next 5 ingredients in a medium bowl; toss gently. Combine mayonnaise, lemon juice, and dillweed, stirring well. Add to tuna mixture, and toss gently. Cover and chill 1 hour or until serving time.

Spoon equal amounts of tuna mixture into each pita half; arrange on a serving platter, and garnish with celery leaves, if desired. Yield: 6 servings (195 calories per serving).

PROTEIN 8.5 / FAT 8.2 / CARBOHYDRATE 20.4 / CHOLESTEROL 18 / IRON 1.7 / SODIUM 158 / CALCIUM 45

PEPPY MEXICAN POPCORN

⅔ cup unpopped popcorn
1 tablespoon vegetable oil
1 tablespoon plus 1½ teaspoons margarine, melted
1 teaspoon chili powder
1 teaspoon paprika
⅛ teaspoon red pepper
⅛ teaspoon garlic powder

Combine popcorn and oil in a Dutch oven; cover and cook over medium-high heat 2 minutes or until popped, shaking pan after corn starts to pop. Place popcorn in bowl; set aside.

Combine margarine and remaining ingredients. Toss with reserved popcorn in bowl. Yield: 8 cups. Serving size: 1 cup (98 calories per serving).

PROTEIN 2.1 / FAT 4.7 / CARBOHYDRATE 12.7 / CHOLESTEROL 0 / IRON 0.5 / SODIUM 29 / CALCIUM 4

Everyone from the kids to Grandpa will love Mini-Melba Pizzas, made with whole grain melba toast rounds, for a quick, light snack.

CINNAMON-PITA CRISPS

3 (6-inch) pita bread rounds
1 egg white, beaten
2 tablespoons sugar
2 teaspoons water
½ teaspoon cinnamon

Split each pita round in half crosswise; quarter each half, making 8 wedges. Place wedges in a jellyroll pan, smooth side down. Combine egg white and remaining ingredients; brush mixture over wedges. Bake at 350° for 12 minutes or until crisp and lightly browned. Yield: 24 crisps (23 calories each).

PROTEIN 0.5 / FAT 0.1 / CARBOHYDRATE 4.6 / CHOLESTEROL 0 / IRON 0.2 / SODIUM 2 / CALCIUM 7

TOASTED WONTON SKINS

20 fresh or frozen wonton skins, thawed
2 teaspoons reduced-sodium soy sauce
2 teaspoons sesame oil
2 teaspoons water
½ teaspoon ground ginger
1 tablespoon plus 2 teaspoons sesame seeds

Work with 1 wonton skin at a time, and keep others covered when not in use. Cut each wonton skin in half crosswise. Place on two ungreased 15- x 10- x 1-inch jellyroll pans. Combine soy sauce, sesame oil, water, and ginger; stir well. Brush mixture evenly over wonton skin halves. Sprinkle evenly with sesame seeds. Bake at 375° for 6 minutes or until crisp and golden brown. Let cool. Store in an airtight container. Yield: 40 skins (16 calories each).

PROTEIN 0.5 / FAT 0.5 / CARBOHYDRATE 2.3 / CHOLESTEROL 4 / IRON 0.2 / SODIUM 40 / CALCIUM 5

APPLE TREATS

2 tablespoons chopped dates
1 ounce Neufchâtel cheese, softened
1 tablespoon peanut butter
½ teaspoon grated orange rind
4 medium-size Red Delicious apples, cored

Combine first 4 ingredients, stirring well. Stuff 1 tablespoon mixture into cavity of each apple. Cut each stuffed apple into 6 slices. Serve immediately. Yield: 24 slices (23 calories each).

PROTEIN 0.4 / FAT 0.7 / CARBOHYDRATE 4.2 / CHOLESTEROL 1 / IRON 0.1 / SODIUM 8 / CALCIUM 3

DRIED FRUIT BALLS

½ cup pitted prunes
½ cup pitted dates
⅓ cup dried apricots
⅓ cup raisins
3 tablespoons unsweetened grated coconut
½ teaspoon grated orange rind
¼ cup plus 2 tablespoons finely chopped unsalted peanuts

Combine all ingredients except peanuts in container of food processor; process until finely chopped. Shape mixture into 1-inch balls. Roll balls in peanuts. Store in an airtight container in refrigerator. Yield: 15 balls (88 calories each).

PROTEIN 1.6 / FAT 2.7 / CARBOHYDRATE 16.3 / CHOLESTEROL 0 / IRON 0.8 / SODIUM 6 / CALCIUM 15

 ### DRIED FRUIT FOR SNACKS

Dried fruit makes a low-fat snack rich in minerals—especially iron, copper, and potassium. Ample quantities of vitamin A are found in apricots, peaches, and prunes.

The drying process that concentrates the nutrients in dried fruits also concentrates the fruit's sugar. The sugar-rich fruit with its sticky texture can bind to teeth, making them susceptible to cavities.

Enjoy dried fruit and reap its healthful benefits. But eat it in small snack-size portions, and make an effort to brush and floss your teeth soon after eating. For a naturally sweet cholesterol-free treat, snack on Dried Fruit Balls.

MINI-MELBA PIZZAS

½ cup no-salt-added tomato sauce
½ teaspoon dried whole oregano
½ teaspoon dried whole basil
24 whole grain melba toast rounds
6 medium-size fresh mushrooms, thinly sliced
2 green onions, sliced
¼ cup (1 ounce) shredded part-skim mozzarella cheese
¼ cup (1 ounce) shredded Cheddar cheese

Combine tomato sauce, oregano, and basil in a small bowl; stir well. Place melba toast rounds on a baking sheet. Spread 1 teaspoon tomato sauce mixture on each round. Evenly distribute mushrooms, onions, and cheeses on top of tomato sauce on each round. Bake at 400° for 3 minutes or until cheeses melt. Yield: 24 pizzas (23 calories each).

PROTEIN 1.1 / FAT 0.9 / CARBOHYDRATE 2.8 / CHOLESTEROL 2 / IRON 0.2 / SODIUM 39 / CALCIUM 16

NUTTY CARROT-CHEESE BALLS

3 ounces Neufchâtel cheese, softened
½ cup (2 ounces) shredded Cheddar cheese
½ cup shredded carrots
3 tablespoons ground pecans, toasted
3 tablespoons wheat germ, toasted

Combine first 3 ingredients; stir well. Cover and chill 1 hour. Shape mixture into 1-inch balls. Combine toasted pecans and wheat germ; stir well. Roll balls in pecan-wheat germ mixture. Cover and chill thoroughly. Yield: 18 cheese balls (38 calories each).

PROTEIN 1.7 / FAT 3.1 / CARBOHYDRATE 1.2 / CHOLESTEROL 7 / IRON 0.2 / SODIUM 39 / CALCIUM 28

FRUIT AND CHEESE SPREAD

1 cup low-fat cottage cheese
1 (8-ounce) can unsweetened crushed pineapple, drained
1 medium-size Red Delicious apple, cored and shredded
¼ cup (1 ounce) shredded Cheddar cheese
2 tablespoons currants

Combine all ingredients in a small bowl; stir until well blended. Cover and chill thoroughly. Serve with assorted fresh fruit. Yield: 2½ cups (13 calories per tablespoon).

PROTEIN 1.0 / FAT 0.4 / CARBOHYDRATE 1.5 / CHOLESTEROL 1 / IRON 0.0 / SODIUM 28 / CALCIUM 10

HERBED HAM AND CHEESE SPREAD

¾ cup low-fat cottage cheese
½ (8-ounce) package Neufchâtel cheese
⅓ cup finely chopped lean cooked ham
1 (2-ounce) jar diced pimiento, drained
2 tablespoons chopped fresh parsley
1 tablespoon grated Parmesan cheese
½ teaspoon dried whole oregano
½ teaspoon dried whole basil

Place cottage cheese in container of an electric blender; process until smooth. Add Neufchâtel; process until combined. Transfer to a small bowl; add remaining ingredients, stirring well. Cover; chill thoroughly. Serve with melba toast rounds or fresh raw vegetables. Yield: 1 cup (35 calories per tablespoon).

PROTEIN 3.1 / FAT 2.2 / CARBOHYDRATE 0.9 / CHOLESTEROL 8 / IRON 0.2 / SODIUM 120 / CALCIUM 19

BANANA-YOGURT POPS

2 medium-size ripe bananas, mashed
2 (8-ounce) cartons vanilla low-fat yogurt
2 tablespoons semisweet chocolate mini-morsels
1 tablespoon honey
10 (3-ounce) paper cups
10 wooden sticks

Combine first 4 ingredients, stirring well. Pour into 10 (3-ounce) paper cups. Cover tops with aluminum foil, and insert a stick through foil into center of each cup. Freeze until firm. To serve, peel paper cup away from pop. Yield: 10 pops (78 calories each).

PROTEIN 2.6 / FAT 1.4 / CARBOHYDRATE 14.8 / CHOLESTEROL 2 / IRON 0.2 / SODIUM 30 / CALCIUM 80

FROZEN PEANUT BUTTER CUPS

12 vanilla wafers, crushed
1 quart vanilla ice milk, softened
¼ cup crunchy peanut butter
2 tablespoons honey

Place ½ teaspoon crushed vanilla wafers into each of 24 paper-lined miniature muffin cups. Set aside.

Place ice milk in a large bowl. Combine peanut butter and honey; stir well. Pour peanut butter mixture over ice milk; gently swirl with a knife. Spoon mixture into prepared muffin pans, filling two-thirds full. Freeze 2 hours or until firm. Yield: 24 cups (61 calories each).

PROTEIN 1.7 / FAT 2.7 / CARBOHYDRATE 8.0 / CHOLESTEROL 3 / IRON 0.1 / SODIUM 38 / CALCIUM 31

These sauces and condiments add flavorful accents to food: (clockwise from front) Autumn Fruit Sauce (page 198), Tomato-Red Pepper Coulis (page 201), Mushroom Sauce (page 201), and Coleslaw Relish (page 204).

Sauces & Condiments

AUTUMN FRUIT SAUCE

1 cup whole berry cranberry sauce
2 tablespoons firmly packed brown sugar
½ teaspoon grated orange rind
2 tablespoons unsweetened orange juice
½ teaspoon ground ginger
½ teaspoon ground nutmeg
⅔ cup finely chopped fresh pineapple
⅔ cup finely chopped unpeeled apple

Combine first 6 ingredients in a medium-size non-aluminum saucepan, stirring well. Stir in chopped pineapple and apple. Cook over low heat 5 minutes or until apple is tender, stirring frequently. Serve warm with chicken, turkey, or pork. Yield: 1⅔ cups (23 calories per tablespoon).

PROTEIN 0.1 / FAT 0.1 / CARBOHYDRATE 6.0 / CHOLESTEROL 0 / IRON 0.1 / SODIUM 3 / CALCIUM 2

BRANDIED APRICOT SAUCE

1 (14½-ounce) can apricot halves in light syrup, undrained
1 tablespoon firmly packed brown sugar
¼ cup apricot-flavored brandy

Drain apricots, reserving juice. Place half of apricot halves in container of electric blender; process until smooth. Coarsely chop remaining apricot halves. Set aside.

Combine reserved apricot juice, brown sugar, and brandy in a small saucepan. Bring to a boil; cook 3 minutes or until slightly thickened, stirring constantly. Remove from heat; stir in reserved pureed and chopped apricots. Cover and chill. Serve with ice milk or pound cake. Yield: 1⅓ cups (25 calories per tablespoon).

PROTEIN 0.1 / FAT 0.0 / CARBOHYDRATE 4.7 / CHOLESTEROL 0 / IRON 0.1 / SODIUM 0 / CALCIUM 3

APPLE-RAISIN SAUCE

1 cup unsweetened apple cider
1 medium cooking apple, peeled and chopped
⅓ cup raisins
1 teaspoon firmly packed brown sugar
1 tablespoon cornstarch
2 tablespoons water
½ teaspoon ground cinnamon

Combine first 4 ingredients in a medium saucepan; bring to a boil. Reduce heat and cook, uncovered, 8 minutes or until apples are tender.

Combine cornstarch and water, stirring well; add to apple mixture. Stir in cinnamon; bring to a boil. Reduce heat; cook, stirring constantly, until thickened. Serve warm with ice milk or angel food cake. Yield: 1½ cups (15 calories per tablespoon).

PROTEIN 0.1 / FAT 0.0 / CARBOHYDRATE 3.9 / CHOLESTEROL 0 / IRON 0.1 / SODIUM 1 / CALCIUM 3

Vanilla ice milk becomes extra special when topped with chunky Brandied Apricot Sauce.

BOURBON-NUTMEG SAUCE

½ cup sugar
1 tablespoon cornstarch
½ teaspoon ground nutmeg
½ cup bourbon
½ cup water
2 tablespoons unsalted margarine, melted

Combine sugar, cornstarch, and nutmeg in a saucepan; stir well. Stir in bourbon and water. Cook over medium heat, stirring constantly, until mixture comes to a full boil and thickens. Remove from heat, and stir in margarine. Serve warm with pound cake, fresh fruit, or ice milk. Yield: 1 cup (39 calories per tablespoon).

PROTEIN 0.0 / FAT 1.4 / CARBOHYDRATE 6.7 / CHOLESTEROL 0 / IRON 0.0 / SODIUM 0 / CALCIUM 0

SCHNAPPY STRAWBERRY SAUCE

½ cup low-sugar strawberry spread
¼ cup strawberry-flavored schnapps
¼ cup unsweetened orange juice

Combine all ingredients in a non-aluminum saucepan. Cook over low heat, stirring frequently, until mixture is thoroughly heated. Serve with cake or ice milk. Yield: ⅔ cup (28 calories per tablespoon).

PROTEIN 0.0 / FAT 0.0 / CARBOHYDRATE 4.3 / CHOLESTEROL 0 / IRON 0.0 / SODIUM 0 / CALCIUM 1

AMARETTO CREAM

1 cup low-fat sour cream
¼ cup sifted powdered sugar
3 tablespoons Amaretto or other almond-flavored liqueur
½ teaspoon vanilla extract

Combine all ingredients in a small bowl; stir with a wire whisk until well blended. Cover and chill thoroughly. Serve with fresh fruit. Yield: 1 cup (37 calories per tablespoon).

PROTEIN 0.4 / FAT 1.8 / CARBOHYDRATE 3.3 / CHOLESTEROL 6 / IRON 0.0 / SODIUM 6 / CALCIUM 16

 LIGHT RECIPES WITH YOGURT CHEESE

Versatile, low-fat yogurt cheese has made its way into American kitchens to shed a new lightness on cheesecakes, bagels with cream cheese, cheese blintzes, salads, dips, and canapé spreads. This deceptively rich-tasting, creamy cheese can be made from commercial yogurt. Using a simple "draining" procedure, the yogurt whey is separated from the curd as in Sweet Yogurt-Cheese Spread. When made from 1½ percent milkfat yogurt, yogurt cheese has 90 percent less fat than commercial cream cheese and almost 75 percent less sodium. Because the separating process removes about half the lactose from yogurt, yogurt cheese makes a good source of calcium for the milk intolerant. Not all yogurts separate well, namely those that contain stabilizers or gelatin. Plain and vanilla flavors make the most versatile substitution for cream cheese, whereas fruited yogurt resembles fruit-flavored cream cheese.

SWEET YOGURT-CHEESE SPREAD

1 (16-ounce) carton vanilla low-fat yogurt
3 tablespoons mixed dried fruit bits
1 teaspoon honey
½ teaspoon ground cinnamon

Line a colander or sieve with a double layer of cheesecloth that has been rinsed out and squeezed dry. Allow cheesecloth to extend over outside edges of colander. Stir yogurt until well blended. Pour yogurt into colander and fold edges of cheesecloth over to cover yogurt. Place colander in a large bowl to drain; refrigerate overnight. Remove yogurt from colander and discard liquid in bowl. Remove cheesecloth from yogurt.

Combine yogurt, dried fruit bits, honey, and cinnamon in a small bowl. Chill mixture thoroughly. Serve as a spread for toast, muffins, or bagels. Yield: 1 cup. Serving size: 1 tablespoon (40 calories per serving).

PROTEIN 1.6 / FAT 0.4 / CARBOHYDRATE 7.5 / CHOLESTEROL 1 / IRON 0.1 / SODIUM 23 / CALCIUM 49

PUMPKIN SPREAD

1 (16-ounce) can pumpkin
1 cup unsweetened apple juice
½ cup honey
½ teaspoon pumpkin pie spice
1 (1¾-ounce) package powdered low-sugar fruit
   pectin

Combine first 4 ingredients in a medium saucepan; stir in pectin. Bring to a boil; boil 1 minute, stirring constantly. Remove from heat, and pour into hot sterilized jars, leaving ½-inch headspace. Cover at once with lids. Let stand at room temperature 24 hours; store in refrigerator. Serve as a spread for toast or muffins. Yield: 3 pints (10 calories per tablespoon).

PROTEIN 0.1 / FAT 0.0 / CARBOHYDRATE 2.6 / CHOLESTEROL 0 /
IRON 0.1 / SODIUM 1 / CALCIUM 2

MOCK SOUR CREAM

1 cup low-fat cottage cheese
¼ cup non-fat buttermilk

Combine cheese and buttermilk in container of electric blender; process until smooth, scraping down sides of container often, using a rubber spatula. Cover and chill thoroughly. Serve as a topping for baked potatoes or fresh fruit. Yield: 1 cup (14 calories per tablespoon).

PROTEIN 2.1 / FAT 0.3 / CARBOHYDRATE 0.7 / CHOLESTEROL 1 /
IRON 0.0 / SODIUM 58 / CALCIUM 14

BUTTERMILK-CHIVE SAUCE

1 tablespoon unsalted margarine
1 tablespoon all-purpose flour
½ cup buttermilk
2 tablespoons reduced-calorie mayonnaise
1 tablespoon chopped fresh chives
⅛ teaspoon white pepper

Melt margarine in a small saucepan over low heat; add flour, stirring until smooth. Cook 1 minute, stirring constantly. Gradually add buttermilk; cook over medium heat, stirring constantly, until thickened and bubbly. Stir in

mayonnaise, chives, and pepper. Serve warm with vegetables. Yield: ½ cup (33 calories per tablespoon).

PROTEIN 0.7 / FAT 2.6 / CARBOHYDRATE 1.8 / CHOLESTEROL 2 /
IRON 0.1 / SODIUM 44 / CALCIUM 19

HOT RED PEPPERS—ADDING THE FIRE

Fresh peppers, dried peppers, and pepper sauces add fire to tasty cuisine. Green and red chili peppers are mainstays for spicy ethnic foods. Hot peppers such as chili and jalapeño peppers contain capsaicin, the tongue-tingling chemical that adds the "fire." A variety of colors, shapes, and sizes are available. As a rule of thumb, the smaller the pepper, the hotter it will be. A burning example is cayenne, the tiny red pepper with the enormous bite.

Surprisingly, most people find the hot, spicy foods that burn the mouth and bring tears to the eyes are gentle on the stomach. Gastric juices, enzymes, and stomach mucus combine to protect the stomach lining from the irritating chemical.

Besides the hot, tingling sensation, hot peppers provide nutritional benefits: lots of vitamins A and C in hot red peppers and vitamin C in hot green peppers. Some studies show that hot spices temporarily speed up the metabolism, causing extra calories to be burned; others suggest they may decrease the ability of blood to clot.

If you scrutinize menus for the most fiery fare, you'll want to try Chile-Cilantro Sauce. Red chiles and the peppery flavor of cilantro make up a truly hot sauce for seafood or vegetables.

CHILE-CILANTRO SAUCE

3 dried red chiles
½ cup loosely packed fresh cilantro
1 large clove garlic
½ (8-ounce) package Neufchâtel cheese
½ cup plain low-fat yogurt
1 teaspoon sherry vinegar
½ teaspoon lime juice

Place chiles in a medium bowl. Cover with water 2 inches above chiles; let soak 8 hours or overnight. Drain chiles. Pat dry with paper towels to remove excess moisture. Remove and discard stems and seeds.

Place chiles in container of an electric blender or food processor. Add cilantro and garlic. Process until finely chopped. Add remaining ingredients. Process until smooth. Cover and chill thoroughly. Serve with seafood or vegetables. Yield: 1¼ cups (24 calories per tablespoon).

PROTEIN 1.1 / FAT 1.5 / CARBOHYDRATE 1.6 / CHOLESTEROL 5 / IRON 0.2 / SODIUM 34 / CALCIUM 19

CUCUMBER-PIMIENTO SAUCE

1 cup shredded cucumber
¼ cup plus 2 tablespoons low-fat sour cream
3 tablespoons plain non-fat yogurt
1 (2-ounce) jar diced pimiento, drained
1 teaspoon lemon juice
¼ teaspoon salt
⅛ teaspoon white pepper
3 drops of hot sauce

Press cucumber between paper towels to remove excess moisture. Combine cucumber and remaining ingredients; stir well. Cover and chill thoroughly. Serve with fish. Yield: 1½ cups (7 calories per tablespoon).

PROTEIN 0.3 / FAT 0.5 / CARBOHYDRATE 0.6 / CHOLESTEROL 1 / IRON 0.0 / SODIUM 28 / CALCIUM 9

MUSHROOM SAUCE

½ teaspoon beef-flavored bouillon granules
½ cup hot water
Vegetable cooking spray
1 tablespoon margarine
1 cup sliced fresh mushrooms
¼ cup chopped shallot
1 tablespoon all-purpose flour
½ teaspoon dried whole dillweed
½ cup plain non-fat yogurt

Dissolve bouillon granules in water, and set aside. Coat a medium skillet with cooking spray; add margarine. Place over medium heat until margarine melts. Add mushrooms and shallot; sauté until tender. Stir in flour and dillweed. Cook over low heat 1 minute, stirring constantly. Gradually add reserved bouillon mixture, and cook over medium heat, stirring constantly, until thickened and bubbly. Remove from heat, and add yogurt, stirring until smooth. Serve with steak or veal. Yield: 1¼ cups (12 calories per tablespoon).

PROTEIN 0.5 / FAT 0.6 / CARBOHYDRATE 1.3 / CHOLESTEROL 0 / IRON 0.1 / SODIUM 23 / CALCIUM 13

SEAFOOD LOUIS SAUCE

¼ cup reduced-calorie mayonnaise
¼ cup plain non-fat yogurt
2 tablespoons reduced-calorie chili sauce
2 tablespoons skim milk
1 tablespoon finely chopped green onions
1 tablespoon finely chopped green pepper
1 tablespoon lemon juice
½ teaspoon Worcestershire sauce

Combine all ingredients in a small mixing bowl; stir well. Cover and chill several hours. Serve sauce with seafood. Yield: 1 cup (14 calories per tablespoon).

PROTEIN 0.3 / FAT 1.0 / CARBOHYDRATE 1.0 / CHOLESTEROL 1 / IRON 0.0 / SODIUM 34 / CALCIUM 10

TOMATO-RED PEPPER COULIS

1½ cups chopped sweet red pepper
1 medium tomato, peeled, seeded, and chopped
¾ cup finely chopped onion
1 clove garlic, finely chopped
1 tablespoon red wine vinegar
1½ teaspoons olive oil
¼ teaspoon salt
¼ teaspoon dried whole oregano
¼ teaspoon dried whole sage
¼ teaspoon dried whole marjoram

Combine all ingredients in a medium-size Dutch oven; bring to a boil. Cover; reduce heat, and simmer 20 minutes. Remove from heat, and cool slightly.
Place mixture in container of electric blender or food processor; process until smooth. Serve warm or chilled with chicken, fish, or beef. Yield: 1½ cups (8 calories per tablespoon).

PROTEIN 0.2 / FAT 0.3 / CARBOHYDRATE 1.2 / CHOLESTEROL 0 / IRON 0.2 / SODIUM 25 / CALCIUM 3

CREAMY VEGETABLE SAUCE

Vegetable cooking spray
¼ cup shredded carrots
¼ cup shredded zucchini
2 tablespoons thinly sliced green onions
2 tablespoons margarine
2 tablespoons all-purpose flour
¼ teaspoon salt
⅛ teaspoon white pepper
¼ teaspoon dried tarragon
1 cup skim milk

Coat a medium skillet with cooking spray; place over medium heat until hot. Add carrots, zucchini, and green onions; sauté until vegetables are tender. Set aside.

Melt margarine in a medium saucepan over low heat; add flour, salt, pepper, and tarragon, stirring until smooth. Cook 1 minute, stirring constantly. Gradually add milk; cook over medium heat, stirring constantly with a wire whisk, until thickened and bubbly. Remove from heat; stir in reserved vegetables. Serve immediately with chicken or fish. Yield: 1¼ cups (19 calories per tablespoon).

PROTEIN 0.6 / FAT 1.2 / CARBOHYDRATE 1.5 / CHOLESTEROL 0 / IRON 0.1 / SODIUM 50 / CALCIUM 17

TEXAS MOPPING SAUCE

½ cup reduced-calorie catsup
3 tablespoons dark corn syrup
2 tablespoons lemon juice
2 tablespoons Worcestershire sauce
2 teaspoons instant coffee granules
2 teaspoons liquid smoke

Combine all ingredients in a small bowl, stirring well. Use as a basting sauce for brisket, beef, or chicken. Yield: ¾ cup plus 2 tablespoons (19 calories per tablespoon).

PROTEIN 0.1 / FAT 0.0 / CARBOHYDRATE 4.6 / CHOLESTEROL 0 / IRON 0.2 / SODIUM 26 / CALCIUM 5

MUSTARD-LEMON MARINADE

⅓ cup lemon juice
2 tablespoons vegetable oil
2 tablespoons Dijon mustard
2 teaspoons grated lemon rind
1 teaspoon pepper
½ teaspoon sugar
¼ teaspoon paprika
1 clove garlic, minced

Combine all ingredients in a small mixing bowl, and stir well. Use to marinate chicken or other poultry. Marinate in refrigerator several hours or overnight. Baste chicken with remaining marinade during cooking. Yield: ¾ cup (26 calories per tablespoon).

PROTEIN 0.1 / FAT 2.5 / CARBOHYDRATE 1.2 / CHOLESTEROL 0 / IRON 0.1 / SODIUM 74 / CALCIUM 2

PICANTE MARINADE

1 (8-ounce) can tomato sauce
2 tablespoons vegetable oil
1 tablespoon liquid jalapeño sauce
2 teaspoons sugar
2 teaspoons vinegar
1 large clove garlic, crushed

Combine all ingredients in a saucepan; cook over medium heat until thoroughly heated. Use to marinate chicken, beef, or pork. Marinate meat in refrigerator several hours or overnight. Baste with remaining marinade during cooking. Yield: 1 cup (22 calories per tablespoon).

PROTEIN 0.2 / FAT 1.8 / CARBOHYDRATE 1.7 / CHOLESTEROL 0 / IRON 0.1 / SODIUM 93 / CALCIUM 2

Make your own hot Cajun Blackened Seasoning to coat fish, chicken, or beef before grilling by browning a mixture of spices.

SHERRIED MARINADE

¼ cup Worcestershire sauce
3 tablespoons dry sherry
3 tablespoons water
2 tablespoons lemon juice
1 tablespoon plus 1½ teaspoons
   reduced-sodium soy sauce
1 tablespoon vegetable oil
1½ teaspoons dry mustard
1 teaspoon pepper
½ teaspoon minced parsley
1 clove garlic, minced

Combine all ingredients in a small bowl; stir well. Use to marinate flank steak or other cuts of beef. Marinate meat in refrigerator several hours or overnight. Baste with remaining marinade during cooking. Yield: 1 cup (17 calories per tablespoon).

PROTEIN 0.3 / FAT 0.9 / CARBOHYDRATE 1.2 / CHOLESTEROL 0 /
IRON 0.1 / SODIUM 92 / CALCIUM 5

CAJUN BLACKENED SEASONING

2 teaspoons black peppercorns, crushed
2 teaspoons dried whole basil
1 teaspoon cumin seeds, crushed
1 teaspoon caraway seeds, crushed
1 teaspoon fennel seeds, crushed
1 teaspoon dried whole thyme
1 teaspoon dried whole oregano
1 teaspoon white pepper
½ teaspoon crushed red pepper
½ teaspoon salt
2 teaspoons paprika

Combine first 10 ingredients in a skillet; place over medium-high heat. Cook 3 minutes or until seeds are lightly browned. Remove from heat; add paprika. Store in an airtight container. Use to coat fish, chicken, or beef before grilling. Yield: ¼ cup (5 calories per teaspoon).

PROTEIN 0.2 / FAT 0.2 / CARBOHYDRATE 1.0 / CHOLESTEROL 0 /
IRON 0.6 / SODIUM 99 / CALCIUM 16

COLESLAW RELISH

3 cups shredded cabbage
1 cup shredded carrots
¼ cup sliced pimiento
1 teaspoon salt
1 cup vinegar
½ cup sugar
1 teaspoon celery seeds
1 teaspoon mustard seeds

Combine first 4 ingredients in a small bowl, stirring well; let stand 3 hours.

Combine remaining ingredients in a small Dutch oven; stir well. Stir in cabbage mixture, and bring to a boil. Boil, uncovered, 4 minutes. Ladle into hot sterilized jars, leaving ½-inch headspace. Gently stir to remove air bubbles. Cover at once with metal lids, and screw bands tight. Process in boiling-water bath 15 minutes. Serve using a slotted spoon. Yield: 3 half pints (12 calories per tablespoon).

PROTEIN 0.1 / FAT 0.1 / CARBOHYDRATE 3.0 / CHOLESTEROL 0 / IRON 0.1 / SODIUM 51 / CALCIUM 4

PICKLED BEET RELISH

1 tablespoon mixed pickling spices
3 (2- x ½-inch) strips orange rind
1 tablespoon plus 1 teaspoon firmly
  packed brown sugar
1 pound fresh beets
½ teaspoon salt
½ cup raspberry vinegar

Combine pickling spices, orange rind, and brown sugar in a cheesecloth bag. Leave root and 1 inch of stem on beets; scrub with a brush. Place beets, spice bag, and salt in a large saucepan, and add water to cover; bring to a boil. Cover; reduce heat, and simmer 30 minutes or until tender. Drain, reserving cooking liquid. Discard spice bag. Peel beets. Transfer beets and reserved cooking liquid to a medium bowl; stir in vinegar. Cover and refrigerate 8 hours or overnight. Drain well. Coarsely grate beets, and transfer to a serving bowl. Serve chilled. Yield: 2 cups (10 calories per tablespoon).

PROTEIN 0.3 / FAT 0.1 / CARBOHYDRATE 2.4 / CHOLESTEROL 0 / IRON 0.2 / SODIUM 47 / CALCIUM 6

VEGETABLE SALSA

1 (14½-ounce) can no-salt-added stewed tomatoes,
  undrained and chopped
1 (8¾-ounce) can whole kernel corn, drained
½ cup shredded jicama
¼ cup minced onion
¼ cup minced fresh cilantro
1 jalapeño pepper, seeded and minced
1 tablespoon minced fresh chives
1 tablespoon vinegar
1½ teaspoons vegetable oil
1 teaspoon sugar
1 clove garlic, crushed

Combine all ingredients. Cover and chill 1 hour. Serve with unsalted chips or grilled meats. Yield: 3 cups (8 calories per tablespoon).

PROTEIN 0.2 / FAT 0.2 / CARBOHYDRATE 1.6 / CHOLESTEROL 0 / IRON 0.1 / SODIUM 2 / CALCIUM 4

CITRUS VINEGAR

½ small grapefruit, thinly sliced
½ medium-size orange, thinly sliced
1 quart white wine vinegar

Fold fruit slices, and thread onto two 10-inch wooden skewers. Place skewers in a sterilized wide mouthed jar. Bring vinegar to a boil; pour over skewered fruit in jar. Cover with a metal lid, and screw band tight. Let stand 10 days at room temperature.

Strain vinegar into a decorative bottle; discard skewered fruit. Seal bottle with a cork or other airtight lid. Use citrus vinegar in salad dressings or serve with raw vegetables. Yield: 1 quart (5 calories per tablespoon).

PROTEIN 0.1 / FAT 0.0 / CARBOHYDRATE 0.6 / CHOLESTEROL 0 / IRON 0.0 / SODIUM 2 / CALCIUM 2

Nutritious fruit and vegetable side dish combinations: (clockwise from front) Jicama-Snow Pea Sauté (page 211), Leeks with Tarragon Vinaigrette (page 211), Lemony Cauliflower (page 210), Tropical Fruit Mélange (page 218), and Sesame Carrots (page 209).

Side Dishes

ARTICHOKES IN CREAMY MUSTARD SAUCE

2 (9-ounce) packages frozen artichoke hearts,
   thawed and drained
¼ cup reduced-calorie mayonnaise
¼ cup low-fat sour cream
2 tablespoons Dijon mustard
1 tablespoon white wine Worcestershire sauce
1 clove garlic, minced
¼ cup fine, dry breadcrumbs
2 tablespoons chopped fresh parsley

Place artichokes in a 1-quart casserole. Combine mayonnaise and next 4 ingredients in a 1-cup measure; stir well. Spread mixture evenly over top of artichokes. Sprinkle with breadcrumbs, and bake at 350° for 25 minutes or until thoroughly heated. Top with fresh parsley. Yield: 6 servings (98 calories per serving).

PROTEIN 3.3 / FAT 4.8 / CARBOHYDRATE 11.8 / CHOLESTEROL 7 / IRON 0.7 / SODIUM 325 / CALCIUM 37

SPINACH-STUFFED ARTICHOKE BOTTOMS

1 (10-ounce) package frozen chopped spinach,
   thawed
Vegetable cooking spray
¼ cup chopped green onions
1 clove garlic, minced
2 ounces Neufchâtel cheese, cut into ½-inch cubes
¼ teaspoon ground nutmeg
1 (14-ounce) can artichoke bottoms, drained
½ cup (2 ounces) shredded part-skim mozzarella
   cheese

Drain thawed spinach; squeeze out excess moisture between paper towels, and set aside.
Coat a large skillet with cooking spray; place over medium heat until hot. Add green onions and garlic; sauté until tender. Stir in reserved spinach, Neufchâtel cheese, and nutmeg. Cook, stirring constantly, until cheese melts. Remove from heat.

Arrange artichoke bottoms in a 1-quart casserole. Spoon spinach mixture evenly over artichoke bottoms, mounding slightly. Bake, uncovered, at 350° for 10 minutes. Sprinkle with mozzarella cheese. Bake an additional 5 minutes or until cheese melts. Yield: 8 servings (59 calories per serving).

PROTEIN 4.1 / FAT 3.0 / CARBOHYDRATE 5.0 / CHOLESTEROL 9 / IRON 1.2 / SODIUM 105 / CALCIUM 103

ASPARAGUS WITH ALMONDS

1 pound fresh asparagus spears
2 teaspoons margarine
1 tablespoon all-purpose flour
½ cup skim milk
1 tablespoon grated Parmesan cheese
1 teaspoon white wine Worcestershire sauce
Dash of pepper
2 tablespoons slivered almonds, toasted

Snap off tough ends of asparagus. Remove scales, using a knife or vegetable peeler, if desired. Cook asparagus, covered, in a small amount of boiling water 6 minutes or until crisp-tender. Drain. Arrange cooked asparagus on a serving platter, and keep warm.

Melt margarine in a small saucepan over low heat; add flour, stirring until smooth. Cook 1 minute, stirring constantly. Gradually add milk; cook over medium heat, stirring constantly, until thickened and bubbly. Stir in cheese, Worcestershire sauce, and pepper.

Pour sauce over asparagus; sprinkle with toasted almonds. Yield: 4 servings (92 calories per serving).

PROTEIN 6.1 / FAT 4.8 / CARBOHYDRATE 8.5 / CHOLESTEROL 2 / IRON 1.0 / SODIUM 78 / CALCIUM 94

HERBED ASPARAGUS SAUTÉ

1 pound fresh asparagus spears
Vegetable cooking spray
1 teaspoon olive oil
1 clove garlic, minced
10 cherry tomatoes, halved
½ teaspoon dried whole oregano
⅛ teaspoon dried whole thyme
Dash of pepper
2 tablespoons grated Parmesan cheese

Snap off tough ends of asparagus. Remove scales, using a knife or vegetable peeler, if desired. Blanch asparagus, covered, in boiling water 1 minute. Drain, and rinse under cold water until cool; drain. Cut diagonally into 1-inch pieces.

Coat a large skillet with cooking spray; add olive oil. Place over medium heat until hot. Add asparagus and garlic; sauté 2 minutes or just until tender. Add tomatoes, oregano, thyme, and pepper. Cook 1 minute or until thoroughly heated. Transfer to a serving dish, and sprinkle with cheese. Yield: 4 servings (55 calories per serving).

PROTEIN 4.9 / FAT 2.2 / CARBOHYDRATE 6.2 / CHOLESTEROL 2 / IRON 1.1 / SODIUM 52 / CALCIUM 67

GREEN BEANS WITH TARRAGON SAUCE

1 pound fresh green beans
Vegetable cooking spray
1 teaspoon olive oil
½ cup finely chopped onion
1 clove garlic, minced
3 medium tomatoes, peeled, seeded, and chopped
1 tablespoon chopped fresh parsley
2 tablespoons tarragon vinegar
¼ teaspoon salt
Dash of pepper

Remove strings from beans. Place beans in vegetable steamer; place steamer over boiling water. Cover and steam 8 minutes or until crisp-tender. Drain, and set aside.

Coat a medium skillet with cooking spray; add oil. Place over medium heat until hot. Add onion and garlic; sauté until tender. Stir in remaining ingredients, and bring to a boil. Reduce heat and simmer, uncovered, 10 minutes.

Arrange beans on a serving platter, and spoon tomato mixture over beans. Yield: 6 servings (48 calories per serving).

PROTEIN 2.2 / FAT 1.0 / CARBOHYDRATE 9.2 / CHOLESTEROL 0 / IRON 1.2 / SODIUM 105 / CALCIUM 41

The flavors of fresh vegetables and herbs found in Herbed Asparagus Sauté will always be popular.

SWISS BROCCOLI BAKE

1 cup low-fat cottage cheese
2 egg yolks
1 tablespoon all-purpose flour
2 (10-ounce) packages frozen chopped broccoli,
  cooked without salt
¾ cup (3 ounces) shredded Swiss cheese
¼ cup minced green onions
¼ teaspoon salt
¼ teaspoon ground nutmeg
⅛ teaspoon pepper
3 egg whites
Vegetable cooking spray

Combine cottage cheese, egg yolks, and flour in container of an electric blender. Process until smooth.

Place broccoli between paper towels; squeeze until barely moist. Combine cottage cheese mixture, broccoli, Swiss cheese and next 4 ingredients; stir well.

Beat egg whites (at room temperature) until stiff but not dry. Gently fold into broccoli mixture. Spoon into an 8-inch square baking dish coated with cooking spray. Bake at 350° for 35 minutes or until puffed and golden brown. Yield: 8 servings (111 calories per serving).

PROTEIN 11.0 / FAT 5.1 / CARBOHYDRATE 6.1 / CHOLESTEROL 80 / IRON 0.9 / SODIUM 254 / CALCIUM 171

SHREDDED BEETS WITH HORSERADISH

6 medium beets
1 tablespoon prepared horseradish
1 tablespoon white wine vinegar
2 teaspoons margarine, melted

Leave root and 1 inch of stem on beets; scrub with a brush. Place beets in a large saucepan, and add water to cover; bring to a boil. Cover; reduce heat, and simmer 40 minutes or until tender. Drain; rinse beets with cold water, and drain again. Peel beets, and coarsely shred.

Combine beets and remaining ingredients, tossing well. Serve immediately. Yield: 12 servings (35 calories per serving).

PROTEIN 1.0 / FAT 0.7 / CARBOHYDRATE 6.7 / CHOLESTEROL 0 / IRON 0.6 / SODIUM 56 / CALCIUM 12

TANGY BEETS WITH GRAPES

2 pounds medium beets
2 teaspoons margarine
¼ cup finely chopped onion
2 tablespoons red wine vinegar
1 tablespoon firmly packed brown sugar
½ cup seedless red grapes, halved

Leave root and 1 inch of stem on beets; scrub with a brush. Place beets in a large saucepan, and add water to cover; bring to a boil. Cover; reduce heat, and simmer 40 minutes or until tender. Drain; rinse beets with cold water, and drain again. Peel beets, and cut into ¼-inch slices; set aside.

Melt margarine in a medium skillet over low heat. Add onion, and sauté until tender. Stir in vinegar, sugar, and grapes. Add beets; cook until thoroughly heated. Yield: 8 servings (74 calories per serving).

PROTEIN 1.8 / FAT 1.2 / CARBOHYDRATE 15.2 / CHOLESTEROL 0 / IRON 1.1 / SODIUM 94 / CALCIUM 22

HONEY-MUSTARD BRUSSELS SPROUTS

1 pound fresh brussels sprouts
1½ cups water
1 teaspoon chicken-flavored bouillon
  granules
2 tablespoons honey
2 teaspoons Dijon mustard
2 teaspoons lemon juice

Remove any discolored leaves from brussels sprouts. Cut off stem ends, and wash sprouts thoroughly. Cut a shallow X in the base of each sprout. Combine water and bouillon granules in a medium saucepan; bring to a boil. Add brussels sprouts, and return to a boil. Cover; reduce heat, and simmer 8 minutes or until brussels sprouts are tender. Drain.

Combine honey, mustard, and lemon juice; pour over sprouts, and toss lightly to coat well. Yield: 4 servings (69 calories per serving).

PROTEIN 3.5 / FAT 0.4 / CARBOHYDRATE 15.2 / CHOLESTEROL 0 / IRON 0.7 / SODIUM 197 / CALCIUM 59

SPICED RED CABBAGE

1 pound red cabbage, shredded
¾ cup unsweetened apple juice
½ cup chopped onion
½ cup water
2 teaspoons sugar
½ teaspoon ground cinnamon
¼ teaspoon ground cloves
1 medium-size Red Delicious apple,
    cored and chopped
2 tablespoons red wine vinegar

Combine shredded cabbage, apple juice, onion, water, sugar, cinnamon, and cloves in a Dutch oven. Bring mixture to a boil. Cover; reduce heat, and simmer 20 minutes. Stir in chopped apple and red wine vinegar. Cover and simmer 5 minutes. Transfer mixture to a serving bowl, and serve immediately. Yield: 10 servings (36 calories per serving).

PROTEIN 0.8 / FAT 0.2 / CARBOHYDRATE 8.5 / CHOLESTEROL 0 / IRON 0.4 / SODIUM 6 / CALCIUM 29

HONEYED CARROTS WITH RAISINS

1 pound medium carrots, scraped and diagonally
    sliced
⅓ cup unsweetened orange juice
¼ cup raisins
1 tablespoon honey
⅛ teaspoon ground nutmeg

Combine carrots, orange juice, raisins, honey, and nutmeg in a medium saucepan. Bring mixture to a boil. Cover; reduce heat, and simmer 12 minutes or until carrots are tender. Transfer mixture to a serving bowl. Serve immediately, using a slotted spoon. Yield: 4 servings (101 calories per serving).

PROTEIN 1.5 / FAT 0.3 / CARBOHYDRATE 25.1 / CHOLESTEROL 0 / IRON 0.9 / SODIUM 43 / CALCIUM 39

LEMONY BABY CARROTS

1 pound baby carrots, scraped
2 tablespoons lemon juice
2 teaspoons margarine, melted
1 teaspoon sugar
Dash of white pepper
Grated lemon rind (optional)

Place carrots in vegetable steamer; place steamer over boiling water. Cover and steam 10 minutes or until crisp-tender. Drain well, and transfer to serving bowl. Combine lemon juice, margarine, sugar, and pepper; pour over carrots, tossing lightly to coat well. Sprinkle with lemon zest, if desired. Yield: 4 servings (72 calories per serving).

PROTEIN 1.2 / FAT 2.1 / CARBOHYDRATE 13.2 / CHOLESTEROL 0 / IRON 0.6 / SODIUM 62 / CALCIUM 32

SESAME CARROTS

2 teaspoons margarine
1 pound medium carrots, scraped and cut into
    julienne strips
2 tablespoons unsweetened orange juice
1 teaspoon brown sugar
¼ teaspoon ground ginger
⅛ teaspoon salt
⅛ teaspoon dry mustard
Dash of pepper
2 teaspoons sesame seeds, toasted

Melt margarine in a large skillet over medium heat. Add carrots; sauté 8 minutes or until crisp-tender. Add orange juice, brown sugar, ginger, salt, mustard, and pepper. Cook over medium-low heat 8 minutes, stirring occasionally. Transfer to a serving bowl. Sprinkle with toasted sesame seeds. Yield: 4 servings (82 calories per serving).

PROTEIN 1.5 / FAT 2.9 / CARBOHYDRATE 13.5 / CHOLESTEROL 0 / IRON 0.9 / SODIUM 136 / CALCIUM 49

LEMONY CAULIFLOWER

1 medium cauliflower (about 2 pounds)
½ cup plain low-fat yogurt
¼ cup reduced-calorie mayonnaise
1 tablespoon lemon juice
2 teaspoons Dijon mustard
½ teaspoon grated lemon rind
1 tablespoon chopped fresh chives

Wash cauliflower; remove leaves, and cut out base. Cover and cook in a small amount of boiling water 5 to 6 minutes or until crisp-tender. Transfer to a serving plate; keep warm.

Combine yogurt and next 4 ingredients; stir well. Pour over hot cauliflower. Sprinkle with chives. Yield: 6 servings (78 calories per serving).

PROTEIN 4.1 / FAT 3.3 / CARBOHYDRATE 9.8 / CHOLESTEROL 4 / IRON 0.9 / SODIUM 160 / CALCIUM 79

CELERY IN LEMON-DIJON SAUCE

3 cups diagonally sliced celery
¼ cup chopped sweet red pepper
1 teaspoon unsalted margarine
3 tablespoons reduced-calorie mayonnaise
1 tablespoon lemon juice
1 tablespoon Dijon mustard
1 teaspoon sugar

Cook celery in a small amount of boiling water 8 minutes or until crisp-tender. Drain. Return celery to saucepan. Add sweet red pepper and margarine. Cook over low heat 2 minutes.

Combine mayonnaise and remaining ingredients, stirring well. Pour over celery; toss gently. Transfer to a serving bowl, and serve immediately. Yield: 4 servings (65 calories per serving).

PROTEIN 0.8 / FAT 4.3 / CARBOHYDRATE 6.1 / CHOLESTEROL 4 / IRON 0.5 / SODIUM 274 / CALCIUM 36

SPICY CORN AND LIMA BEANS

2 cups fresh or frozen lima beans
2 cups fresh corn, cut from cob
1 (10-ounce) can chopped tomatoes with green chiles, undrained
1 clove garlic, minced
¼ teaspoon salt

Cook lima beans in a small amount of boiling water 15 minutes or until tender. Drain. Return beans to saucepan. Add remaining ingredients; stir well. Bring to a boil. Cover; reduce heat, and simmer 15 minutes or until thoroughly heated. Yield: 8 servings (84 calories per serving).

PROTEIN 4.0 / FAT 0.8 / CARBOHYDRATE 17.0 / CHOLESTEROL 0 / IRON 1.6 / SODIUM 267 / CALCIUM 26

SAUTÉED CUCUMBER MEDLEY

Vegetable cooking spray
3 medium cucumbers, peeled, seeded, and chopped
1 medium tomato, seeded and chopped
¼ cup shredded carrots
¼ teaspoon salt
¼ teaspoon dried whole dillweed

Coat a large skillet with cooking spray; place over medium heat until hot. Add cucumber, tomato, and carrots. Sauté 3 minutes or until crisp-tender. Add salt and dillweed. Serve immediately. Yield: 4 servings (35 calories per serving).

PROTEIN 1.4 / FAT 0.3 / CARBOHYDRATE 7.9 / CHOLESTEROL 0 / IRON 0.8 / SODIUM 162 / CALCIUM 36

HERBED EGGPLANT SAUTÉ

Vegetable cooking spray
1 teaspoon olive oil
2 cloves garlic, minced
1 medium eggplant, peeled and cubed
3 tablespoons chopped fresh parsley
½ teaspoon dried whole thyme
¼ teaspoon salt
¼ teaspoon dried whole marjoram
¼ teaspoon summer savory
⅛ teaspoon freshly ground pepper
1 cup chopped tomato

Coat a skillet with cooking spray; add oil. Place over medium heat until hot. Add garlic. Sauté 1 minute. Add eggplant and next 6 ingredients. Sauté 8 minutes or until eggplant is tender. Stir in tomato. Cook until heated. Yield: 6 servings (35 calories per serving).

PROTEIN 1.2 / FAT 0.9 / CARBOHYDRATE 6.7 / CHOLESTEROL 0 / IRON 0.9 / SODIUM 104 / CALCIUM 38

LEEKS WITH TARRAGON VINAIGRETTE

6 medium-size leeks (2½ pounds)
2 cups water
1 teaspoon chicken-flavored bouillon granules
⅛ teaspoon freshly ground pepper
2 tablespoons tarragon vinegar
1 tablespoon chopped fresh parsley
1 tablespoon reduced-calorie Italian salad dressing
¼ teaspoon dried whole tarragon

Remove roots, tough outer leaves, and tops from leeks, leaving 2 inches of dark leaves. Split leeks in half lengthwise to within 1 inch of bulb end. Set aside.

Combine water, bouillon granules, and pepper in a large heavy skillet. Bring to a boil. Add leeks. Cover; reduce heat, and simmer 10 minutes or just until tender. Drain. Place leeks on a serving platter.

Combine vinegar and remaining ingredients, stirring well. Pour over leeks. Serve immediately. Yield: 6 servings (118 calories per serving).

PROTEIN 2.9 / FAT 0.7 / CARBOHYDRATE 27.1 / CHOLESTEROL 0 / IRON 3.9 / SODIUM 124 / CALCIUM 113

MUSHROOMS ITALIANO

1 pound small fresh mushrooms
Vegetable cooking spray
1 teaspoon olive oil
2 teaspoons chopped fresh basil
2 teaspoons chopped fresh oregano
1 teaspoon lemon juice
¼ teaspoon garlic salt
Dash of red pepper
1 tablespoon diced pimiento

Clean mushrooms with damp paper towels; set aside.

Coat a large skillet with cooking spray; add olive oil, and place over medium-high heat until hot. Add basil, oregano, lemon juice, garlic salt, and pepper; sauté 1 minute. Add reserved mushrooms, and sauté 3 to 5 minutes, stirring frequently. Stir in chopped pimiento, and serve immediately. Yield: 4 servings (43 calories per serving).

PROTEIN 2.5 / FAT 1.7 / CARBOHYDRATE 6.3 / CHOLESTEROL 0 / IRON 1.8 / SODIUM 137 / CALCIUM 22

JICAMA-SNOW PEA SAUTÉ

6 ounces fresh snow peas
Vegetable cooking spray
¼ pound jicama, peeled and cut into julienne strips
1 medium-size sweet red pepper, seeded and cut into strips
1 cup sliced fresh mushrooms
1 tablespoon teriyaki sauce

Trim ends from fresh snow peas. Set snow peas aside.

Coat a large nonstick skillet with cooking spray. Place over medium-high heat until hot. Add jicama and sweet red pepper; sauté 2 minutes. Add reserved snow peas and mushrooms; sauté 2 minutes. Add teriyaki sauce, stirring well. Transfer to a serving platter. Serve immediately. Yield: 6 servings (29 calories per serving).

PROTEIN 1.6 / FAT 0.2 / CARBOHYDRATE 5.6 / CHOLESTEROL 0 / IRON 1.1 / SODIUM 118 / CALCIUM 17

JICAMA AND SNOW PEAS—A COMPLEMENTARY COMBO

East meets West when you combine crunchy Mexican jicamas and crisp Asian snow peas in Jicama-Snow Pea Sauté. Somewhat of a newcomer to the marketplace, jicama is a sweet, juicy tuber with a texture like that of the water chestnut. Raw strips of jicama make ideal dippers, and when cut into flat rounds, make pretty canapés. For more crunch and flavor, add strips of jicama to stir-fries. Each cup has only 49 calories and lots of vitamin C. The perfect complement to the creamy white flesh of jicama is the crescent-shaped snow pea with its own crisp texture and sweet taste. Whether steamed, stir-fried, or blanched, snow peas are also low in calories (67 per cup) and rich in vitamin C.

OKRA SKILLET MEDLEY

Vegetable cooking spray
1 teaspoon vegetable oil
½ cup chopped green pepper
½ cup chopped onion
1 clove garlic, minced
2 cups sliced fresh okra
2 medium tomatoes, seeded and chopped
1 cup fresh corn, cut from cob
2 tablespoons water
½ teaspoon chili powder
¼ teaspoon salt
⅛ teaspoon pepper

Coat a large skillet with cooking spray; add oil. Place over medium heat until hot. Add green pepper, onion, and garlic. Sauté until tender. Add okra and remaining ingredients; stir well. Cover; reduce heat, and simmer 15 minutes or until corn is tender. Yield: 8 servings (45 calories per serving).

PROTEIN 1.7 / FAT 1.0 / CARBOHYDRATE 8.6 / CHOLESTEROL 0 / IRON 0.7 / SODIUM 83 / CALCIUM 28

SKILLET CREOLE PEAS

1 (10-ounce) package frozen black-eyed peas
Vegetable cooking spray
¾ cup chopped onion
½ cup chopped celery
½ cup chopped green pepper
1 clove garlic, minced
1 (14½-ounce) can whole tomatoes, undrained and chopped
¼ teaspoon dried whole thyme
¼ teaspoon red pepper
⅛ teaspoon hot sauce
Dash of ground allspice
1 bay leaf

Cook peas according to package directions, omitting salt and fat; drain and set aside.
Coat a large skillet with cooking spray; place over medium heat until hot. Add onion, celery, green pepper, and garlic. Sauté until tender. Stir in reserved peas and remaining ingredients. Cook over medium-low heat 10 minutes, stirring

occasionally. Remove and discard bay leaf before serving. Yield: 6 servings (93 calories per serving).

PROTEIN 5.4 / FAT 0.6 / CARBOHYDRATE 17.7 / CHOLESTEROL 0 / IRON 2.0 / SODIUM 125 / CALCIUM 44

OKRA IS O.K.

Fried by Southerners, pickled by Texans, and stewed by Cajuns and Creoles, slender, tapering pods of okra add body, color, and texture to dishes. One cup of boiled, cooked okra has only 38 calories and supplies one-third of the vitamin C and almost all of the folate needed each day. This is good information when you consider okra's low-fat culinary possibilities. Steamed for three to five minutes, it makes crunchy vegetable dippers. Side dishes with vegetable combinations and main-dish gumbos and stews offer plenty of reasons to serve okra. Each serving of Okra Skillet Medley has only 45 calories.

ZESTY SUGAR SNAP PEAS

½ pound fresh Sugar Snap peas
1 tablespoon plain low-fat yogurt
1 tablespoon reduced-calorie mayonnaise
1 teaspoon prepared horseradish
1 teaspoon unsweetened orange juice
½ teaspoon grated orange rind

Trim ends from peas. Place peas in a vegetable steamer; place steamer over boiling water. Cover and steam 3 to 5 minutes or until crisp-tender.
Transfer peas to a serving platter and keep warm. Combine yogurt and remaining ingredients, stirring well. Pour over peas. Serve immediately. Yield: 4 servings (37 calories per serving).

PROTEIN 1.8 / FAT 1.2 / CARBOHYDRATE 5.1 / CHOLESTEROL 1 / IRON 1.2 / SODIUM 34 / CALCIUM 32

Parmesan Potato Puffs are elegant, golden swirls of potato and Parmesan cheese.

PARMESAN POTATO PUFFS

2 large baking potatoes, peeled and sliced (1 pound)
3 tablespoons skim milk, divided
¼ cup freshly grated Parmesan cheese
¼ teaspoon salt
⅛ teaspoon white pepper
⅛ teaspoon ground nutmeg
2 eggs, separated
Vegetable cooking spray

Combine potatoes and water to cover in a large saucepan; bring to a boil. Cover; reduce heat, and simmer 20 minutes or until tender. Drain. Place potatoes in a medium mixing bowl; add 2 tablespoons skim milk. Mash until smooth. Add remaining skim milk and next 4 ingredients. Beat at low speed of an electric mixer until smooth and blended.

Beat egg yolks in a small bowl until thick and lemon colored. Stir into potato mixture.

Beat egg whites (at room temperature) in a medium bowl until stiff, but not dry. Gently fold into potato mixture. Spoon or pipe potato mixture into 6 mounds on a baking sheet coated with cooking spray. Bake at 350° for 25 to 30 minutes or until golden brown. Yield: 6 servings (104 calories per serving).

PROTEIN 5.2 / FAT 3.0 / CARBOHYDRATE 14.3 / CHOLESTEROL 94 / IRON 1.0 / SODIUM 191 / CALCIUM 71

GARLIC-ROSEMARY OVEN POTATOES

3 medium baking potatoes (1¼ pounds)
3 tablespoons water
1 tablespoon vegetable oil
1 teaspoon dried whole rosemary, crushed
2 cloves garlic, crushed
¼ teaspoon salt
¼ teaspoon paprika
⅛ teaspoon pepper
Vegetable cooking spray

Cut potatoes crosswise into ⅛-inch-thick slices. Combine water and next 6 ingredients in a large shallow container, stirring well. Add potatoes. Toss gently to coat well.

Arrange potato slices in a 13- x 9- x 2-inch baking dish coated with cooking spray. Brush remaining marinade over potatoes. Bake at 475° for 30 minutes or until tender, turning potato slices after 15 minutes. Serve immediately. Yield: 6 servings (93 calories per serving).

PROTEIN 2.2 / FAT 2.4 / CARBOHYDRATE 16.2 / CHOLESTEROL 0 / IRON 1.2 / SODIUM 105 / CALCIUM 17

GINGERED SPINACH STIR-FRY

1 pound fresh spinach
1 tablespoon vinegar
1 teaspoon sugar
1 teaspoon grated fresh gingerroot
⅛ teaspoon salt
⅛ teaspoon hot sauce
Vegetable cooking spray
2 teaspoons vegetable oil
½ cup chopped green onions
1 (8-ounce) can sliced water chestnuts, drained

Remove stems from spinach; wash leaves, and drain. Set aside.

Combine vinegar, sugar, gingerroot, salt, and hot sauce; stir well, and set aside.

Coat a wok or large skillet with cooking spray; add oil. Heat at medium-high until hot. Add onions and water chestnuts; stir-fry 1 minute. Add spinach and vinegar mixture; stir-fry 2 minutes or until spinach is wilted. Serve hot. Yield: 6 servings (55 calories per serving).

PROTEIN 1.8 / FAT 1.7 / CARBOHYDRATE 8.8 / CHOLESTEROL 0 / IRON 1.5 / SODIUM 91 / CALCIUM 54

TROPICAL BUTTERNUT SQUASH

1 (2-pound) butternut squash
1 (8-ounce) can unsweetened pineapple tidbits, undrained
½ cup unsweetened orange juice
1 tablespoon rum
2 teaspoons cornstarch
1 teaspoon grated orange rind
¼ teaspoon salt

Cut squash in half lengthwise, and remove seeds. Place cut side down in a large Dutch oven; add boiling water to a depth of 1 inch in Dutch oven. Cover and cook over medium-high heat 12 minutes or until squash is tender. Drain. Let cool to touch. Peel and cube squash.

Drain pineapple, reserving juice. Set pineapple aside. Combine pineapple juice and remaining ingredients in a medium saucepan over medium heat. Bring to a boil. Boil 1 minute. Remove from heat. Add reserved squash and pineapple. Toss gently. Transfer to a serving bowl. Yield: 6 servings (115 calories per serving).

PROTEIN 2.1 / FAT 0.2 / CARBOHYDRATE 28.0 / CHOLESTEROL 0 / IRON 1.3 / SODIUM 100 / CALCIUM 56

MEXICAN SPAGHETTI SQUASH

2 (3-pound) spaghetti squash
Vegetable cooking spray
1 small onion, chopped
1 clove garlic, minced
1 (14½-ounce) can no-salt-added whole tomatoes, undrained and chopped
1 (4-ounce) can chopped green chiles, drained
½ teaspoon chili powder
⅛ teaspoon red pepper
½ cup (2 ounces) shredded Monterey Jack cheese

Wash squash; pierce with a fork several times. Place squash in a large baking dish. Bake at 350° for 1 hour or until squash yield to pressure. Let cool to touch. Cut squash in half lengthwise; discard seeds. Remove spaghetti-like strands from squash using a fork. Place squash in a large serving bowl. Set aside and keep warm. Discard squash shells.

Coat a large skillet with cooking spray; place over medium-high heat until hot. Add onion and garlic; sauté until tender. Stir in tomatoes, green chiles, chili powder, and red pepper. Bring to a boil. Cover; reduce heat, and simmer 10 minutes. Add tomato mixture and cheese to reserved squash, tossing gently. Serve immediately. Yield: 12 servings (96 calories per serving).

PROTEIN 3.1 / FAT 2.1 / CARBOHYDRATE 17.5 / CHOLESTEROL 4 / IRON 1.1 / SODIUM 185 / CALCIUM 101

SPICY SQUASH AND PEPPER CASSEROLE

2 medium-size yellow squash, chopped
2 medium zucchini, chopped
Vegetable cooking spray
1 banana pepper, seeded and chopped
1 medium-size green pepper, seeded and chopped
¼ cup minced onion
1 tablespoon margarine
2 tablespoons all-purpose flour
¾ cup skim milk
½ cup (2 ounces) shredded sharp Cheddar cheese
3 drops of hot sauce
1 egg, beaten

Cook yellow squash and zucchini separately in a small amount of boiling water for 5 minutes. Drain, and set aside.

Coat a large skillet with cooking spray; place over medium-high heat until hot. Add peppers and onion; sauté until tender. Remove from heat, and stir in reserved squash. Set aside.

Melt margarine in a heavy saucepan over low heat. Add flour, stirring until smooth. Cook 1 minute, stirring constantly. Gradually add milk. Cook over medium heat, stirring constantly, until thickened and bubbly. Stir in cheese and hot sauce. Gradually stir about one-fourth of hot mixture into egg; add to remaining hot mixture, stirring constantly. Add reserved squash mixture, stirring well. Spoon mixture into a 1-quart casserole coated with cooking spray. Cover and bake at 350° for 30 minutes. Yield: 6 servings (110 calories per serving).

PROTEIN 5.8 / FAT 6.3 / CARBOHYDRATE 8.3 / CHOLESTEROL 56 / IRON 0.9 / SODIUM 112 / CALCIUM 128

OVEN-FRIED ZUCCHINI CHIPS

3 medium zucchini (1 pound)
1 egg
2 tablespoons reduced-calorie Italian
  salad dressing
½ cup fine, dry breadcrumbs
2 tablespoons all-purpose flour
2 tablespoons grated Parmesan cheese
⅛ teaspoon freshly ground pepper
Vegetable cooking spray

Cut zucchini into ¼-inch-thick slices. Combine egg and salad dressing; stir well. Combine breadcrumbs and next 3 ingredients; stir well. Dip zucchini in egg mixture; dredge in breadcrumbs. Place on baking sheets coated with cooking spray. Bake at 475° for 5 minutes on each side or until golden brown. Serve immediately. Yield: 6 servings (77 calories per serving).

PROTEIN 4.0 / FAT 1.9 / CARBOHYDRATE 11.2 / CHOLESTEROL 47 /
IRON 0.9 / SODIUM 151 / CALCIUM 50

PEPPER-STUFFED TOMATOES

6 medium tomatoes
2 tablespoons reduced-calorie Italian salad dressing
1 medium-size green pepper, seeded and chopped
1 medium-size sweet red pepper, seeded and chopped
1 medium-size sweet yellow pepper, seeded and chopped
½ cup (2 ounces) shredded part-skim mozzarella cheese

Cut off top of each tomato. Scoop out pulp, leaving shells intact. Chop 1 cup of pulp; drain, and set aside. Discard remaining pulp. Invert tomato shells on paper towels to drain.

Pour salad dressing into a large skillet. Place over medium heat until hot. Add peppers, and sauté until tender. Stir in reserved tomato pulp.

Spoon mixture into shells. Place in a 12- x 8- x 2-inch baking dish. Bake, uncovered, at 350° for 10 minutes. Remove from oven. Sprinkle with cheese. Broil 6 inches from heating element until cheese melts. Serve immediately. Yield: 6 servings (65 calories per serving).

PROTEIN 3.9 / FAT 2.0 / CARBOHYDRATE 9.4 / CHOLESTEROL 5 /
IRON 1.3 / SODIUM 101 / CALCIUM 74

ORANGE-TURNIP MÉLANGE

Vegetable cooking spray
1 teaspoon margarine
1 pound turnips, peeled and grated
2 medium carrots, scraped and grated
2 tablespoons minced onion
¼ teaspoon grated orange rind
¾ cup unsweetened orange juice
2 tablespoons firmly packed brown sugar
⅛ teaspoon salt
⅛ teaspoon ground ginger
2 tablespoons chopped fresh parsley

Coat a large skillet with cooking spray; add margarine. Place over medium-high heat until margarine melts. Add turnips, carrots, and onion; cook over medium-high heat 2 minutes, stirring frequently.

Combine remaining ingredients, except parsley, and add to skillet. Cook over medium-high heat 5 minutes or until thoroughly heated, stirring frequently. Transfer to a serving platter, and sprinkle with parsley. Yield: 6 servings (65 calories per serving).

PROTEIN 1.0 / FAT 0.8 / CARBOHYDRATE 14.2 / CHOLESTEROL 0 /
IRON 0.6 / SODIUM 105 / CALCIUM 34

GETTING ENOUGH POTASSIUM

Are you getting enough potassium? As nature's foods are processed into convenience foods, potassium stores are reduced. Preliminary studies suggest that some people who consume diets low in potassium are more likely to have high blood pressure. Potassium guidelines are not set but the American Heart Association suggests two times your sodium intake. (See page 12 for sodium guidelines.)

Unprocessed fruit and vegetables are the best sources of potassium. Potassium-rich fruits include melons, bananas, and citrus fruits and juices. Vegetables that are potassium rich include potatoes, dried peas and beans, tomatoes, and all varieties of greens—spinach, turnip, mustard, and kale.

Rich potassium stores also exist in other foods, such as 8 ounces of milk or 3 ounces of fish. A product listing 300 milligrams of potassium on the label is considered a good source. Consider serving potassium-rich Honeyed Banana Sauté (page 216) as a special side-dish treat.

APPLE-SWEET POTATO MEDLEY

1 pound sweet potatoes, peeled and cubed
⅔ cup unsweetened apple juice
2 teaspoons cornstarch
¼ teaspoon ground cinnamon
⅛ teaspoon ground nutmeg
2 medium apples, peeled, cored, and coarsely chopped

Place sweet potato cubes in vegetable steamer. Place over boiling water; cover and steam 5 to 6 minutes or until tender. Transfer potatoes to a serving bowl, and keep warm.

Combine apple juice, cornstarch, cinnamon, and nutmeg in a small saucepan. Cook over medium heat, stirring constantly, until thickened and bubbly. Stir in chopped apple. Reduce heat, and simmer 5 minutes or until apples are tender. Add apple mixture to reserved sweet potatoes; toss gently. Yield: 8 servings (89 calories per serving).

PROTEIN 1.0 / FAT 0.3 / CARBOHYDRATE 21.2 / CHOLESTEROL 0 / IRON 0.5 / SODIUM 8 / CALCIUM 17

BAKED MANDARIN APRICOTS

1 (14½-ounce) can unsweetened apricot halves, drained
1 (11-ounce) can unsweetened mandarin oranges, drained
8 gingersnaps, finely crushed
1 tablespoon firmly packed brown sugar
1 tablespoon margarine, melted
1 teaspoon grated orange rind

Place apricot halves, cut side up, in a 1-quart casserole. Top with mandarin oranges. Combine remaining ingredients and sprinkle over oranges. Bake, uncovered, at 325° for 15 minutes or until hot and bubbly. Serve immediately. Yield: 6 servings (96 calories per serving).

PROTEIN 0.9 / FAT 3.4 / CARBOHYDRATE 16.0 / CHOLESTEROL 3 / IRON 0.8 / SODIUM 39 / CALCIUM 24

HONEYED BANANA SAUTÉ

2 teaspoons margarine
⅛ teaspoon grated lemon rind
1 tablespoon lemon juice
1 tablespoon plus 1½ teaspoons honey
Dash of ground nutmeg
3 medium bananas, split lengthwise and halved

Melt margarine in a large skillet over medium heat. Add lemon rind, juice, honey, and nutmeg; stir well. Add bananas to skillet; cook over medium heat 2 to 3 minutes or until bananas are slightly soft, basting frequently with honey mixture. Serve immediately. Yield: 6 servings (83 calories per serving).

PROTEIN 0.6 / FAT 1.5 / CARBOHYDRATE 18.6 / CHOLESTEROL 0 / IRON 0.2 / SODIUM 16 / CALCIUM 5

CURRIED PEARS

4 medium pears, peeled, cored, and cut into wedges
½ cup unsweetened apple juice
1 tablespoon lemon juice
1 tablespoon honey
1 teaspoon curry powder

Combine all ingredients in a non-aluminum saucepan. Bring mixture to a boil. Cover; reduce heat, and simmer 8 to 10 minutes or until pears are tender. Serve hot, using a slotted spoon. Yield: 6 servings (72 calories per serving).

PROTEIN 0.4 / FAT 0.4 / CARBOHYDRATE 18.6 / CHOLESTEROL 0 / IRON 0.4 / SODIUM 1 / CALCIUM 13

Pear-Apple Fans are a unique presentation of two favorites.

PEAR-APPLE FANS

3 medium pears
2 teaspoons lemon juice
1 medium-size Red Delicious apple
¾ cup unsweetened apple juice
1 tablespoon honey
¼ teaspoon ground cinnamon

Cut pears in half lengthwise, removing core from bottom end and leaving stem intact. Cut 4 lengthwise slits on the rounded side of each pear half from the stem end to the base. Place pears, cut side down, in a 13- x 9- x 2-inch baking dish. Brush with lemon juice to prevent browning. Core apple and cut into 24 thin wedges. Place apple wedges, skin side up, into pear slits.

Combine remaining ingredients in a small bowl, and pour over pears. Cover and bake at 350° for 30 minutes or until pears are tender. Serve warm. Yield: 6 servings (103 calories per serving).

PROTEIN 0.5 / FAT 0.6 / CARBOHYDRATE 26.4 / CHOLESTEROL 0 / IRON 0.5 / SODIUM 2 / CALCIUM 17

PINEAPPLE WITH SPICED MERINGUE

1 fresh pineapple (about 4 pounds)
1 tablespoon rum
2 egg whites
½ teaspoon ground cinnamon
⅛ teaspoon ground nutmeg
1 tablespoon firmly packed brown sugar

Peel and trim eyes from pineapple; remove core. Cut pineapple into 1-inch cubes. Combine pineapple cubes and rum, tossing gently. Transfer mixture to a 1½-quart casserole. Cover and chill 1 hour.

Beat egg whites (at room temperature) with cinnamon and nutmeg until soft peaks form. Gradually add brown sugar, beating until stiff peaks form. Spread meringue over pineapple mixture, carefully sealing to edge of casserole. Bake at 350° for 12 to 15 minutes or until meringue is golden brown. Serve immediately. Yield: 6 servings (84 calories per serving).

PROTEIN 1.6 / FAT 0.6 / CARBOHYDRATE 18.5 / CHOLESTEROL 0 / IRON 0.6 / SODIUM 19 / CALCIUM 15

GRILLED FRUIT KABOBS

⅓ cup unsweetened pineapple juice
1 tablespoon reduced-sodium soy sauce
1 tablespoon honey
½ teaspoon grated fresh gingerroot
½ teaspoon cornstarch
1 (11-ounce) can unsweetened mandarin oranges, drained
1½ cups cubed fresh pineapple
Vegetable cooking spray

Combine first 5 ingredients in a non-aluminum saucepan. Cook over medium heat, stirring constantly, until mixture thickens. Set aside.

Alternate orange sections and pineapple on six 10-inch wooden skewers. Coat grill with cooking spray. Grill kabobs 6 inches over medium coals 5 minutes, turning and basting often with reserved pineapple juice mixture. Yield: 6 servings (61 calories per serving).

PROTEIN 0.4 / FAT 0.2 / CARBOHYDRATE 15.1 / CHOLESTEROL 0 / IRON 0.3 / SODIUM 100 / CALCIUM 6

TROPICAL FRUIT MÉLANGE

1 mango, peeled and coarsely chopped
1 cup fresh pineapple cubes
2 medium kiwifruit, peeled and sliced
1 large-size ripe banana, sliced
2 tablespoons lime juice
1 tablespoon cream of coconut

Combine first 4 ingredients in a medium bowl. Combine lime juice and cream of coconut; pour over fruit, and toss gently to coat well. Cover and chill at least 1 hour. Yield: 6 servings (96 calories per serving).

PROTEIN 1.1 / FAT 1.4 / CARBOHYDRATE 22.5 / CHOLESTEROL 0 / IRON 0.4 / SODIUM 3 / CALCIUM 18

BAKED PLUMS MADEIRA

1½ pounds small ripe plums, peeled, halved, and pitted
⅓ cup Madeira wine
¼ cup unsweetened orange juice
1 teaspoon grated orange rind
Dash of ground allspice

Place plums in a 2-quart casserole. Combine remaining ingredients, stirring well. Pour wine mixture over plums. Bake, uncovered, at 350° for 30 minutes or until plums are soft. Serve, using a slotted spoon. Yield: 6 servings (81 calories per serving).

PROTEIN 0.5 / FAT 0.0 / CARBOHYDRATE 18.1 / CHOLESTEROL 0 / IRON 0.5 / SODIUM 2 / CALCIUM 19

Chunks of fresh red snapper and potatoes are the basis of Red Snapper Stew (page 228).

Sweet Cherry Soup is a cold dessert or appetizer soup featuring plump, sweet cherries and flavored with Burgundy and cardamom.

BANANA SOUP WITH CINNAMON CROUTONS

2 medium-size ripe bananas, peeled
  and cubed
1½ cups plain low-fat yogurt
1 cup unsweetened orange juice
½ cup skim milk
1 tablespoon sugar
1 tablespoon light rum
⅛ teaspoon ground cinnamon
Cinnamon Croutons

Combine all ingredients, except Cinnamon Croutons, in container of electric blender or food processor; process until smooth. Cover and chill 2 hours. Sprinkle each serving with ¼ cup Cinnamon Croutons. Yield: 4 cups (203 calories per 1-cup serving).

Cinnamon Croutons:

2 teaspoons margarine, melted
¼ teaspoon ground cinnamon
2 slices day-old bread, cut into ½-inch cubes

Combine margarine and cinnamon in a small bowl, stirring well. Add bread cubes, and toss gently to coat well. Arrange bread cubes in a single layer in an 8-inch square baking pan. Bake at 275° for 45 minutes, stirring at 15 minute intervals. Remove from oven, and let cool before serving. Yield: 1 cup.

PROTEIN 7.5 / FAT 3.9 / CARBOHYDRATE 33.7 / CHOLESTEROL 6 / IRON 0.4 / SODIUM 162 / CALCIUM 214

SWEET CHERRY SOUP

2 cups plus 2 tablespoons water, divided
1 cup unsweetened white grape juice
1 (3-inch) stick cinnamon
1 pound fresh sweet cherries, pitted
1 tablespoon cornstarch
¼ teaspoon ground cardamom
¼ cup Burgundy or other dry red wine

Combine 2 cups water, grape juice, and cinnamon in a large saucepan. Bring to a boil, and add cherries. Cover; reduce heat, and simmer 15 minutes or until cherries are tender. Discard cinnamon stick.

Combine cornstarch, cardamom, and remaining 2 tablespoons water; stir well. Add to cherry mixture. Cook, stirring constantly, until mixture is clear and thickened. Remove from heat. Pour into a bowl; cover and chill thoroughly. Stir in wine before serving. Yield: 3 cups (77 calories per ½-cup serving).

PROTEIN 0.8 / FAT 0.2 / CARBOHYDRATE 17.1 / CHOLESTEROL 0 / IRON 0.6 / SODIUM 4 / CALCIUM 24

FRESH BERRY SOUP

2 cups fresh raspberries
1 cup sliced fresh strawberries
1 (8-ounce) carton vanilla low-fat yogurt
1 cup unsweetened orange juice
¼ cup rosé wine
1 teaspoon grated orange rind
1½ teaspoons powdered sugar

Place berries in container of an electric blender or food processor; process until smooth. Press berry mixture through a sieve lined with two layers of cheesecloth; lift cheesecloth from sieve, and squeeze to drain remaining juice. Discard seeds.

Return pureed berry mixture to container of blender. Add yogurt, orange juice, wine, and orange rind; process until smooth. Pour into a bowl; cover and chill thoroughly. Sift powdered sugar over soup before serving. Yield: 4 cups (150 calories per 1-cup serving).

PROTEIN 4.3 / FAT 1.5 / CARBOHYDRATE 29.6 / CHOLESTEROL 3 / IRON 1.2 / SODIUM 40 / CALCIUM 133

CARROT SOUP À L'ORANGE

Vegetable cooking spray
1 medium onion, chopped
1 teaspoon chicken-flavored bouillon granules
2¼ cups water
1 cup unsweetened orange juice
4 cups sliced carrots
1 tablespoon honey
1 teaspoon grated orange rind
¼ teaspoon ground ginger

Coat a small Dutch oven with cooking spray; place over medium heat until hot. Add onion, and sauté until tender. Dissolve bouillon granules in water, and add to Dutch oven. Stir in remaining ingredients. Bring mixture to a boil. Cover; reduce heat, and simmer 15 minutes or until carrots are tender.

Transfer mixture in batches into container of an electric blender or food processor; process until smooth. Repeat with remaining mixture. Pour into a bowl; cover and chill thoroughly. Yield: 6 cups (70 calories per 1-cup serving).

PROTEIN 1.3 / FAT 0.3 / CARBOHYDRATE 16.6 / CHOLESTEROL 0 / IRON 0.5 / SODIUM 90 / CALCIUM 30

ASPARAGUS-EGG DROP SOUP

¼ pound fresh asparagus spears
4 cups water
1 teaspoon chicken-flavored bouillon granules
¾ cup sliced fresh mushrooms
1 tablespoon plus 2 teaspoons reduced-sodium soy sauce
1 teaspoon minced fresh gingerroot
1 clove garlic, minced
Dash of pepper
2 tablespoons dry sherry
1 tablespoon plus 1 teaspoon cornstarch
1 egg, lightly beaten
2 green onions, chopped

Snap off tough ends of asparagus. Remove scales, using a knife or vegetable peeler, if desired. Cut asparagus into 1-inch pieces. Set aside.

Combine water and bouillon granules in a large saucepan. Bring to a boil. Add reserved asparagus, mushrooms, and next 4 ingredients. Reduce heat, and simmer, uncovered, 3 minutes or until asparagus is crisp-tender.

Combine sherry and cornstarch; stir until well blended. Add to soup mixture. Cook, stirring constantly, until thickened. Slowly pour beaten egg into soup, stirring constantly. (The egg will form lacy strands as it cooks.) Ladle hot soup into serving bowls; sprinkle with onions. Yield: 4 cups (59 calories per 1-cup serving).

PROTEIN 3.4 / FAT 1.6 / CARBOHYDRATE 5.9 / CHOLESTEROL 68 / IRON 0.7 / SODIUM 357 / CALCIUM 20

DELICIOUS CAULIFLOWER SOUP

1 small cauliflower
2 cups water, divided
Vegetable cooking spray
¾ cup chopped onion
1 carrot, shredded
1 clove garlic, minced
⅓ cup all-purpose flour
1 tablespoon chicken-flavored bouillon granules
½ teaspoon Worcestershire sauce
¼ teaspoon celery salt
⅛ teaspoon ground nutmeg
⅛ teaspoon pepper
2 cups skim milk
1 cup (4 ounces) shredded Cheddar cheese
Chopped fresh parsley (optional)

Wash cauliflower, and break into flowerets. Cover and cook in 1 cup of boiling water 5 to 6 minutes or until crisp-tender. Drain, reserving liquid. Reserve 1 cup cauliflower flowerets; set aside. Place remaining cauliflower and reserved liquid in container of electric blender or food processor; process until smooth. Set aside.

Coat a large Dutch oven with cooking spray; place over medium heat until hot. Add onion, carrot, and garlic; sauté until tender. Combine flour and remaining cup of water, stirring well; add to onion mixture. Add bouillon granules and next 4 ingredients. Cook over medium heat, stirring constantly, until thickened. Stir in reserved pureed cauliflower mixture, flowerets, and milk; cook until thoroughly heated. Add cheese, and continue cooking until cheese melts. Garnish with chopped parsley, if desired. Yield: 5 cups (103 calories per ½-cup serving).

PROTEIN 6.4 / FAT 4.2 / CARBOHYDRATE 10.7 / CHOLESTEROL 13 / IRON 0.6 / SODIUM 276 / CALCIUM 166

 LEGUMES—GOOD VEGETABLE PROTEIN

The richest source of vegetable protein is found in legumes, represented by dried peas and beans and peanuts. When combined with grains, nuts, or seeds, legumes serve as a substitute for animal protein. Nutty Whole Grain Crackers (page 102) make an ideal complementary dish to serve with Creamy Navy Bean Soup.

CUCUMBER-LIME SOUP

2 medium cucumbers, peeled, seeded, and chopped
1 cup plain low-fat yogurt
1½ cups skim milk
¼ cup chopped green onions
2 tablespoons freshly squeezed lime juice
2 teaspoons grated lime rind
½ teaspoon salt
Dash of white pepper
2 tablespoons chopped fresh chives

Combine first 8 ingredients in container of an electric blender or food processor; process until smooth. Pour into a bowl; cover and chill thoroughly. Sprinkle with chives before serving. Yield: 5 cups (71 calories per 1-cup serving).

PROTEIN 5.6 / FAT 0.9 / CARBOHYDRATE 10.8 / CHOLESTEROL 4 / IRON 0.5 / SODIUM 310 / CALCIUM 197

TOMATO SOUP WITH BASIL

Vegetable cooking spray
6 medium tomatoes, peeled, seeded, and chopped
1 medium onion, chopped
½ cup chopped celery
1 cup water
1 teaspoon chicken-flavored bouillon granules
½ teaspoon sugar
¼ teaspoon freshly ground pepper
⅓ cup fresh basil leaves, chopped

Coat a Dutch oven with cooking spray; place over medium heat until hot. Add tomatoes, onion, and celery; sauté 5 minutes or until onion is tender.

Add remaining ingredients except basil to Dutch oven; bring to a boil. Cover; reduce heat, and simmer 30 minutes, stirring occasionally. Transfer mixture in batches into container of an electric blender or food processor; process until smooth. Stir in chopped basil. Chill thoroughly before serving. Yield: 4 cups (60 calories per 1-cup serving).

PROTEIN 2.9 / FAT 0.7 / CARBOHYDRATE 13.0 / CHOLESTEROL 0 / IRON 2.8 / SODIUM 116 / CALCIUM 126

BRIE SOUP

Vegetable cooking spray
½ cup chopped green onions
1 cup water
1 teaspoon chicken-flavored bouillon granules
¼ cup all-purpose flour
2 cups skim milk
1 (4½-ounce) round Brie cheese, cut into ½-inch cubes
¼ cup Chablis or other dry white wine
⅛ teaspoon white pepper
3 tablespoons chopped fresh chives

Coat a small Dutch oven with cooking spray, and place over medium heat until hot. Add onions; sauté until tender. Combine water, bouillon granules, and flour, stirring well; add to sautéed onion. Gradually add milk; cook over medium heat, stirring constantly, until slightly thickened. Stir in cheese, and continue to cook until cheese is melted.

Transfer mixture in batches into container of an electric blender or food processor; process until smooth. Return mixture to Dutch oven. Stir in wine and pepper; cook over medium heat until mixture is thoroughly heated. Ladle into serving bowls, and sprinkle with chopped chives. Yield: 3 cups (126 calories per ½-cup serving).

PROTEIN 8.0 / FAT 6.2 / CARBOHYDRATE 9.6 / CHOLESTEROL 23 / IRON 0.5 / SODIUM 241 / CALCIUM 147

PEPPERY GARBANZO BEAN SOUP

1 (15-ounce) can garbanzo beans
Vegetable cooking spray
1 medium onion, chopped
1 medium-size green pepper, seeded and chopped
¼ cup chopped fresh parsley
2½ cups water
2½ teaspoons chicken-flavored bouillon granules
1 medium tomato, peeled and chopped
⅛ teaspoon red pepper
1 bay leaf

Place garbanzo beans in a colander, and rinse under cold tap water 1 minute; set colander aside to let beans drain 1 minute.

Coat a small Dutch oven with cooking spray; place over medium heat until hot. Add chopped onion, green pepper, and parsley; sauté until tender.

Stir in reserved beans and remaining ingredients; cover and bring to a boil. Reduce heat, and simmer 20 minutes. Remove and discard bay leaf before serving. Yield: 1½ quarts (58 calories per 1-cup serving).

PROTEIN 2.9 / FAT 1.4 / CARBOHYDRATE 10.0 / CHOLESTEROL 0 / IRON 1.0 / SODIUM 322 / CALCIUM 26

CREAMY NAVY BEAN SOUP

1½ cups dried navy beans
Vegetable cooking spray
1 medium onion, chopped
½ cup chopped carrots
½ cup chopped celery
4 cups water
1 tablespoon plus 1 teaspoon chicken-flavored bouillon granules
⅛ teaspoon pepper
1 bay leaf

Sort and wash beans; place in a large Dutch oven. Cover with water 2 inches above beans; let soak overnight. Drain beans, and set aside.

Coat a large skillet with cooking spray. Place over medium heat until hot. Add onion, carrots, and celery. Sauté until vegetables are crisp-tender. Remove from heat. Combine reserved beans and vegetable mixture in a large Dutch oven. Stir in water and remaining ingredients. Bring to a boil. Cover; reduce heat, and simmer 1 hour. Remove and discard bay leaf.

Pour half of mixture into container of an electric blender or food processor; process until smooth. Return to Dutch oven; stir well. Cook over low heat until thoroughly heated. Yield: 5 cups (230 calories per 1-cup serving).

PROTEIN 14.4 / FAT 1.5 / CARBOHYDRATE 41.6 / CHOLESTEROL 0 / IRON 5.1 / SODIUM 331 / CALCIUM 105

MINTED PEA SOUP

2 (10-ounce) packages frozen English peas
1 medium onion, coarsely chopped
2 cups water
2 tablespoons minced fresh mint leaves
1 tablespoon margarine
2 tablespoons all-purpose flour
2 cups skim milk
⅛ teaspoon salt
⅛ teaspoon pepper
½ cup plain low-fat yogurt
Fresh mint sprigs (optional)

Combine peas, onion, and water in a small Dutch oven; cover and bring to a boil. Reduce heat, and simmer 15 minutes. Remove from heat, and stir in minced mint. Pour mixture into container of an electric blender or food processor; process until smooth. Set aside.

Melt margarine in Dutch oven over low heat; add flour, stirring until smooth (mixture will be dry). Cook 1 minute, stirring constantly. Gradually add milk; cook over medium heat, stirring constantly with a wire whisk, until thickened and bubbly. Add reserved pea mixture, salt, and pepper, stirring until smooth. Cook over low heat until thoroughly heated.

Ladle into soup bowls, and top each serving with 1 tablespoon yogurt. Garnish each serving with a mint sprig, if desired. Yield: 8 cups (118 calories per 1-cup serving).

PROTEIN 7.1 / FAT 1.8 / CARBOHYDRATE 16.8 / CHOLESTEROL 2 / IRON 1.3 / SODIUM 181 / CALCIUM 123

CURRIED BUTTERNUT SQUASH SOUP

Vegetable cooking spray
1 medium onion, chopped
1 (1-pound) butternut squash, peeled and chopped
1 cup water
1 teaspoon chicken-flavored bouillon granules
1 cup unsweetened apple juice
½ teaspoon curry powder
1 cup skim milk

Coat a medium Dutch oven with cooking spray; place over medium heat until hot. Add onion; sauté until tender.

Add squash and next 4 ingredients. Cover; reduce heat, and simmer 30 minutes. Remove from heat. Transfer mixture in batches into container of an electric blender or food processor; process until smooth. Return mixture to Dutch oven; stir in milk. Continue to cook until mixture is thoroughly heated. Serve hot. Yield: 4 cups (111 calories per 1-cup serving).

PROTEIN 3.6 / FAT 0.5 / CARBOHYDRATE 24.9 / CHOLESTEROL 1 / IRON 1.1 / SODIUM 131 / CALCIUM 117

VEGETABLE-BARLEY SOUP

Vegetable cooking spray
1 cup chopped onion
½ cup chopped celery
2 tablespoons chopped fresh parsley
1 clove garlic, minced
7 cups water
1 (28-ounce) can whole tomatoes, undrained and chopped
1 cup thinly sliced carrots
½ cup barley
1 tablespoon beef-flavored bouillon granules
¼ teaspoon pepper
¼ teaspoon dried whole oregano
¼ teaspoon dried whole basil
¼ teaspoon dried whole thyme
¼ teaspoon curry powder
1 bay leaf
1 cup thinly sliced leeks
1 cup shredded cabbage
½ cup peeled, diced turnip

Coat a large Dutch oven with cooking spray; place over medium heat until hot. Add onion, celery, parsley, and garlic; sauté until vegetables are tender.

Add water and next 10 ingredients; stir well, and bring to a boil. Cover; reduce heat, and simmer 20 minutes. Stir in leeks, cabbage, and turnip; cover and simmer an additional 15 minutes. Remove and discard bay leaf before serving. Yield: 12 cups (71 calories per 1-cup serving).

PROTEIN 2.1 / FAT 0.5 / CARBOHYDRATE 15.6 / CHOLESTEROL 0 / IRON 1.4 / SODIUM 257 / CALCIUM 43

BEEFY EGGPLANT SOUP

Vegetable cooking spray
1 pound ground chuck
3 cups water
1 tablespoon beef-flavored bouillon granules
1 (28-ounce) can no-salt-added whole tomatoes, undrained and chopped
1 medium eggplant, peeled and diced
1 medium onion, chopped
1 cup chopped celery
1 cup chopped carrots
2 cloves garlic, minced
½ teaspoon pepper
½ teaspoon dried whole oregano
½ teaspoon dried whole thyme

Coat a Dutch oven with cooking spray, and place over medium heat until hot. Add ground chuck; cook until meat is browned, stirring to crumble. Drain meat in a colander; pat dry with paper towels to remove excess fat. Wipe Dutch oven clean with paper towels.

Return meat to Dutch oven; add remaining ingredients. Bring to a boil. Cover; reduce heat, and simmer 45 minutes. Yield: 6 cups (205 calories per 1-cup serving).

PROTEIN 17.4 / FAT 9.6 / CARBOHYDRATE 14.4 / CHOLESTEROL 46 / IRON 2.9 / SODIUM 297 / CALCIUM 94

PORK AND CABBAGE SOUP

1 pound lean boneless pork
Vegetable cooking spray
½ pound cabbage, shredded
2 medium-size green peppers, seeded and chopped
1 medium onion, chopped
1 clove garlic, minced
1½ quarts water
2 (14½-ounce) cans no-salt-added whole tomatoes, undrained and chopped
1 tablespoon Worcestershire sauce
2 teaspoons vegetable-flavored bouillon granules
¼ teaspoon salt
⅛ teaspoon pepper
1 bay leaf

Trim excess fat from pork; cut into ½-inch pieces. Coat a large Dutch oven with cooking spray. Place over medium-high heat until hot. Add pork; brown on all sides. Drain. Wipe Dutch oven dry with a paper towel. Return pork to Dutch oven.

Add cabbage, green pepper, onion, and garlic to Dutch oven. Cook over medium heat until vegetables are tender. Stir in water and remaining ingredients. Bring to a boil. Cover; reduce heat, and simmer 1 hour. Remove and discard bay leaf before serving. Yield: 3 quarts (72 calories per 1-cup serving).

PROTEIN 7.4 / FAT 2.2 / CARBOHYDRATE 6.2 / CHOLESTEROL 18 / IRON 0.9 / SODIUM 156 / CALCIUM 40

Vegetable-Barley Soup is hearty, wholesome, and packed to the brim with nutritious barley and garden vegetables.

CURRIED CHICKEN AND APPLE SOUP

Vegetable cooking spray
1 cup chopped onion
1 cup shredded carrot
1 cup chopped celery
1 medium cooking apple, cored and chopped
1¼ cups hot water
1 tablespoon chicken-flavored bouillon granules
¼ cup all-purpose flour
2 cups water
1 teaspoon curry powder
¼ teaspoon pepper
1½ cups skim milk
2 cups chopped, cooked chicken breast (skinned before cooking and cooked without salt)

Coat a Dutch oven with cooking spray; place over medium heat until hot. Add onion, carrot, and celery; sauté until tender. Add apple.

Combine hot water, bouillon granules, and flour; stir well. Add to vegetable mixture, stirring well. Stir in water, curry powder, and pepper. Cover and bring to a boil; reduce heat, and simmer 5 minutes or until slightly thickened. Stir in milk and chicken. Cook over low heat, stirring constantly, until thoroughly heated. Yield: 3 quarts (78 calories per 1-cup serving).

PROTEIN 9.0 / FAT 1.1 / CARBOHYDRATE 7.8 / CHOLESTEROL 20 / IRON 0.6 / SODIUM 141 / CALCIUM 53

CREAMED ZUCCHINI SOUP WITH SHRIMP

4½ cups water, divided
½ pound small fresh shrimp
Vegetable cooking spray
1 medium onion, chopped
1 clove garlic, minced
6 small zucchini, sliced
1 tablespoon chicken-flavored bouillon granules
1 tablespoon chopped fresh basil
⅛ teaspoon pepper
1 cup skim milk
¼ cup grated Parmesan cheese

Bring 1½ cups water to a boil in a saucepan; add shrimp. Reduce heat; cook 3 to 4 minutes. (Do not boil.) Drain, and rinse in cold water. Peel, devein, and coarsely chop shrimp.

Coat a small Dutch oven with cooking spray; place over medium heat until hot. Add onion and garlic; sauté until tender.

Stir in zucchini, 3 cups water, bouillon granules, basil, and pepper. Cover and bring to a boil; reduce heat, and simmer 10 minutes or until zucchini is tender. Transfer zucchini mixture in batches into container of an electric blender or food processor; process until smooth. Return to Dutch oven, and stir in milk and cheese. Cook over low heat, stirring constantly, until cheese melts. Add shrimp, and heat thoroughly. Yield: 1½ quarts (84 calories per 1-cup serving).

PROTEIN 9.7 / FAT 1.8 / CARBOHYDRATE 8.2 / CHOLESTEROL 46 / IRON 1.3 / SODIUM 318 / CALCIUM 150

MEXICAN CHICKEN CHOWDER

1 (3½-pound) broiler fryer, skinned
2 quarts water
1 stalk celery, cut into 2-inch pieces
2 cloves garlic, minced
½ teaspoon pepper
1 (16-ounce) can no-salt-added whole tomatoes, undrained and chopped
1 (10-ounce) can tomatoes and green chiles, undrained
1 medium onion, chopped
1 medium-size green pepper, chopped
1 cup fresh corn, cut from cob
4 green onions, chopped
1½ teaspoons chili powder
1 tablespoon chopped fresh parsley
¼ teaspoon ground cumin

Trim excess fat from chicken; combine chicken and next 4 ingredients in a large Dutch oven. Bring to a boil. Cover; reduce heat, and simmer 30 minutes or until chicken is tender. Remove chicken; skim off fat from broth. Reserve broth. Bone chicken, and cut meat into bite-size pieces. Set aside.

Combine reserved broth and remaining ingredients except chicken in Dutch oven. Bring to a boil. Cover; reduce heat, and simmer 30 minutes or until vegetables are tender, stirring occasionally. Stir in chicken, and cook until thoroughly heated. Yield: 10 cups (144 calories per 1-cup serving).

PROTEIN 17.8 / FAT 4.6 / CARBOHYDRATE 8.2 / CHOLESTEROL 50 / IRON 1.5 / SODIUM 214 / CALCIUM 42

SALMON AND VEGETABLE CHOWDER

Vegetable cooking spray
2 teaspoons unsalted margarine
2 cloves garlic, minced
1 cup chopped celery
1 cup chopped green pepper
1 cup chopped onion
2 cups diced carrots
1 cup diced potato
1 (17-ounce) can no-salt-added cream-style corn
1 (14½-ounce) can no-salt-added whole tomatoes, undrained and chopped
4 cups water
1 tablespoon chicken-flavored bouillon granules
1 teaspoon dried whole thyme
½ teaspoon pepper
¼ teaspoon hot sauce
1 (15½-ounce) can salmon, rinsed, drained, and flaked
1 cup evaporated skim milk

Coat a large Dutch oven with cooking spray; add margarine. Place over medium heat until margarine melts. Add garlic, celery, green pepper, and onion; sauté until tender. Stir in carrots and next 8 ingredients; bring to a boil. Reduce heat; cover and simmer 30 minutes. Stir in salmon and milk; simmer, uncovered, 5 minutes or until thoroughly heated. Yield: 3 quarts (118 calories per 1-cup serving).

PROTEIN 8.7 / FAT 2.1 / CARBOHYDRATE 17.8 / CHOLESTEROL 10 / IRON 1.2 / SODIUM 160 / CALCIUM 125

HEARTY HAMBURGER STEW

Vegetable cooking spray
1 pound ground chuck
1 medium onion, chopped
1 (14½-ounce) can whole tomatoes, undrained and chopped
½ cup chopped celery
3 cups water
2 teaspoons beef-flavored bouillon granules
2 teaspoons Worcestershire sauce
⅛ teaspoon pepper
1 bay leaf
1 (8¾-ounce) can cream-style corn
1 (10-ounce) package frozen baby lima beans
4 ounces small shell macaroni

Coat a Dutch oven with cooking spray. Add ground chuck and onion; cook until meat is browned, stirring to crumble. Drain meat mixture in a colander; pat dry with paper towels. Wipe Dutch oven dry with paper towels.

Return meat mixture to Dutch oven; add tomatoes and next 6 ingredients. Bring to a boil. Cover; reduce heat, and simmer 30 minutes. Add corn, lima beans, and macaroni. Bring to a boil; reduce heat, and simmer, uncovered, 20 minutes, stirring occasionally. Remove and discard bay leaf before serving. Yield: 8 cups (244 calories per 1-cup serving).

PROTEIN 17.0 / FAT 7.5 / CARBOHYDRATE 28.4 / CHOLESTEROL 35 / IRON 3.1 / SODIUM 380 / CALCIUM 44

GRECIAN BEEF STEW

½ cup (2 ounces) crumbled feta cheese
2 pounds lean round steak (about ½-inch thick)
Vegetable cooking spray
2 medium onions, cut into wedges
1 (14½-ounce) can whole tomatoes, undrained and chopped
½ cup Burgundy or other dry red wine
½ cup water
½ cup cider vinegar
2 tablespoons no-salt-added tomato paste
1 teaspoon dried whole oregano
½ teaspoon ground cinnamon
¼ teaspoon pepper
1 bay leaf
2 cups hot cooked parboiled rice (cooked without salt or fat)

Place feta cheese in a colander and rinse under cold tap water 1 minute; set colander aside to let cheese drain 1 minute.

Trim excess fat from steak, and cut steak into 1-inch cubes. Coat a Dutch oven with cooking spray; place over medium heat until hot. Add steak; cook until browned on all sides, stirring frequently. Add onions and next 9 ingredients; bring to a boil. Cover; reduce heat, and simmer 1 hour and 30 minutes or until meat is tender. Remove and discard bay leaf. To serve, stir in rice, and sprinkle with reserved cheese. Yield: 6 cups (256 calories per ¾-cup serving).

PROTEIN 28.0 / FAT 7.4 / CARBOHYDRATE 18.2 / CHOLESTEROL 72 / IRON 3.7 / SODIUM 230 / CALCIUM 81

SAVORY CHICKEN STEW

1 (3½-pound) broiler fryer, skinned
2 quarts plus 1 cup water, divided
3 medium carrots, scraped and cut
   into 1-inch pieces
2 medium onions, quartered
2 stalks celery, cut into 1-inch
   pieces
¾ teaspoon dried whole tarragon
¼ teaspoon salt
⅛ teaspoon pepper
⅓ cup skim milk
3 tablespoons all-purpose flour

Remove giblets and neck from chicken, and reserve for other uses. Trim excess fat from chicken. Place chicken in a large Dutch oven. Add 2 quarts water. Bring to a boil. Cover; reduce heat, and simmer 45 minutes.

Remove chicken from Dutch oven, and let cool to touch. Reserve 3 cups stock in Dutch oven. Skim fat from top of stock, and discard.

Bone and cut chicken into 1-inch pieces. Add chicken pieces, 1 cup water, carrots, onions, celery, tarragon, salt, and pepper to stock in Dutch oven. Bring to a boil. Cover; reduce heat, and simmer 1 hour.

Combine skim milk and flour, stirring until well blended. Add to stew. Cook over medium-high heat, stirring constantly, until thickened and bubbly. Yield: 6 cups (234 calories per 1-cup serving).

PROTEIN 29.1 / FAT 7.2 / CARBOHYDRATE 11.7 / CHOLESTEROL 84 / IRON 1.7 / SODIUM 211 / CALCIUM 60

RED SNAPPER STEW

Vegetable cooking spray
2 cups chopped onion
1 cup chopped celery
½ cup chopped green pepper
1 clove garlic, minced
1½ cups water
1 teaspoon chicken-flavored bouillon granules
1 cup Chablis or other dry white wine
1 large potato (½ pound), peeled and cut
   into 1-inch cubes
1 (14½-ounce) can whole tomatoes, undrained
   and chopped
¼ teaspoon salt
¼ teaspoon red pepper
1 bay leaf
1½ pounds red snapper fillets, skinned
Chopped fresh parsley (optional)

Coat a large Dutch oven with cooking spray; place over medium heat until hot. Add onion, celery, pepper, and garlic; sauté until vegetables are tender. Stir in water and next 7 ingredients; bring to a boil. Cover; reduce heat, and simmer 20 minutes.

Rinse fish with cold water, and pat dry. Cut fish into 1-inch cubes, and add to stew. Cover and simmer for 10 minutes or until fish flakes easily when tested with a fork. Remove and discard bay leaf. Ladle into serving bowls, and sprinkle with parsley, if desired. Yield: 8 cups (138 calories per 1-cup serving).

PROTEIN 18.6 / FAT 1.1 / CARBOHYDRATE 12.9 / CHOLESTEROL 47 / IRON 1.7 / SODIUM 236 / CALCIUM 219

Calories are streamlined in this version of Baked Alaska (page 234). A low-fat cake base, chocolate ice milk, and strawberry sorbet make for elegant results with lighter and healthier appeal.

Desserts

ISLAND FRUIT IN CHOCOLATE CRÊPE CUPS

1 tablespoon unsweetened orange juice
1 tablespoon honey
¼ teaspoon ground ginger
1¼ cups sliced strawberries
1 medium kiwifruit, peeled and thinly sliced
1 medium banana, thinly sliced
Chocolate Crêpe Cups
2 tablespoons flaked coconut, toasted

Combine orange juice, honey, and ginger; set aside. Combine strawberries, kiwifruit, and banana; toss gently. Pour reserved honey mixture over fruit mixture; toss gently.

To serve, spoon ⅓ cup fruit mixture into each crêpe cup. Top each serving with 1 teaspoon coconut. Serve immediately. Yield: 6 servings (174 calories per serving).

Chocolate Crêpe Cups:

1 egg white
¼ cup all-purpose flour
¼ cup plus 1 tablespoon skim milk
¼ cup sugar
2 tablespoons vegetable oil
1 tablespoon flaked coconut
1 tablespoon plus 1½ teaspoons unsweetened cocoa
1 tablespoon dark rum
Dash of salt

Combine all ingredients in container of an electric blender or food processor; process 30 seconds. Scrape sides of container using a rubber spatula; process an additional 30 seconds. Refrigerate batter 2 hours. (This allows flour particles to swell and soften so crêpes are light in texture.)

Place a 6-inch non-stick skillet over medium heat just until hot, not smoking. Pour 2 tablespoons batter onto pan. Quickly tilt pan in all directions so batter covers bottom of pan in a thin film. Cook 1 minute or until lightly browned. Lift edge of crêpe to test for doneness. Crêpe is ready for flipping when it can be shaken loose from pan. Flip crêpe, and cook 30 seconds. (This side is rarely more than spotty brown, and is the side on which the filling is placed.) Repeat procedure until all batter is used. Place crêpes in six 6-ounce custard cups. Gently place a large ball of aluminum foil in center of each cup, shaping crêpes into cups. Bake at 400° for 2 minutes. Remove from oven. Discard foil. Bake cups an additional 2 minutes or until crisp; cool. Yield: 6 crêpe cups.

PROTEIN 2.7 / FAT 6.7 / CARBOHYDRATE 25.6 / CHOLESTEROL 0 / IRON 0.8 / SODIUM 41 / CALCIUM 30

FRESH FRUIT WITH ALMOND CREAM

½ (8-ounce) package Neufchâtel cheese
2 tablespoons honey
1 tablespoon skim milk
½ teaspoon almond extract
1⅓ cups sliced bananas
1⅓ cups fresh blueberries
1⅓ cups fresh raspberries

Combine first 4 ingredients in container of an electric blender or food processor; process until smooth. Cover and chill thoroughly.

Combine bananas, blueberries, and raspberries in a medium bowl; toss gently. Spoon fruit mixture into individual serving bowls. Top each serving with 1 tablespoon chilled cheese mixture. Serve immediately. Yield: 8 servings (101 calories per serving).

PROTEIN 2.1 / FAT 3.6 / CARBOHYDRATE 16.5 / CHOLESTEROL 11 / IRON 0.3 / SODIUM 60 / CALCIUM 21

CHOCOLATE-TOPPED STRAWBERRIES

½ cup low-fat sour cream
½ (8-ounce) carton low-fat vanilla yogurt
2 tablespoons sifted powdered sugar
1 tablespoon unsweetened cocoa
1 quart fresh strawberries, washed, hulled, and chilled

Combine first 4 ingredients in a small bowl, stirring well. Cover and chill thoroughly.

Divide strawberries among 4 individual dessert dishes, reserving 4 strawberries for garnish. Spoon ¼ cup of chilled chocolate mixture over individual servings of strawberries; garnish with a reserved strawberry. Yield: 4 servings (130 calories per serving).

PROTEIN 3.6 / FAT 4.7 / CARBOHYDRATE 20.0 / CHOLESTEROL 13 / IRON 0.8 / SODIUM 32 / CALCIUM 103

SHERRIED BAKED PEARS

4 medium pears, peeled
1 tablespoon sugar
2 tablespoons water
2 tablespoons sweet sherry
⅛ teaspoon almond extract
Vanilla Sauce
2 tablespoons plus 2 teaspoons finely chopped
   almonds, toasted

Cut pears in half lengthwise; remove cores. Arrange pears, cut side up, in a 10- x 6- x 2-inch baking dish. Combine sugar, water, sherry, and almond extract; pour over pears. Cover and bake at 350° for 30 minutes or until pears are tender. Serve warm with Vanilla Sauce. Sprinkle each serving with 1 teaspoon almonds. Yield: 8 servings (82 calories per serving plus 41 calories per 2 tablespoons sauce).

Vanilla Sauce:

2 egg yolks, beaten
2 tablespoons sugar
1 teaspoon cornstarch
¾ cup skim milk
2 teaspoons vanilla extract

Combine egg yolks, sugar, and cornstarch in a small heavy saucepan, stirring well. Gradually add milk, beating well with a wire whisk. Cook over medium heat, stirring constantly, 10 minutes or until thickened. Remove from heat, and stir in vanilla. Serve warm. Yield: 1 cup.

PROTEIN 2.5 / FAT 3.8 / CARBOHYDRATE 19.7 / CHOLESTEROL 69 / IRON 0.6 / SODIUM 42 / CALCIUM 52

DESSERT OMELET WITH FRESH FRUIT

1 cup fresh blueberries
1 cup sliced fresh strawberries
1 tablespoon strawberry schnapps
4 eggs, separated
2 egg whites
¼ cup water
3 tablespoons sugar
Vegetable cooking spray
1 tablespoon sifted powdered sugar
Fresh mint sprig (optional)

Combine blueberries, strawberries, and schnapps, tossing gently. Set aside.

Beat egg yolks until thick and lemon colored. Beat egg whites (at room temperature) until foamy. Add water and 3 tablespoons sugar. Beat until stiff peaks form. Gently fold egg whites into yolks. Coat a 10-inch nonstick skillet or omelet pan with cooking spray; place over medium heat until hot enough to sizzle a drop of water. Spoon in egg mixture. Cook over medium-low heat 5 minutes. Transfer omelet to oven; bake at 350° for 10 minutes or until puffed and golden brown.

Spoon half of reserved fruit mixture over half of omelet; loosen omelet with spatula, and carefully fold in half. Slide omelet onto a serving platter. Spoon remaining fruit mixture over omelet. Sprinkle with powdered sugar. Garnish with mint sprig, if desired. Serve immediately. Yield: 4 servings (173 calories per serving).

PROTEIN 8.3 / FAT 5.9 / CARBOHYDRATE 20.8 / CHOLESTEROL 274 / IRON 1.3 / SODIUM 97 / CALCIUM 37

A light-as-a-feather Dessert Omelet with Fresh Fruit bursts with the flavors of fresh blueberries, strawberries and strawberry schnapps.

STRAWBERRY-ROSÉ ICE

1 (25.4-ounce) bottle rosé wine
¾ cup water
½ cup sugar
2 cups whole strawberries, washed, hulled, and mashed
⅓ cup freshly squeezed orange juice
1 teaspoon grated orange rind

Combine wine, water, and sugar in a large saucepan. Bring to a boil; boil 3 minutes. Remove from heat. Stir in strawberries, orange juice, and orange rind. Pour strawberry mixture into a 9-inch square baking pan; freeze until mixture becomes slushy.

Scoop strawberry mixture into container of an electric blender or food processor; process until smooth. Return strawberry mixture to baking pan. Freeze until firm. Scoop strawberry mixture into dessert bowls, and serve immediately. Yield: 5 cups (63 calories per ½-cup serving).

PROTEIN 0.3 / FAT 0.1 / CARBOHYDRATE 16.1 / CHOLESTEROL 0 / IRON 0.4 / SODIUM 4 / CALCIUM 12

PEACH-BRANDY SORBET

1 cup peach nectar
⅓ cup peach-flavored brandy
⅓ cup unsweetened orange juice
¼ cup sugar
4 cups sliced fresh peaches
1½ teaspoons lime juice

Combine first 4 ingredients in a non-aluminum saucepan; cover and bring mixture to a boil. Boil 1 minute. Remove from heat, and set mixture aside to cool.

Place peaches in container of an electric blender or food processor; process until smooth. Combine reserved brandy mixture, pureed peaches, and lime juice, stirring well.

Pour peach mixture into freezer can of a hand-turned or electric freezer. Freeze according to manufacturer's instructions. Scoop peach mixture into individual dessert bowls, and serve immediately. Yield: 5 cups (68 calories per ½-cup serving).

PROTEIN 0.6 / FAT 0.1 / CARBOHYDRATE 17.6 / CHOLESTEROL 0 / IRON 0.1 / SODIUM 2 / CALCIUM 6

PEACH-YOGURT FREEZE

1 envelope unflavored gelatin
½ cup cold water
2 eggs
⅓ cup sugar
½ cup unsweetened orange juice
2 (16-ounce) cartons low-fat vanilla yogurt
3 cups peeled, chopped fresh peaches

Soften gelatin in cold water in a small saucepan; let stand 1 minute. Cook over medium heat, stirring constantly, until gelatin dissolves. Set aside.

Beat eggs and sugar until thick and lemon colored. Stir in reserved gelatin mixture, orange juice, and yogurt.

Place peaches in container of an electric blender or food processor; process until smooth. Add pureed peaches to yogurt mixture; stir well.

Pour peach mixture into freezer can of a hand-turned or electric freezer. Freeze according to manufacturer's instructions. Scoop peach mixture into individual dessert bowls, and serve immediately. Yield: 2 quarts (94 calories per ½-cup serving).

PROTEIN 4.2 / FAT 1.4 / CARBOHYDRATE 16.7 / CHOLESTEROL 37 / IRON 0.2 / SODIUM 47 / CALCIUM 103

PUMPKIN-HAZELNUT ICE MILK

3 cups vanilla ice milk, softened
1 cup canned pumpkin
1 tablespoon firmly packed brown sugar
¾ teaspoon ground cinnamon
½ teaspoon ground nutmeg
¼ teaspoon ground cloves
2 tablespoons Frangelico or other hazelnut-flavored liqueur
½ cup finely chopped blanched hazelnuts or filberts

Combine all ingredients in a large bowl, blending well. Spoon pumpkin mixture into a chilled 8½- x 4½- x 3-inch loafpan; cover and freeze until firm. Scoop pumpkin mixture into individual dessert bowls, and serve immediately. Yield: 6 cups (96 calories per ½-cup serving).

PROTEIN 2.2 / FAT 4.5 / CARBOHYDRATE 11.6 / CHOLESTEROL 5 / IRON 0.6 / SODIUM 28 / CALCIUM 61

Pumpkin-Hazelnut Ice Milk is reminiscent of fall.

FROZEN STRAWBERRY-BANANA CREAM

2 medium bananas
2 cups frozen whole strawberries
¾ cup skim milk
2 tablespoons sifted powdered sugar
1 tablespoon Triple Sec or other orange-flavored liqueur
1 teaspoon lemon juice

Peel bananas. Wrap in aluminum foil, and freeze until firm.

Slice frozen bananas. Place bananas and strawberries in container of an electric blender or food processor; process 30 seconds or until well-blended. Add milk, sugar, Triple Sec, and lemon juice; process until smooth. Pour into individual dessert dishes. Serve immediately. Yield: 4 servings (123 calories per serving).

PROTEIN 2.5 / FAT 0.4 / CARBOHYDRATE 27.8 / CHOLESTEROL 1 / IRON 0.8 / SODIUM 26 / CALCIUM 72

FROZEN RASPBERRY DESSERT

2 egg whites
¼ cup sugar
2 tablespoons unsweetened orange juice
1 teaspoon grated orange rind
1 (10-ounce) package frozen raspberries in light syrup, thawed and undrained
1 cup evaporated skim milk, chilled
¼ cup vanilla wafer crumbs

Place electric mixer beaters and bowl in freezer to chill. Beat egg whites (at room temperature) until foamy. Add sugar, orange juice, and rind; beat until soft peaks form. Fold raspberries into egg white mixture; set aside.

Place evaporated milk in cold bowl; beat at high speed of an electric mixer until stiff peaks form. Fold whipped milk into reserved raspberry mixture. Spoon raspberry mixture into a 9-inch square baking pan. Sprinkle with vanilla wafer crumbs. Freeze overnight or until firm. Yield: 12 servings (70 calories per serving).

PROTEIN 2.4 / FAT 0.5 / CARBOHYDRATE 14.4 / CHOLESTEROL 1 / IRON 0.3 / SODIUM 41 / CALCIUM 67

APPLES JUBILEE

1 tablespoon cornstarch
1 tablespoon firmly packed brown sugar
½ cup unsweetened apple juice
½ cup water
¼ teaspoon apple pie spice
1 pound cooking apples, peeled, cored, and thinly sliced
¼ cup brandy
1 quart vanilla ice milk

Combine cornstarch and brown sugar in a large skillet. Stir in apple juice, water, and apple pie spice; bring to a boil. Add apple slices. Reduce heat, and simmer 10 minutes, stirring occasionally. Transfer apple mixture to a chafing dish and keep warm.

Place brandy in a small, long-handled saucepan; heat just until warm. (Do not boil.) Ignite brandy with a long match, and pour over apple mixture. Let stand until flames die down. Scoop ½ cup ice milk into individual dessert dishes. Spoon ⅓ cup apple mixture over each serving. Yield: 8 servings (153 calories per serving).

PROTEIN 2.7 / FAT 3.0 / CARBOHYDRATE 25.7 / CHOLESTEROL 9 / IRON 0.4 / SODIUM 54 / CALCIUM 94

CRÈME DE CASSIS SUNDAES

2 cups fresh or frozen blackberries, thawed
¼ cup crème de cassis
2½ cups vanilla ice milk
Fresh mint sprigs (optional)

Place blackberries in container of an electric blender or food processor; process until smooth. Press blackberry puree through a sieve to remove seeds. Stir in crème de cassis. Cover and chill thoroughly.

Scoop ½ cup ice milk into individual parfait glasses. Top each with ¼ cup blackberry mixture. Garnish with mint sprigs, if desired. Yield: 5 servings (138 calories per serving).

PROTEIN 3.0 / FAT 3.0 / CARBOHYDRATE 22.7 / CHOLESTEROL 9 / IRON 0.4 / SODIUM 53 / CALCIUM 107

BAKED ALASKA

1 pint chocolate ice milk, slightly softened
1 pint strawberry sorbet, slightly softened
Angel Layer Cake
5 egg whites
½ teaspoon cream of tartar
1 teaspoon vanilla extract
¼ cup sugar

Line two 8-inch round cakepans with wax paper, leaving an overhang around edges. Spread ice milk evenly into one pan, and spread sorbet in remaining pan. Freeze 2 hours or until ice milk and sorbet are firm.

Place Angel Layer Cake on an ovenproof wooden board or serving dish. Invert ice milk layer onto cake; remove pan and wax paper. Invert sorbet layer onto ice milk layer; remove pan and wax paper. Freeze layers 1 hour.

Beat egg whites (at room temperature) until foamy. Add cream of tartar and vanilla; beat until soft peaks form. Gradually add sugar, 1 tablespoon at a time, beating until stiff peaks form. Remove layers from freezer, and quickly spread meringue over entire surface, making sure edges are sealed to serving board or dish.

Bake at 475° for 1 minute or until meringue peaks are lightly browned. Slice into wedges, and serve immediately. Yield: 12 servings (138 calories per serving).

Angel Layer Cake:

6 egg whites
½ teaspoon cream of tartar
½ teaspoon vanilla extract
⅛ teaspoon salt
¼ cup plus 2 tablespoons sugar
½ cup sifted cake flour

Beat egg whites (at room temperature) in a large bowl until foamy. Add cream of tartar, vanilla, and salt; beat until soft peaks form. Gradually add sugar, 1 tablespoon at a time, beating until stiff peaks form.

Gently fold flour, one-third at a time, into egg whites. Pour batter into an ungreased 9-inch round cakepan. Bake at 325° for 30 minutes. Cool in pan on a wire rack 40 minutes. Remove cake from pan, and cool completely. Yield: 12 servings.

PROTEIN 4.0 / FAT 0.7 / CARBOHYDRATE 29.2 / CHOLESTEROL 5 / IRON 0.0 / SODIUM 111 / CALCIUM 4

CHOCOLATE-RASPBERRY SHERBET TORTE

Vegetable cooking spray
2 cups raspberry sherbet, slightly softened
⅔ cup all-purpose flour
¼ cup unsweetened cocoa
1¼ teaspoons baking powder
3 eggs, separated
2 egg whites
⅔ cup sugar
½ teaspoon vanilla extract
¼ teaspoon almond extract
Chocolate Frosting
2 tablespoons sifted powdered sugar

Coat three 8-inch round cakepans with cooking spray; line bottoms with wax paper. Spread sherbet into one cakepan, and freeze until sherbet is firm.

Combine flour, cocoa, and baking powder in a medium bowl; set aside. Beat egg whites (at room temperature) until foamy. Gradually add ⅔ cup sugar, 2 tablespoons at a time, beating until soft peaks form. Set aside.

Beat egg yolks 5 minutes or until thick and lemon colored; stir in flavorings. Gently fold yolk mixture into reserved egg whites; fold reserved dry ingredients into egg mixture. Spread batter evenly in pans. Bake at 350° for 12 minutes or until a wooden pick inserted in center comes out clean. When cake layers are done, immediately loosen from sides of pan, and turn out onto wire racks; peel off wax paper. Let cool 30 minutes.

Place one cake layer on a serving plate. Invert sherbet layer onto cake; remove pan and wax paper. Top with second cake layer. Spread Chocolate Frosting over top of torte. Sift powdered sugar over torte in desired pattern. Yield: 12 servings (184 calories per serving).

Chocolate Frosting:

1 tablespoon margarine, softened
¾ cup sifted powdered sugar
2 tablespoons unsweetened cocoa
2 tablespoons skim milk
½ teaspoon vanilla extract

Cream margarine; add powdered sugar, cocoa, milk, and vanilla; beat until smooth. Yield: ½ cup.

PROTEIN 4.1 / FAT 3.1 / CARBOHYDRATE 35.3 / CHOLESTEROL 69 / IRON 1.0 / SODIUM 92 / CALCIUM 49

STRAWBERRIES AND CUSTARD

2 eggs
3 tablespoons sugar
1 tablespoon plus 1½ teaspoons all-purpose flour
⅛ teaspoon salt
1 cup skim milk, scalded
1 tablespoon Cointreau or other orange-flavored liqueur
1 teaspoon vanilla extract
Strawberry Sauce
1 cup sliced fresh strawberries

Beat eggs in top of a double boiler at medium speed of an electric mixer until foamy. Combine sugar, flour, and salt, stirring well; gradually add to eggs, beating until thick.

Gradually stir about one-fourth of hot milk into egg mixture; add remaining milk, stirring constantly. Cook 20 minutes over simmering water, stirring occasionally, until custard thickens and coats a metal spoon. Stir in Cointreau and

vanilla. Cover and chill thoroughly.

To serve, spoon custard evenly into 4 individual dessert dishes. Spoon Strawberry Sauce evenly over custard; top each serving with ¼ cup sliced strawberries. Yield: 4 servings (178 calories per serving).

Strawberry Sauce:

1 cup fresh strawberries
2 tablespoons sugar
¼ teaspoon grated orange rind
1 tablespoon unsweetened orange juice
2 teaspoons cornstarch

Place strawberries in container of an electric blender or food processor; process until smooth. Combine strawberry puree, sugar, orange rind, juice, and cornstarch in a small non-aluminum saucepan. Cook over medium heat, stirring constantly, until thickened and bubbly. Remove from heat, and cool completely. Yield: ⅔ cup.

PROTEIN 6.0 / FAT 3.2 / CARBOHYDRATE 29.6 / CHOLESTEROL 138 / IRON 0.9 / SODIUM 141 / CALCIUM 101

BUTTERSCOTCH-BROWN RICE PUDDING

1⅓ cups skim milk
2 eggs, beaten
2 cups cooked brown rice (cooked without salt or fat)
2 tablespoons firmly packed brown sugar
1 teaspoon vanilla extract
Vegetable cooking spray
¼ cup butterscotch morsels

Place milk in a saucepan; cook over medium heat until thoroughly heated. (Do not boil.) Remove from heat.

Gradually stir about one-fourth of hot milk into eggs; add to remaining hot milk, stirring constantly. Stir in rice, sugar, and vanilla. Pour into a 1-quart baking dish coated with cooking spray. Sprinkle with butterscotch morsels.

Place dish in a shallow pan; add water to a depth of 1 inch in pan. Bake at 350° for 30 minutes or until set. Remove dish from pan; let pudding cool slightly before serving. Yield: 6 servings (170 calories per serving).

PROTEIN 5.5 / FAT 4.1 / CARBOHYDRATE 26.8 / CHOLESTEROL 93 / IRON 0.8 / SODIUM 59 / CALCIUM 96

CINNAMON-CHOCOLATE PUDDING

½ cup sifted powdered sugar
¼ cup unsweetened cocoa
2 tablespoons all-purpose flour
¼ teaspoon ground cinnamon
2 cups skim milk
1 egg yolk, lightly beaten
1 teaspoon vanilla extract
2 tablespoons plus 2 teaspoons chopped pecans, toasted

Combine first 4 ingredients in a medium saucepan; stir in milk and egg yolk. Cook over medium heat, stirring constantly, until mixture boils; cook an additional minute, stirring constantly. Remove from heat; stir in vanilla.

Pour into 4 individual dessert dishes. Top each with 2 teaspoons pecans. Serve warm or chilled. Yield: 4 servings (193 calories per serving).

PROTEIN 7.3 / FAT 5.7 / CARBOHYDRATE 28.1 / CHOLESTEROL 71 / IRON 1.5 / SODIUM 67 / CALCIUM 170

APRICOT-ALMOND MOUSSE

1 (14½-ounce) can apricot halves in light syrup, undrained
1 tablespoon Amaretto or other almond-flavored liqueur
1 teaspoon lemon juice
1 envelope unflavored gelatin
¼ cup cold water
2 tablespoons sugar
¾ cup evaporated skim milk, chilled
Fresh mint sprig

Place electric mixer beaters and bowl in freezer. Drain apricot halves, reserving liquid. Set aside 1 apricot half. Place remaining apricots in container of an electric blender or food processor; process until smooth. Add amaretto and lemon juice. Process until well blended.

Sprinkle unflavored gelatin over water in a small bowl; let stand 3 minutes. Combine reserved apricot liquid and sugar in a medium saucepan. Bring to a boil, stirring constantly, until sugar dissolves. Remove from heat. Add gelatin mixture, stirring until gelatin dissolves. Stir in pureed apricot mixture. Chill until consistency of unbeaten egg white.

Place milk in cold bowl; beat at high speed of an electric mixer until stiff peaks form. Fold whipped milk into chilled apricot mixture. Spoon into 8 individual dessert dishes. Chill until firm. Slice reserved apricot half into 8 thin wedges. Garnish each serving with 1 apricot wedge and a mint sprig. Yield: 8 servings (74 calories per serving).

PROTEIN 2.9 / FAT 0.1 / CARBOHYDRATE 15.0 / CHOLESTEROL 1 / IRON 0.2 / SODIUM 29 / CALCIUM 75

KENTUCKY BOURBON SOUFFLÉ

Vegetable cooking spray
2 envelopes unflavored gelatin
½ cup cold water
1 cup boiling water
¾ cup firmly packed brown sugar, divided
¼ cup bourbon
5 egg whites
1 teaspoon vanilla extract
½ teaspoon cream of tartar
½ teaspoon ground cinnamon
2 tablespoons finely chopped pecans, toasted

Cut a piece of aluminum foil to fit around a 1-quart soufflé dish, allowing a 1-inch overlap; fold foil lengthwise into thirds. Lightly coat one side of foil with cooking spray; wrap foil around outside of dish, coated side against dish, allowing foil to extend 3 inches above rim to form a collar. Secure with freezer tape. Set aside.

Soften gelatin in cold water in a medium saucepan; let stand 2 minutes. Add 1 cup boiling water and ½ cup brown sugar. Cook over low heat, stirring constantly, until gelatin dissolves. Remove from heat; stir in bourbon. Chill to consistency of unbeaten egg white.

Combine egg whites (at room temperature), vanilla, cream of tartar, and cinnamon in a large bowl; beat until foamy. Add remaining ¼ cup sugar, 1 tablespoon at a time, beating until stiff peaks form.

Gently fold egg white mixture into chilled bourbon mixture. Gently spoon soufflé into prepared dish; chill until firm. Remove collar from dish; sprinkle top of soufflé with pecans. Yield: 6 servings (167 calories per serving).

PROTEIN 5.0 / FAT 1.7 / CARBOHYDRATE 27.7 / CHOLESTEROL 0 / IRON 1.1 / SODIUM 70 / CALCIUM 30

LOW-IMPACT AEROBICS—SOFT AND SAFE

Exercising to upbeat music is fun, so it's no wonder aerobics classes are very popular. But repeated jumping, bouncing, jarring movements make injuries all too common.

Legs, ankles, and feet are designed to carry the body forward and absorb shock. Landing on the balls of your feet without using heels as shock absorbers forces feet, ankles, calves, knees, and lower back to take the added stress.

Low-impact aerobic workouts provide a safer exercise alternative—with all the fat-burning, cardiovascular benefits of a full body workout. This "soft" aerobics replaces the up and down motion of the high-impact aerobics with side-to-side gliding and forward lunges. One foot is always kept on the floor, which helps to avoid impact stress on joints and muscles caused by jumping and bouncing.

While low-impact aerobics diminishes the risk of injury, any exercise done too often or too long without proper warm-up, suitable shoes, or a safe workout surface can cause injury. Remember to start slowly, and gradually increase the time and intensity of your workout.

LEMON-CREAM SOUFFLÉ

½ (8-ounce) package Neufchâtel cheese, softened
½ cup lemon low-fat yogurt
3 tablespoons sifted powdered sugar
¼ cup freshly squeezed lemon juice
1 envelope unflavored gelatin
¼ cup water
2 egg whites
1 teaspoon grated lemon rind

Combine first 3 ingredients in a large bowl; stir well. Add lemon juice. Stir until smooth.

Sprinkle gelatin over water in a small saucepan; let stand 5 minutes. Cook over low heat, stirring constantly, until gelatin dissolves. Add to cheese mixture, beating well.

Beat egg whites (at room temperature) until stiff peaks form. Gently fold egg whites and lemon rind into cheese mixture. Spoon into 4 individual dessert dishes; chill until set. Yield: 4 servings (138 calories per serving).

PROTEIN 7.5 / FAT 7.1 / CARBOHYDRATE 12.0 / CHOLESTEROL 23 / IRON 0.1 / SODIUM 172 / CALCIUM 69

BLUEBERRY-LEMON SHORTCAKE

2 cups all-purpose flour
¼ cup plus 1 tablespoon sugar, divided
2 teaspoons baking powder
½ teaspoon baking soda
⅛ teaspoon salt
¼ cup margarine
1 (8-ounce) carton plain low-fat yogurt
1 egg, beaten
Vegetable cooking spray
2 tablespoons cornstarch
¾ cup skim milk
1 egg yolk
½ teaspoon vanilla extract
1 (8-ounce) carton lemon low-fat yogurt
1 teaspoon grated lemon rind
1½ cups fresh blueberries

Combine flour, 2 tablespoons sugar, baking powder, soda, and salt; cut in margarine with a pastry blender until mixture resembles coarse meal. Add plain low-fat yogurt and beaten egg to flour mixture; stir with a fork just until dry ingredients are moistened.

Turn dough out onto a lightly floured surface; knead 1 minute. Pat dough evenly in a 9-inch square baking pan coated with cooking spray. Bake at 450° for 15 minutes. Cool in pan 10 minutes. Remove cake from pan; split cake horizontally into 2 layers. Set aside.

Combine cornstarch, milk, and remaining 3 tablespoons sugar in a saucepan. Bring mixture to a boil over medium-high heat; reduce heat, and cook, stirring constantly, until thickened. Beat egg yolk until thick and lemon colored. Gradually stir about one-fourth of hot mixture into yolk; add to remaining hot mixture, stirring constantly. Stir in vanilla. Remove from heat; add lemon low-fat yogurt and lemon rind, stirring well.

To serve, spread half of lemon low-fat yogurt mixture over bottom half of reserved shortcake; top with half of blueberries. Place top half of reserved shortcake over blueberries. Top with remaining half of yogurt mixture and blueberries. Yield: 12 servings (199 calories per serving).

PROTEIN 5.7 / FAT 5.7 / CARBOHYDRATE 31.3 / CHOLESTEROL 48 / IRON 0.9 / SODIUM 203 / CALCIUM 132

MANGO PICNIC CAKE

¼ cup plus 2 tablespoons sugar
¼ cup vegetable oil
1 egg
1½ cups all-purpose flour
1 teaspoon baking soda
¼ teaspoon ground nutmeg
⅛ teaspoon salt
1 medium mango, peeled and coarsely chopped
1 tablespoon plus 1½ teaspoons lime juice
1 teaspoon grated lime rind
½ teaspoon vanilla extract
¼ teaspoon almond extract
Vegetable cooking spray

Combine sugar, oil, and egg in a medium bowl. Beat at medium speed of an electric mixer until well blended; set aside. Combine flour, soda, nutmeg, and salt; set aside.

Process mango and next 4 ingredients in container of food processor until smooth. Add flour mixture to sugar mixture alternately with mango mixture, beginning and ending with flour mixture. Beat just until blended.

Spoon batter into an 8-inch square baking pan coated with cooking spray. Bake at 350° for 25 minutes or until a wooden pick inserted in center comes out clean. Cool in pan. Yield: 9 servings (196 calories per serving).

PROTEIN 3.2 / FAT 7.0 / CARBOHYDRATE 30.4 / CHOLESTEROL 30 / IRON 0.8 / SODIUM 133 / CALCIUM 29

TROPICAL CHIFFON CAKE

1½ cups sifted cake flour
¾ cup sugar, divided
2 teaspoons baking powder
⅛ teaspoon salt
4 eggs, separated
¼ cup plus 2 tablespoons unsweetened orange juice
¼ cup vegetable oil
1 teaspoon grated orange rind
½ teaspoon vanilla extract
¼ teaspoon coconut extract
¼ teaspoon rum extract
1 (8-ounce) can unsweetened crushed pineapple, drained
2 egg whites
½ teaspoon cream of tartar

Sift together flour, ¼ cup sugar, baking powder, and salt in a large mixing bowl. Make a well in center of dry ingredients; add egg yolks, orange juice, oil, orange rind, and flavorings. Beat at high speed of electric mixer 5 minutes or until smooth. Stir in pineapple.

Beat egg whites (at room temperature) and cream of tartar in a large mixing bowl at high speed of electric mixer until soft peaks form. Gradually add remaining ½ cup sugar, 2 tablespoons at a time, beating 4 minutes at high speed or until stiff peaks form and sugar dissolves.

Gently fold egg white mixture into batter. Pour batter into an ungreased 10-inch tube pan, spreading evenly with a spatula. Bake at 325° for 1 hour or until cake springs back when lightly touched. Remove from oven; invert pan, and let cool completely before removing cake from pan. Yield: 16 servings (129 calories per serving).

PROTEIN 2.7 / FAT 4.9 / CARBOHYDRATE 18.6 / CHOLESTEROL 68 / IRON 0.4 / SODIUM 86 / CALCIUM 34

SPICED PEAR UPSIDE-DOWN CAKE

Vegetable cooking spray
2 tablespoons firmly packed brown sugar
2 tablespoons margarine, melted
2 medium pears, peeled, cored, and sliced
3 eggs, separated
½ cup sugar
1 cup all-purpose flour
1 teaspoon baking powder
1 teaspoon ground cinnamon
¼ teaspoon ground ginger
⅛ teaspoon ground nutmeg
⅓ cup skim milk
1 teaspoon grated lemon rind
1 teaspoon vanilla extract

Coat a 9-inch square baking pan with cooking spray; line with wax paper. Combine brown sugar and margarine; spread in bottom of prepared pan. Arrange pear slices in a single layer over brown sugar mixture; set aside.

Beat egg yolks until thick and lemon colored; gradually add sugar, beating well. Combine flour and next 4 ingredients; add to egg mixture. Stir in milk, lemon rind, and vanilla.

Beat egg whites (at room temperature) until stiff peaks form; fold into flour mixture. Spread batter evenly over pear slices. Bake at 350° for 30 minutes or until a wooden pick inserted in center comes out clean. Cool for 1 minute; invert cake onto a plate. Yield: 9 servings (186 calories per serving).

PROTEIN 4.1 / FAT 4.7 / CARBOHYDRATE 32.3 / CHOLESTEROL 92 / IRON 1.1 / SODIUM 92 / CALCIUM 55

SWEET POTATO CAKE ROLL

Vegetable cooking spray
3 eggs
½ cup sugar
½ cup peeled, grated raw sweet potato
1 teaspoon vanilla extract
¾ cup all-purpose flour
1 teaspoon baking powder
2 teaspoons ground cinnamon
1 teaspoon ground ginger
1 teaspoon grated orange rind
¼ teaspoon salt
¼ teaspoon ground nutmeg
2 tablespoons sifted powdered sugar
Creamy Filling

Coat a 15- x 10- x 1-inch jellyroll pan with cooking spray, and line with wax paper. Coat wax paper with cooking spray; set aside.

Beat eggs at high speed of electric mixer 5 minutes or until thick and lemon colored. Gradually add ½ cup sugar, 1 tablespoon at a time, beating well after each addition; fold in sweet potato and vanilla.

Combine flour and next 6 ingredients; fold into sweet potato mixture. Spread batter evenly in pan. Bake at 375° for 12 minutes or until surface springs back when touched.

Sift powdered sugar in a 15- x 10-inch rectangle on a linen towel. When cake is done, immediately loosen from sides of pan, and turn out onto powdered sugar; peel off wax paper. Starting at narrow end, roll up cake and towel together, jellyroll fashion; let cool on a wire rack, seam side down.

Unroll cake, and remove towel. Spread cake with Creamy Filling; reroll. Place on a serving plate, seam side down. Cut cake roll into 1-inch slices to serve. Yield: 10 servings (199 calories per serving).

Creamy Filling:

1 (8-ounce) package Neufchâtel cheese, softened
3 tablespoons sifted powdered sugar
2 tablespoons unsweetened orange juice
½ teaspoon vanilla extract
2 tablespoons finely chopped pecans

Beat cheese at medium speed of an electric mixer until fluffy; gradually add sugar, beating well after each addition. Add orange juice, vanilla, and pecans; stir well. Yield: about ¾ cup.

PROTEIN 5.5 / FAT 8.2 / CARBOHYDRATE 26.2 / CHOLESTEROL 99 / IRON 1.0 / SODIUM 202 / CALCIUM 56

COCOA-BANANA CUPCAKES

1½ cups all-purpose flour
2 tablespoons Dutch process or unsweetened cocoa
1½ teaspoons baking powder
¼ cup margarine, softened
¼ cup sugar
1 egg
1 cup mashed, ripe banana
⅔ cup skim milk
½ teaspoon vanilla extract

Combine flour, cocoa, and baking powder in a small bowl, stirring well; set aside.

Cream margarine in a medium bowl; gradually add sugar, beating well. Add egg and banana, beating well. Add reserved dry ingredients to creamed mixture alternately with skim milk, beginning and ending with flour mixture. Mix well after each addition. Stir in vanilla.

Spoon batter into 12 paper-lined muffin cups, filling two-thirds full. Bake at 350° for 25 to 30 minutes. Remove from pans, and cool completely on wire racks. Yield: 1 dozen cupcakes (155 calories each).

PROTEIN 3.4 / FAT 4.7 / CARBOHYDRATE 25.1 / CHOLESTEROL 23 / IRON 0.8 / SODIUM 96 / CALCIUM 50

INDIVIDUAL LIME CHEESECAKES

12 vanilla wafers
¾ cup low-fat cottage cheese
1 (8-ounce) package Neufchâtel cheese, softened
¼ cup plus 2 tablespoons sugar
2 eggs
1 tablespoon grated lime rind
1 teaspoon vanilla extract
½ cup vanilla low-fat yogurt
2 medium kiwifruit, peeled and sliced

Line 12 (2½-inch) muffin pans with paper baking cups. Place 1 wafer in the bottom of each liner.

Place cottage cheese in container of an electric blender or food processor; process until smooth. Combine Neufchâtel and cottage cheese in a medium bowl; beat at medium speed of an electric mixer until creamy. Gradually add sugar; mix well. Add eggs, lime rind, and vanilla; beat until smooth. Spoon mixture evenly into muffin cups.

Bake at 350° for 20 minutes or until set but centers are still creamy (do not overbake). Remove muffin pan from oven to wire racks and cool to room temperature.

Remove cakes from pans, and refrigerate until thoroughly chilled. Spread vanilla yogurt over each cheesecake and top with a kiwifruit slice. Serve immediately. Yield: 12 servings (136 calories per serving).

PROTEIN 5.7 / FAT 6.7 / CARBOHYDRATE 13.2 / CHOLESTEROL 62 / IRON 0.4 / SODIUM 167 / CALCIUM 51

INDIVIDUAL CHERRY COBBLERS

4 cups pitted fresh sweet cherries
1 tablespoon sugar
1 tablespoon quick-cooking tapioca, uncooked
¾ teaspoon almond extract
Vegetable cooking spray
½ cup all-purpose flour
¼ cup whole wheat flour
1 tablespoon sugar
¼ teaspoon salt
⅛ teaspoon ground cinnamon
2 tablespoons shortening
2 tablespoons skim milk
1 egg white, beaten

Combine first 4 ingredients. Spoon cherry mixture evenly into 6 (6-ounce) custard cups coated with cooking spray.

Combine flours, 1 tablespoon sugar, salt, and cinnamon in a bowl; cut in shortening with a pastry blender until mixture resembles coarse meal. Add milk; stir with a fork just until dry ingredients are moistened. Divide dough into 6 balls. Roll each ball into a 5-inch circle on a lightly floured surface. Place a circle over each custard cup. Seal and flute edges; brush with egg white. Cut slits in top to allow steam to escape. Bake at 350° for 30 minutes or until lightly browned. Yield: 6 servings (187 calories per serving).

PROTEIN 3.8 / FAT 4.7 / CARBOHYDRATE 34.1 / CHOLESTEROL 0 / IRON 0.9 / SODIUM 109 / CALCIUM 27

Individual Cherry Cobblers are cherry delicious.

APPLE-SOUR CREAM PASTRY

1½ pounds cooking apples, peeled,
  cored, and sliced (4 cups)
1¼ cups all-purpose flour
1 tablespoon sugar
¼ teaspoon ground cinnamon
⅓ cup margarine
3 tablespoons water
¼ teaspoon vanilla extract
Vegetable cooking spray
1 (8-ounce) carton low-fat sour cream
2 tablespoons firmly packed brown
  sugar
1 egg
½ teaspoon grated lemon rind
¼ teaspoon vanilla extract
⅛ teaspoon salt
2 tablespoons firmly packed brown
  sugar
½ teaspoon ground cinnamon
⅛ teaspoon ground cardamom

Place apple slices in a 13- x 9- x 2-inch baking dish. Cover and bake at 400° for 15 minutes. Set aside.

Combine flour, 1 tablespoon sugar, and ¼ teaspoon cinnamon in a bowl. Cut in margarine with a pastry blender until mixture resembles coarse meal. Sprinkle water and ¼ teaspoon vanilla over surface; stir with a fork just until dry ingredients are moistened. Shape dough into a ball. Roll into an 11-inch circle on a lightly floured surface. Press circle into the bottom and 1½ inches up sides of a 9-inch springform pan coated with cooking spray. Bake at 400° for 5 minutes. Set aside.

Combine sour cream, 2 tablespoons brown sugar, egg, lemon rind, ¼ teaspoon vanilla, and salt. Beat at medium speed of an electric mixer until mixture is well blended. Spoon sour cream mixture into reserved crust. Top with reserved apple slices.

Combine remaining 2 tablespoons brown sugar, cinnamon, and cardamom. Sprinkle over apples. Bake at 400° for 40 minutes or until set. Let cool completely. Remove from pan. Yield: 12 servings (169 calories per serving).

PROTEIN 2.7 / FAT 8.1 / CARBOHYDRATE 22.0 / CHOLESTEROL 30 /
IRON 0.8 / SODIUM 99 / CALCIUM 34

KEY LIME MERINGUE PIE

1 cup all-purpose flour
1 tablespoon flaked coconut
Dash of salt
3 tablespoons shortening
3 tablespoons cold water
¼ cup cornstarch
¼ cup sugar
⅛ teaspoon salt
2 cups water
2 egg yolks
¼ cup Key lime juice
2 teaspoons margarine
2 teaspoons grated lime rind
3 egg whites
⅛ teaspoon cream of tartar
2 tablespoons plus 1½ teaspoons sugar

Combine flour, coconut, and dash of salt; stir well. Cut in shortening with a pastry blender until mixture resembles coarse meal. Sprinkle 3 tablespoons water, 1 tablespoon at a time, over surface; stir with a fork until dry ingredients are moistened. Shape into a ball, and chill.

Roll dough into an 11-inch circle on a lightly floured surface; fit into a 9-inch pieplate. Trim excess pastry. Fold edges under, and flute. Prick bottom and sides of shell with a fork. Bake at 425° for 12 minutes or until golden brown.

Combine cornstarch, ¼ cup sugar, and ⅛ teaspoon salt in a saucepan. Gradually add 2 cups water, stirring until smooth. Cook over medium heat, stirring constantly, until thickened.

Beat egg yolks until thick and lemon colored. Gradually stir about one-fourth of hot mixture into egg yolks; add to remaining hot mixture, stirring constantly. Cook, stirring constantly, 2 minutes or until mixture thickens. Remove from heat; stir in lime juice, margarine, and lime rind. Spoon filling into pastry shell.

Combine egg whites (at room temperature) and cream of tartar; beat until foamy. Gradually add remaining sugar, beating until stiff peaks form. Spread meringue over filling, sealing to edge of piecrust. Bake at 350° for 12 minutes or until meringue peaks are golden brown. Cool to room temperature. Chill before serving. Yield: 8 servings (188 calories per serving).

PROTEIN 3.8 / FAT 6.9 / CARBOHYDRATE 27.7 / CHOLESTEROL 68 /
IRON 0.8 / SODIUM 91 / CALCIUM 13

This Fresh Strawberry Tart makes a spectacular appearance. Get ready for the oohs and aahs!

FRESH STRAWBERRY TART

¾ cup all-purpose flour
1 teaspoon sugar
¾ teaspoon grated orange rind
Dash of salt
3 tablespoons margarine
3 tablespoons cold water
Vegetable cooking spray
¾ cup lemon low-fat yogurt
1 pint fresh strawberries, washed, hulled, and sliced
¼ cup low-sugar strawberry spread, melted
Fresh mint sprig (optional)

Combine first 4 ingredients in a medium bowl; cut in margarine with a pastry blender until mixture resembles coarse meal. Sprinkle cold water evenly over surface of flour mixture; stir with a fork until dry ingredients are moistened. Shape dough into a ball; chill.

Pat dough into a 9-inch springform pan coated with cooking spray. Prick with a fork. Bake at 375° for 15 minutes or until lightly browned. Remove tart shell from oven, and let cool in pan 5 minutes. Transfer to a wire rack to cool completely.

Place cooled tart shell on a serving platter. Spread yogurt evenly over tart shell. Arrange strawberry slices over yogurt. Brush with melted strawberry spread. Garnish with mint sprig, if desired. Yield: 6 servings (182 calories per serving).

PROTEIN 3.3 / FAT 6.4 / CARBOHYDRATE 28.5 / CHOLESTEROL 0 / IRON 1.0 / SODIUM 111 / CALCIUM 53

PRALINE-BANANA TART

2 tablespoons firmly packed dark brown sugar
1 tablespoon cornstarch
¾ cup skim milk
1 egg yolk
½ teaspoon vanilla extract
¼ teaspoon maple flavoring
2 medium bananas, sliced
Oatmeal Crust
2 tablespoons finely chopped pecans, toasted

Combine brown sugar and cornstarch in top of a double boiler; gradually stir in milk. Cook over simmering water, stirring constantly, until mixture thickens. Remove from heat.

Stir about one-fourth of hot mixture into egg yolk; add to remaining hot mixture, stirring constantly. Return to heat, and cook, stirring constantly, until smooth and thickened.

Remove from heat; stir in vanilla and maple flavorings. Chill thoroughly.

Arrange banana slices on oatmeal crust. Spread chilled filling evenly over bananas. Sprinkle with toasted pecans. Cover and chill 1 hour. Yield: 8 servings (195 calories per serving).

Oatmeal Crust:

1 cup quick-cooking oats, uncooked
⅓ cup whole wheat flour
¼ cup margarine, melted
3 tablespoons water
2 tablespoons plus 1 teaspoon firmly packed brown sugar
Vegetable cooking spray

Combine all ingredients, except cooking spray in a medium bowl; mix well. Shape oatmeal mixture into a ball and place on a baking sheet coated with cooking spray. With lightly floured hands, press mixture into a 9-inch circle. Bake at 375° for 8 to 10 minutes. Let cool 10 minutes. Transfer to a wire rack, and cool completely. Yield: one 9-inch crust.

PROTEIN 3.7 / FAT 8.7 / CARBOHYDRATE 27.0 / CHOLESTEROL 35 / IRON 1.1 / SODIUM 83 / CALCIUM 50

FRESH FIG STREUSEL

½ cup quick-cooking oats, uncooked
⅓ cup all-purpose flour
3 tablespoons firmly packed brown sugar
3 tablespoons margarine, softened
Vegetable cooking spray
3 cups fresh figs, quartered
½ teaspoon ground cinnamon
¼ cup evaporated skim milk
1 egg
½ teaspoon vanilla extract

Combine oats, flour, and brown sugar; cut in margarine with a pastry blender until mixture resembles coarse meal. Place half of mixture in a 9-inch pieplate coated with cooking spray.

Arrange figs in pieplate. Sprinkle with cinnamon. Combine milk, egg, and vanilla; pour over figs. Sprinkle with remaining crumb mixture. Bake at 350° for 40 minutes or until golden brown. Serve warm or at room temperature. Yield: 8 servings (192 calories per serving).

PROTEIN 4.1 / FAT 6.1 / CARBOHYDRATE 32.2 / CHOLESTEROL 35 / IRON 1.3 / SODIUM 71 / CALCIUM 66

FRUIT: A NATURAL FOR DESSERTS

Want something sweet to follow your light dinners? How about nature's own dessert—fruit. Eaten out of hand or in a spectacular dessert, fruit is ready-made, already endowed with extraordinary color and shape. Its delicate sweetness and succulent texture always please, and the selection is always varied. Choose from exotic mangos found in Strawberry-Mango Compote (page 35) to cool, plump blueberries found in the Blueberry-Lemon Shortcake (page 237). Nutritionally, calorie- and fat-conservative fruit is a natural—chock full of vitamins, minerals, and fiber.

Cooking Light uses the wonderful attributes of fruit to enhance custards, cakes, and cookies; sorbets, sundaes, and soufflés.

MELTING MOMENTS

½ cup margarine, softened
½ cup sifted powdered sugar
¾ cup all-purpose flour
½ cup cornstarch
¼ teaspoon salt
¼ teaspoon orange extract
¼ teaspoon almond extract
Vegetable cooking spray

Cream margarine; add sugar, and beat well. Gradually add flour and cornstarch, beating until smooth. Add salt and flavorings, beating until well blended.

Press dough from a small cookie press onto a baking sheet coated with cooking spray. Bake at 325° for 15 minutes. (Cookies do not brown on top.) Remove from cookie sheets, and cool completely on wire racks. Yield: 3 dozen cookies (46 calories each).

PROTEIN 0.3 / FAT 2.6 / CARBOHYDRATE 5.4 / CHOLESTEROL 0 / IRON 0.1 / SODIUM 46 / CALCIUM 2

APPLE-DATE COOKIES

⅓ cup margarine, softened
¼ cup firmly packed brown sugar
2 tablespoons honey
1 egg
1 teaspoon vanilla extract
¾ cup all-purpose flour
¼ cup whole wheat flour
½ teaspoon baking soda
½ teaspoon ground cinnamon
¼ teaspoon ground ginger
⅛ teaspoon ground nutmeg
¾ cup regular oats, uncooked
½ cup grated Red Delicious apple
¼ cup chopped dates
Vegetable cooking spray

Cream softened margarine in a medium bowl; gradually add brown sugar and honey, beating well. Add egg and vanilla; beat well. Combine all-purpose flour, whole wheat flour, soda, cinnamon, ginger, and nutmeg in a small bowl; gradually add to sugar mixture, beating well. Stir in oats, apple, and chopped dates.

Drop dough by rounded teaspoonfuls 2 inches apart onto cookie sheets coated with cooking spray. Bake at 350° for 12 to 14 minutes. Remove from cookie sheets, and cool completely on wire racks. Yield: 3½ dozen cookies (44 calories each).

PROTEIN 0.7 / FAT 1.8 / CARBOHYDRATE 6.6 / CHOLESTEROL 7 / IRON 0.3 / SODIUM 29 / CALCIUM 7

Chocolate-Mint Cookies, Apple-Date Cookies, and Honey Graham Crackers (page 246) are special enough for gifts!

CARROT-PINEAPPLE COOKIES

2 cups all-purpose flour
1½ teaspoons baking powder
1½ teaspoons ground cinnamon
1½ teaspoons ground ginger
1 teaspoon ground nutmeg
½ cup margarine, softened
⅓ cup firmly packed brown sugar
1 egg
½ teaspoon vanilla extract
1 cup shredded carrots
1 (8-ounce) can unsweetened crushed pineapple, drained
Vegetable cooking spray

Combine first 5 ingredients; stir well. Set aside.
Cream margarine in a medium bowl; gradually add sugar, beating well. Add egg and vanilla; beat well. Stir in reserved flour mixture. Gently stir in carrots and pineapple.
Drop dough by rounded teaspoonfuls 2 inches apart onto cookie sheets coated with cooking spray. Bake at 350° for 12 minutes or until golden brown. Remove from cookie sheets, and cool completely on wire racks. Yield: 5 dozen cookies (39 calories each).

PROTEIN 0.6 / FAT 1.7 / CARBOHYDRATE 5.4 / CHOLESTEROL 5 / IRON 0.2 / SODIUM 28 / CALCIUM 9

LEMON-OATMEAL CRISPIES

⅓ cup shortening
⅓ cup firmly packed brown sugar
1 egg
1 tablespoon lemon juice
1½ teaspoons grated lemon rind
½ teaspoon vanilla extract
½ cup all-purpose flour
½ cup quick-cooking oats, uncooked
¼ teaspoon baking powder
¼ teaspoon baking soda
¾ cup crispy rice cereal

Cream shortening; gradually add sugar, beating until light and fluffy. Add egg, lemon juice, rind, and vanilla. Beat well. Combine flour, oats, baking powder, and soda; stir well. Gradually add to creamed mixture, beating well. Stir in cereal.

Drop dough by heaping teaspoonfuls 2 inches apart onto ungreased cookie sheets. Bake at 375° for 8 to 10 minutes. Remove from cookie sheets, and cool completely on wire racks. Yield: 32 cookies (48 calories each).

PROTEIN 0.9 / FAT 2.2 / CARBOHYDRATE 6.4 / CHOLESTEROL 9 / IRON 0.3 / SODIUM 17 / CALCIUM 8

WATER: THE CHOICE SPORTS DRINK

Water is the ideal sports drink. The body needs water to regulate its temperature through perspiration, to eliminate toxic wastes, to maintain proper volume and pressure of blood, to supply oxygen and nutrients to muscles and vital organs, and to permit the energy-producing chemical reactions in muscle cells to take place.
"Camel up" before exercise with 8 to 12 ounces of water. If you work out beyond 20-30 minutes, drink one glass of water every half hour. Don't rely on thirst; it lags behind the body's need for water.

CHOCOLATE-MINT COOKIES

¼ cup plus 2 tablespoons margarine, softened
¼ cup sugar
1 egg
¼ teaspoon mint extract
1 cup all-purpose flour
½ teaspoon baking powder
¼ cup semisweet chocolate mini-morsels

Cream margarine in a medium bowl; gradually add sugar, beating at medium speed of an electric mixer. Add egg and mint extract, beating well.
Combine flour and baking powder; add to creamed mixture, beating at medium speed of an electric mixer until well blended. Stir in chocolate morsels.
Drop by rounded teaspoonfuls 2 inches apart onto ungreased cookie sheets. Bake at 300° for 20 minutes or until lightly browned. Let cool 1 minute on cookie sheets. Remove from cookie sheets, and cool completely on wire racks. Yield: 3 dozen cookies (45 calories each).

PROTEIN 0.6 / FAT 2.5 / CARBOHYDRATE 5.0 / CHOLESTEROL 8 / IRON 0.2 / SODIUM 29 / CALCIUM 5

HONEY GRAHAM CRACKERS

1½ cups whole wheat flour
1 cup all-purpose flour
1¼ teaspoons ground cinnamon
¾ teaspoon baking soda
¼ teaspoon salt
½ cup unsalted margarine, softened
⅓ cup firmly packed brown sugar
¼ cup honey
1 teaspoon vanilla extract
¼ cup skim milk

Combine first 5 ingredients; stir well, and set aside. Cream margarine; add brown sugar, honey, and vanilla. Beat well. Add reserved flour mixture alternately with skim milk, beginning and ending with flour mixture. Mix just until blended after each addition. Shape dough into a flat rectangle. Cover and chill 2 hours.

Divide chilled dough onto 2 ungreased cookie sheets. Roll each portion directly on baking sheets to 12- x 10-inch rectangles. Cut each portion into 12 (5- x 2-inch) rectangles. Lightly score each rectangle in half using the dull side of a knife. Prick surface of each square in 3 parallel rows, using a fork.

Bake at 350° for 12 to 15 minutes on top rack of oven. Separate crackers; remove from cookie sheets, and cool completely on wire racks. Store in an airtight container. Yield: 4 dozen crackers (52 calories each).

PROTEIN 0.9 / FAT 2.0 / CARBOHYDRATE 7.9 / CHOLESTEROL 0 / IRON 0.3 / SODIUM 26 / CALCIUM 9

APPLESAUCE-GINGERBREAD BARS

1 cup unsweetened applesauce
⅓ cup molasses
1 teaspoon baking soda
2 eggs
¼ cup sugar
¼ cup vegetable oil
1½ cups all-purpose flour
1½ teaspoons ground ginger
1 teaspoon ground cinnamon
¼ teaspoon ground cloves
⅛ teaspoon salt
Vegetable cooking spray

Place applesauce in a small saucepan. Cook over low heat, stirring constantly, until applesauce boils. Remove from heat; stir in molasses and soda. Set aside to cool.

Combine eggs and sugar in a large bowl; gradually beat in oil. Combine flour, spices, and salt; stir well. Add flour mixture to creamed mixture alternately with applesauce mixture, beginning and ending with flour mixture.

Spoon batter into an 8-inch square baking pan coated with cooking spray. Bake at 350° for 30 minutes or until a wooden pick inserted in center comes out clean.

Cool in pan on a wire rack. Cut into bars; serve warm or at room temperature. Yield: 12 servings (163 calories per serving).

PROTEIN 2.9 / FAT 5.7 / CARBOHYDRATE 25.4 / CHOLESTEROL 46 / IRON 1.3 / SODIUM 109 / CALCIUM 52

KAHLÚA SQUARES

⅓ cup plus 1 tablespoon margarine, softened
3 tablespoons plus 2 teaspoons unsweetened cocoa, divided
½ cup firmly packed brown sugar
½ teaspoon vanilla extract
1 cup all-purpose flour
1 teaspoon baking powder
¼ teaspoon salt
2 eggs
1½ teaspoons instant coffee granules
¼ cup Kahlúa or other coffee-flavored liqueur
Vegetable cooking spray

Combine margarine and 3 tablespoons cocoa in a medium saucepan. Cook over low heat until margarine melts. Stir in sugar and vanilla. Set aside.

Combine flour, baking powder, and salt in a large bowl. Add eggs, one at a time, beating well after each addition. Add chocolate mixture; mix well. Dissolve coffee granules in liqueur; add to chocolate mixture. Mix well.

Pour batter into an 8-inch square baking pan coated with cooking spray. Bake at 350° for 20 minutes. Cool completely. Dust top of cake with 2 teaspoons cocoa. Cut into squares. Yield: 16 squares (125 calories each).

PROTEIN 2.1 / FAT 5.5 / CARBOHYDRATE 15.0 / CHOLESTEROL 34 / IRON 0.8 / SODIUM 119 / CALCIUM 27

What's New In The Marketplace?

Turn shopping cents into fitness sense. Here's a shortcut for the on-the-go consumer who wants to make health-conscious choices at the marketplace. This chapter interprets the latest "labelese," the language of food labels; it separates what's hot from what's not in supermarket fare. Here are new products and new trends that can add interest and pleasure to your pursuit of a healthier lifestyle.

Interpreting "Labelese"

BEEFING UP MEAT LABELS

The meaning of "Lean" and "Extra Lean" on fresh meat and poultry packages has been clearly defined by the U.S. Department of Agriculture (USDA) as of April 1, 1987. "Lean" now indicates no more than 10 percent fat by weight; "Extra Lean," no more than 5 percent; and "Leaner," 25 percent less fat than the standard product. (Keep in mind that if the standard product is high in fat, the word "leaner" could really mean "not as fat.")

The matter is not settled, however. Compliance dates were modified when some members of the meat industry wanted to keep ground meat out of the ratings altogether, presumably because of its high-fat status when compared to "whole" beef products such as steaks and roasts. Until the controversy is resolved, the "Lean" ground beef you purchase will not be subject to the new regulations.

Expect to find other new labels in the meat department. Nutritional Effects Foundation (NEF) seals are available to any meat producer who voluntarily complies with NEF standards. NEF-1 indicates less than 3.5 percent fat and NEF-2, less than 6 percent. The meat industry's own Nutri-Facts labels for beef, pork, and lamb are affixed to meat counters in many large supermarket chains. They list the amount of calories, fat, cholesterol, and seven other nutrients for 3 ounces of well-trimmed cooked meat (the equivalent of about 4 ounces raw). A Nutri-Facts label showing less than 8 grams of fat indicates a relatively good low-fat choice.

The familiar USDA grades ("Prime," "Choice," "Good") are a reliable fat gauge when used in reverse: Beef labeled "Good" contains the least fat and "Prime," the most. The USDA has just recently decided to label "Good" beef "Select" to make it more attractive in the marketplace.

If you don't see a label, look for well-trimmed cuts with the least internal marbling. It may be that only your butcher knows the meaning of "Lean." When in doubt, ask.

Instead of what goes onto the label, some members of the meat industry are concentrating more on what goes into the beef. A new brand of corn-fed beef is available at the supermarket. Processed when cattle are only 10 to 12 months old, it is a leaner product: 50 percent less fat than regular beef and about 25 percent less cholesterol. The new brand of beef is about equivalent in fat content to USDA "Select" beef. Of course, the sacrifice of processing beef with less weight and fat is passed on to the consumer; expect to pay more.

"LIGHT" TALK

"Light" food labels are ambiguous. They often refer to color, taste, or texture, not fat. Compare 5 ounces of flounder at 140 calories to an equal portion of breaded "light" fillets at 300 calories. In this case, the light fillets are lighter than the standard breaded fillets, not flounder fillets in general. And "light" vegetable oils may be lighter in color, but never in calories.

CHOLESTEROL LABELS: TO INFORM OR DECEIVE?

The food industry knows that nutrition is a dynamic concept for boosting sales, and so do regulatory agencies, consumer advocates, and nutrition professionals. The cross-purposes of these groups often clash when efforts are made to clarify and standardize food labels.

Manufacturers use the claim of "no cholesterol" to suggest "good for the heart" to consumers. When shoppers see the label on vegetable oils, they often overlook the fact that vegetable products never contain cholesterol anyway. The claim skillfully camouflages the fact that saturated fat is also associated with increased blood cholesterol. While it's true that most vegetable oils are unsaturated, the exceptions (coconut, palm, and palm kernel oils) are highly saturated.

Similarly, claims such as "pure vegetable oil" and "made with vegetable shortening" suggest "good fat" and skirt the complete fat story.

The Food and Drug Administration (FDA) has proposed standardized cholesterol labeling for those products specifically altered to reduce cholesterol.

"Cholesterol free" would mean less than 2 milligrams of cholesterol per serving; "low cholesterol," less than 20 milligrams; and "cholesterol reduced" would identify products modified to contain only 25 percent of the cholesterol in the standard product. Ideally, labels making these claims would simultaneously list saturated and unsaturated fat content, but the current proposal makes this information voluntary, thereby allowing foods high in saturated fat to make low-cholesterol claims. The jury is still out, so the final rule could be different.

HEALTH MESSAGES TO BE REGULATED

Disease-prevention claims and health messages on products present an equally challenging dilemma for the FDA. High-fiber cereal and cancer, dairy products and osteoporosis, polyunsaturated oil and heart disease—links such as these are used to sell products. New guidelines, not yet in place, will probably require that disease-prevention claims be backed by scientific studies; that health messages equate good nutrition with a person's total diet, not just the product bearing the health message; that the messages be consistently expressed from product to product; and that manufacturers avoid overfortification of products.

Food and Fitness Shopper Stoppers

COLD FRUIT TREATS ARE HOT ITEMS

Frozen fruit and juice bars, made essentially of water and natural fruit chunks or juice, are the fastest growing "frozen novelty," according to *Advertising Age* magazine. Already out in front of gelatin and pudding bars, they are rapidly gaining on ice cream, the persistent leader. Options are as diverse as the colors: fruit and cream bars, fruit and juice bars, fruit bars without juice added, and fruit-flavored bars. All contain some sugar, but most are fat-free. A ½-cup serving of ice cream has 134 calories and about 7 grams of fat. Frozen fruit snack bars average only 64 calories per serving and 1 gram or less of fat. Other nutrient values vary with the type of fruit and the amount used. Select those with more real fruit, less sugar, and higher amounts of vitamins A

Frozen fruit bars vary in shape, color, and composition, but all are virtually fat-free.

and C. These cooling treats make a low-fat alternative to ice cream, but think twice before using them as a replacement for fresh fruit in your diet. They are not fruit on a stick.

DO FROZEN DINNERS MEASURE UP?

When it comes to frozen dinners, labels once again reveal the nutritional scoop. Calorie counts range from around 300 in diet dinners to over 600 in gourmet dinners. Overall, calcium (especially for postmenopausal women) and fiber are low. (A simple fruit or vegetable salad and a glass of skim milk can balance a frozen dinner without adding too many calories.) Cholesterol and saturated fat information is rarely provided; the total fat content, even in the low-calorie meals, can be high. Ten grams of fat per serving or less makes a good low-fat choice. Finding a dinner low in sodium may be difficult; most contain over 800 milligrams. Overall, frozen dinners can offer more nutritious dining than other fast-food options, but they are not a substitute for meals planned around freshness and the Basic Four.

PUTTING A CAP ON WATER

Bottled water has captured the imagination of Americans. Even though a glass of water from a well-regulated public water supply remains as wholesome a way to rehydrate the body as any, many consumers don't flinch at the 25- to 50-cent price for, say, a glass of mineral water. In fact, they'll pay considerably more in a restaurant or "water bar," where enhancing flavors and cocktail garnishes add to low-calorie appeal.

When an 8-ounce glass of tap water costs only about .02 cent, one might well ask the difference. For the most part, the popularity of bottled waters seems to be based on the benefits outlined in a marketing strategy over a decade ago, when bottled water was introduced to the American market. Importers first positioned bottled water as a no-calorie, no-caffeine, wholesome alternative to alcoholic beverages and soda pop. And that is what it continues to be. It does not, on the other hand, hold the preventive or regenerative powers that many Europeans and Americans have attributed to mineral water over the years. Such claims have never been proven. In fact, the FDA prohibits health claims on bottled waters.

Selecting a bottled water is a matter of personal taste. Hard waters high in mineral content have a more pronounced taste than soft waters. Carbonated waters such as sparkling water, club soda, and seltzer are refreshing straight from the bottle, but they also give "sparkle" to "still" drinks. Sparkling water and club soda are relatively high in sodium, whereas seltzer has no added mineral salts. ("No-sodium" labels are showing up on some carbonated waters.) The FDA has received complaints concerning some beverages that use the word "seltzer" when in fact they are sweetened sodas. A true seltzer may have added flavor, but supposedly no sugar. If you're buying seltzer beverages because they are calorie-free, read the labels carefully. Some pack a sweet 100-calorie wallop per 8-ounce serving.

NEW VARIATIONS IN YOGURT

There's no end to the versatility of yogurt. A new high-calcium yogurt on the market in some parts of the country supplies 650-1,300 milligrams per eight ounces as opposed to the usual 300-400 milligrams. What else? Yogurt with vegetables instead of fruit. And kefir, yogurt's European relation, has arrived. Kefir tastes less sour than yogurt, but has comparable nutritive value.

QUASI YOGURT

For those who don't like yogurt's tang and bite, new "yogurtlike" products are making dairy-case appearances. A tofu-based, non-dairy product, similar nutritionally to low-fat yogurt, but without the riboflavin, is being touted as an "answer to yogurt." Since calcium sulfate is used as the coagulating agent in the tofu-making process, it still delivers calcium, regardless of its non-dairy status.

Fresh cheese and fruit is another yogurtlike concept. It's "a creamy delicate blend of fresh cheese and fruit" that contains more milk than yogurt, making it slightly higher in protein, but similar in calcium and riboflavin. Fat content is slightly higher, but low-fat versions are on the drawing board. Two major yogurt producers are planning to introduce their own fresh cheese and fruit products.

CANOLA—NO AVERAGE OIL

Vegetable oils all have some saturated fat, but a newcomer has the least. In 1985, the FDA approved canola oil, a hybrid variety of rapeseed oil already familiar to Europeans. Its unique properties may eventually make it the leading consumer choice for vegetable oil. Not only is it 50 percent less saturated than other popular vegetable oils, but also, like olive oil, it is high in monounsaturated fat, thought to be beneficial to the heart.

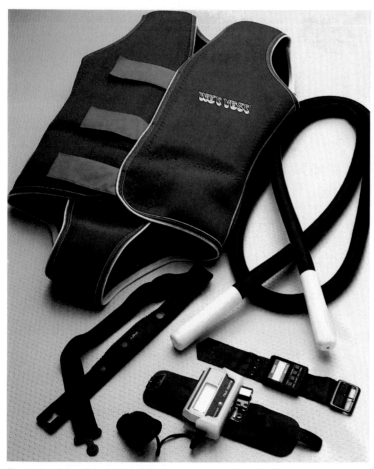

The Wet Vest,® weighted jump rope, and wrist heart rate monitors (with chest or finger sensor).

VESTED INTEREST IN WATER

Strap on a vest, jump in the water, and start running to your heart and lung's content. Novice and elite athletes alike are using the Wet Vest® (developed by Bioenergetics of Birmingham, Alabama) to build strength and endurance in the water. Light-weight and snug fitting, the Wet Vest allows a person to run or exercise against the resistance of water in an upright position. Because water creates a stress-free environment, water running is ideal for runners who want to increase mileage without risk of injury or continue running while recovering from an injury. Moreover, pregnant women, arthritis victims, cardiac rehab patients, the elderly, and physically impaired can use the vest to improve fitness under friendly conditions. The vest costs $110.

JUMP ROPE THAT CARRIES MORE WEIGHT

Professional basketball teams, home-town volleyball teams, novice athletes, and ordinary fitness seekers are using weighted jump ropes to enhance their aerobic workouts. Sold as 3½-, 5-, and 6-pound ropes, these portable and relatively inexpensive ($35) training devices increase upper-body exertion. Because the muscles are forced to participate more intensely in the activity, jumping with a weighted rope makes for an all-in-one aerobic and strength workout. Before you modify your workout with a heavier rope, however, make sure your heart is fit enough to take the effort, and request safety information as well as guidelines for duration and progression.

MESSAGES FROM THE HEART DURING EXERCISE

"Your heart rate tells you how much exercise you need," says the American Heart Association. And for a quick message from your heart during a workout, you need only to glance at your wrist. A heart rate monitor, worn wristwatch fashion, can transmit signals from the heart to a digital printout via a chest sensor or sensor attached to the fingertip or ear-lobe. The type of feedback from the workout varies with the model and the price ($45-$300). All can be programmed with your target heart rate zone to signal when to pick up the pace or ease off. Some show how your heart rate varies over the entire exercise period, and others compute the time you actually spend exercising while your heart rate is in the target heart rate zone. Heart rate monitors can take all the guesswork out of exercise. According to *The Physician and Sportsmedicine* magazine, heart rate monitors are as reliable as an electrocardiogram heart rate measurement.

SOUNDS LIKE FITNESS FICTION

Feel like a three-mile jog in the country, complete with sound effects—without ever leaving the city? Want to pit yourself against some absentee competition? Need something to talk you through your workout and then tell you just how fit you are? High-tech programmable exercise gear lets you do all that. Computerized rowing machines, cycles, and stairclimbs are getting some people interested in health and keeping them active. Instant readouts that gauge the intensity and duration of the activity can feed motivation. But high tech is generally synonomous with high cost ($1900-$3600). Although the home market is making a sizable contribution to the growth of this unique industry, a health club may present the only opportunity for most of us to program a workout.

Trends on the Light Side

FITNESS HOLIDAYS

"Vacation" generally conjures up the image of lounging in a beach chair until the sun's disappearance signals that it's time for gorging on calorie-laden delicacies. Hundreds of fitness spas and cruise lines are altering that image. They're selling the concept of fitness holidays: Take a holiday; get plenty of good exercise; eat the right foods; and return home in high performance gear.

More and more, spas are breaking away from their jet-setter stereotype of $300-a-day diet food. Instead, they are staffing up with qualified personnel who counsel clients on healthy eating and exercise practices. In addition to tempting fitness options and fitness cuisine, many conduct nutrition and cooking classes.

Fitness cruises are such spas in transit. You may find yourself striding around the jogging track while en route to Mazátlan, where you will participate in a 5K run before heading back to the ship for delectable high-carbohydrate, low-fat dining. The next day, en route to Cabo San Lucas, you can attend classes on health, beauty, and stress management before your workout. Then a sauna, massage, or whirlpool session will ready tired muscles for an evening of dancing.

To plan a successful fitness holiday, ask questions up front. If possible, tour the facility and talk with the owner and instructors. Consult a travel agent to give you the particulars of a fitness cruise. Always inquire about professional credentials. ("Nutritionist" is a title up for grabs; it does not mean registered dietitian.) Be certain diet and exercise regimes are not faddish or unrealistic. If weight loss is your goal, determine whether or not the principles of the program are structured to promote permanent changes in diet and exercise patterns.

GOING OFF TO CAMP HEALTH

While Mom and Dad are off on a cruise getting fit, where are the kids? In a slim-down camp, where food and fitness know-how is integrated into the usual summer fun for children. This innovative concept of summer camp comes as a welcome resource at a time when statistics give children bad marks for fitness and when the importance of a positive self-image is increasingly recognized as vital to a child's development. In these camps, children attend instructional sessions on nutrition and exercise but are also exposed to experiences involving sports, the performing arts, and computers.

Parents should check the camp's references and visit the site, if possible; select a licensed and accredited camp with a program appropriate for their child; and determine if the principles of weight loss seek to modify poor eating and exercise habits. Sessions typically run three to six weeks and prices vary accordingly, ranging from $1800 to $3400.

Cooking Light '88 Menu Plans

This plan for seven days of calorie-controlled meals provides a healthful approach to weight loss. Follow the plan precisely, or use it as a model for planning your own balanced meals by substituting any foods of comparable calories and nutrients. (Asterisks represent recipes which can be located in the menu and recipe sections.) Of the total calories provided, over 50 percent are from carbohydrates, less than 30 percent from fat, and less than 20 percent from protein. Most women can safely lose weight while eating 1,200 calories per day and most men, while eating 1,600. Once weight is lost, modify the menu plan according to the calories needed to maintain your ideal weight. Plan on losing about two pounds per week (possibly more the first two weeks). If you feel you are losing weight too slowly, keep in mind that eating fewer calories to speed up weight loss may rob you of the nutrients your body needs to stay healthy. Also, your metabolism may slow down to accommodate a very limited food supply and cause you to burn calories even more slowly. Exercise is the key to speeding up weight loss.

1200 calories		DAY 1	1600 calories	
		Breakfast		
2 pancakes	136	*Lemon-Wheat Germ Pancakes	3 pancakes	198
2 tbsp	12	Reduced-Calorie Maple Syrup	3 tbsp	18
—	—	Lean Cooked Ham	2 ounces	120
1 cup	86	Skim Milk	1 cup	86
	234			422
		Lunch		
⅔ cup	136	Low-Fat Cottage Cheese	1 cup	204
½ cup	38	Fresh Pineapple	½ cup	38
1 cup	55	Fresh Strawberries	1 cup	55
3 crackers	96	*Nutty Whole-Grain Crackers	4 crackers	128
	325			425
		Dinner		
1 serving	258	*Saucy Beef and Noodles	1 serving	258
1 serving	92	*Asparagus with Almonds	1 serving	92
1 cup	7	Iceberg Lettuce Salad	1 cup	7
1 tbsp	16	*Creamy Country Dressing	1 tbsp	16
1 serving	63	*Strawberry-Rosé Ice	1 serving	63
	436			436
		Snack		
1 cup	86	Skim Milk	1 cup	86
½ muffin	92	Whole Wheat English Muffin	1 muffin	183
1 tbsp	20	Reduced-Calorie Marmalade	1 tbsp	20
—	—	Margarine	1 tsp	33
	198			322
Total	1193		Total	1605

1200 calories		DAY 2	1600 calories	
		Breakfast		
—	—	Hot Oatmeal	1 cup	145
1 serving	161	*Breakfast Bagels	1 serving	161
1 cup	86	Skim Milk	1 cup	86
1 cup	42	Tomato Juice	½ cup	21
	289			413
		Lunch		
1 serving	234	*Savory Chicken Stew	1 serving	234
3 crackers	60	*Blue Cornmeal Crackers	5 crackers	100
1 cup	58	Peach Halves	½ cup	29
—	—	*Angel Food Cake with Berries	1 serving	125
	352			488
		Dinner		
1 serving	155	*Hot and Spicy Seafood Kabobs	1 serving	155
1 serving	77	*Oven-Fried Zucchini Chips	1 serving	77
1 ear of corn	81	Grilled Corn-on-the-Cob	1 ear of corn	81
1 biscuit	69	*Cheddar Cheese Biscuits	2 biscuits	138
—	—	Margarine	1 tsp	33
1 serving	89	*Raspberry-Pear Sorbet	1 serving	89
	471			573
		Snack		
1 cup	86	Skim Milk	1 cup	86
—	—	Dried Apricot Halves	6 halves	50
	86			136
Total	1198		Total	1610

1200 calories		DAY 3	1600 calories	
		Breakfast		
1 serving	200	*Yogurt Crunch Parfaits	1 serving	200
½ cup	56	Orange Juice	½ cup	56
—	—	Whole Wheat Toast	1 slice	61
	256			317
		Lunch		
1 serving	253	*Grilled Fish Sandwiches	1 serving	253
½ cup	12	*Coleslaw Relish	½ cup	12
—	—	*Cocoa-Banana Cupcakes	1 cupcake	155
1 cup	86	Skim Milk	1 cup	86
	351			506
		Dinner		
1 serving	182	*Chicken Étouffée	1 serving	182
½ cup	30	Steamed Brussels Sprouts	½ cup	30
1 serving	82	*Sesame Carrots	1 serving	82
1 roll	88	Hard Roll	1 roll	88
1 cookie	43	*Lemon-Oatmeal Crispies	2 cookies	86
—	—	*Spiced Cranberry Tea	1 serving	80
	425			548
		Snack		
½ cup	43	Skim Milk	½ cup	43
2 crackers	104	*Honey Graham Crackers	2 crackers	104
—	—	Peanut Butter	1 tbsp	95
	147			242
Total	1179		Total	1613

1200 calories		DAY 4	1600 calories	
		Breakfast		
—	—	Broiled Grapefruit	½ grapefruit	43
1 cup	127	Bran Flakes	1 cup	127
1 tbsp	27	Raisins	2 tbsp	54
1 cup	86	Skim Milk	1 cup	86
	240			310
		Lunch		
1 serving	209	*Vegetarian Chef Salad	1 serving	209
1 slice	70	Sour Dough Bread	2 slices	139
—	—	Margarine	1 tsp	33
1 serving	87	*Four Fruit Shake	1 serving	87
	366			468
		Dinner		
1 serving	134	*Orange Flounder in Papillote	1 serving	134
1 serving	30	*Nouvelle Tossed Salad	1 serving	30
½ cup	102	Cooked Brown Rice	½ cup	102
1 roll	88	Hard Roll	2 rolls	176
—	—	Margarine	1 tsp	33
1 serving	188	*Key Lime Meringue Pie	1 serving	188
	542			663
		Snack		
1 cup	56	Honeydew Melon Balls	1 cup	56
—	—	*Amaretto Cream	2 tbsp	74
	56			130
Total	1204		Total	1571

1200 calories		DAY 6	1600 calories	
		Breakfast		
1 serving	100	*Baked Apple Omelet	1 serving	100
1 slice	61	Whole Wheat Bread	2 slices	122
—	—	Margarine	1 tsp	33
1 cup	86	Skim Milk	1 cup	86
	247			341
		Lunch		
1 serving	207	*Turkey Chili	1 serving	207
1 serving	144	*Indian Flat Bread	1 serving	144
1 serving	46	*Jicama Chips	1 serving	46
—	—	*Mocha-Drenched Chocolate Cake	1 serving	138
	397			535
		Dinner		
1 serving	246	*Vegetable-Cheese Cannelloni	1 serving	246
1 cup	12	Spinach Salad	1 cup	12
1 tbsp	14	*Poppy Seed Dressing	2 tbsp	28
—	—	*Hot Cross Rolls	1 roll	150
1 serving	101	*Fresh Fruit with Almond Cream	1 serving	101
1 cup	39	Wine Spritzer	1 cup	39
	412			576
		Snack		
1 cup	86	Skim Milk	1 cup	86
½ banana	55	Banana	½ banana	55
	141			141
Total	1197		Total	1593

1200 calories		DAY 5	1600 calories	
		Breakfast		
1 egg	79	Poached Egg	1 egg	79
1 biscuit	110	*Rye Biscuits	2 biscuits	220
1 cup	86	Skim Milk	1 cup	86
—	—	Canadian Bacon	1 ounce	53
	275			438
		Lunch		
2 servings	182	*Smoked Turkey and Wild Rice Salad	2 servings	182
1 serving	53	*Summer Squash Medley	1 serving	53
—	—	*Hearty Whole Wheat Muffins	1 muffin	139
1 serving	103	*Pear-Apple Fans	1 serving	103
	338			477
		Dinner		
1 serving	155	*Lemon-Garlic Veal	1 serving	155
1 serving	89	*Apple-Sweet Potato Medley	1 serving	89
½ cup	26	Steamed Broccoli	½ cup	26
1 roll	70	*Herbed Dinner Rolls	2 rolls	140
—	—	Margarine	1 tsp	33
1 square	125	*Kahlúa Squares	1 square	125
	465			568
		Snack		
1 serving	94	*Peach-Yogurt Freeze	1 serving	94
Total	1172		Total	1577

1200 calories		DAY 7	1600 calories	
		Breakfast		
1 muffin	136	*Peach-Almond Muffins	2 muffins	272
1 cup	86	Skim Milk	1 cup	86
—	—	Orange Sections	½ cup	42
	222			400
		Lunch		
1 serving	123	*Shredded Chicken Salad	1 serving	123
½ round	73	Pita Bread Round	1 round	147
8 ounces	193	Vanilla Low-Fat Yogurt	8 ounces	193
½ cup	41	Fresh Blueberries	½ cup	41
	430			504
		Dinner		
1 serving	178	*Crustless Ham Quiche	1 serving	178
½ cup	20	Sliced Tomato and Cucumber Salad	½ cup	20
1 slice	134	*Brown Rice Bread	1 slice	134
—	—	Margarine	1 tsp	33
½ cup	29	Peach Halves	1 cup	58
2 cookies	90	*Chocolate-Mint Cookies	3 cookies	135
	451			558
		Snack		
4 cups	92	Air-Popped Popcorn	4 cups	92
—	—	Parmesan Cheese	2 tbsp	46
	92			138
Total	1195		Total	1600

Index

Subject Index